Electronic
Circuits
and
Systems

VOLUME IV

BASIC ELECTRONIC CIRCUITS AND SYSTEMS

Other Volumes in Electronic Circuits and Systems Series:

Volume V — Advanced Electronic Circuit Technology

Volume VI — Industrial and Microwave Electronic Technology

Electronic Circuits and Systems supplements the previously published series entitled:

ELECTRONIC AND ELECTRICAL FUNDAMENTALS

Volume I — Basic Concepts and D-C Circuits

Volume II — Fundamentals of AC and A-C Circuit Analysis

Volume III — Vacuum Tube and Semiconductor Fundamentals

Other PHILCO TechRep Division Publications:

AN-167 Cable Fabrication

AN-169 Shop Practices

AN-195 Electrical Power Equipment (Generators and Motors)

AN-234 Antenna Construction

AN-252 Radio Communications System Measurements

AN-256 Synchros and Servo Mechanisms

AN-296 Electronic Circuit Directory

AN-320 Electronic Navigation Systems

AN-374 Antennas

AN-401 Single Sideband Communications

AN-407 Field Engineers' Data Handbook

AN-430 Technical Writing Guide

AN-447 Radar Systems Measurements

Basic Electronic
Circuits
and
Systems

By Members of the Staff

of the

Technical Department

published by

PHILCO TECHREP DIVISION

PHILCO CORPORATION

PHILADELPHIA, PENNSYLVANIA

1 9 6 0

PRINTED IN THE UNITED STATES OF AMERICA

at Williams Brothers Printing Co., Philadelphia, Pa.

AN-460

Preface

This is the first of a series of three volumes on the subject, *Electronic Circuits and Systems;* the series is divided into the following general phases — basic circuits, application of basic circuits to communication, advanced circuits, special applications of advanced circuits, and examples of typical electronic systems in common use. This first volume covers the first two of these phases — basic circuits and the application of basic circuits to communication. The other two volumes cover the remaining phases.

The need for a treatment of circuit concepts and systems has been emphasized by the introduction of electronics into the curriculum of many vocational and technical high schools. Accordingly, this series of texts was prepared primarily to fill this need.

This series represents a cooperative effort on the part of many members of the Technical Department of the Philco TechRep Division, and is the result of a wide background in the field of electronics training for schools, industry, and the Armed Forces. This background in training and training materials development has given the Technical Department an insight into the comparative advantages of many teaching methods, and has thus made it possible for them to use the most effective approach in presenting this kind of material. The application of mathematics to the circuit design principles has been minimized; however, certain formulas which provide a close correlation between theory and practice are presented, to aid the student in solving the problems encountered in actual electronics work.

The order and methods of presentation of the various topics are logical and straightforward, and should pose no problems for the vocational h i g h school class. Example problems are included at appropriate points in the text, and review questions and problems are provided at the end of each chapter.

John E. Remich
Manager, Technical Department
TechRep Division

Philadelphia, Pennsylvania
July, 1960

Contents

Introduction

Assuming that the student has acquired a thorough knowledge of electronic components, fundamental circuit arrangements, and the effects of applied d-c and a-c voltages, he is now ready to study basic electronic circuits and the use of these circuits to make up a communication system. This volume, *Basic Electronic Circuits and Systems*, seeks to guide the student in this study.

The volume shows how, by the proper control of circuit constants and by the proper selection and arrangement of resistors, capacitors, inductors, vacuum tubes, and transistors, it is possible to design various kinds of functional circuits such as d-c voltage supplies, audio- and radio-frequency amplifiers, and audio and radio-frequency oscillators. It also shows how such circiuts, when properly arranged and used with sound-energy transducers (microphones and loudspeakers), can be made into a complete communication system for the transmission and reception of intelligence-bearing radio-frequency energy. Both amplitude-modulation (AM) and frequency-modulation (FM) principles are covered.

The circuits discussed in this volume are limited to those which are designed to generate and process sinusoidal voltages and currents. The circuit modifications required for the handling of nonsinusoidal waveshapes are discussed in Volume 5 of this series.

CHAPTER ONE

Radio Circuits and Systems

1-1 Introduction

The science of radio communication has evolved as a result of man's constant effort to improve his methods of transferring information. Although the telegraph and the telephone represent a tremendous advance in communication, they require wires, and therefore are not suitable for shipboard and other mobile installations. The need was for a method of transferring information over long distances without the use of wires. Today radio is common, and has advanced to the stage where it provides a highly efficient and reliable means of communication which directly or indirectly affects everyday life. The home radio provides news and entertainment; radio dispatching of transportation such as taxicabs and trucks provides faster and more efficient service; the radio-telephone makes it possible to talk to people almost anywhere in the world; and radio communications is essential to the control of aircraft traffic. These are only a few examples of how radio reaches into our everyday life.

1

1-2 HISTORICAL DEVELOPMENT

The history of radio began in 1832 with the invention of the electric telegraph by Samuel F. B. Morse. Morse found that electrical impulses from a battery could be sent along a wire to actuate the spring-loaded armature of an electromagnet at the other end of the line, causing an audible click. By using a predetermined coding of dots and dashes, known as the *Morse code,* messages could be transmitted along the wire. This was a great forward step in long-distance communications, since wires could be strung for many miles and messages quickly transferred over great distances. Great progress was made, and in 1866 the first message was sent through a cable laid along the floor of the Atlantic Ocean. The telegraph is commonplace and available everywhere today, and has advanced from the old electromagnets to the m o d e r n teletypewriter which automatically prints the messages.

The telegraph still requires wires, a feature which makes it useless in many applications, such as communication with ships and aircraft. Many scientists experimented with the phenomenon known as *electromagnetic induction* in an effort to develop a system of wireless transmission. As early as 1834, Joseph Henry succeeded in magnetizing needles at a distance of over 200 feet from telegraph wires, and shortly after, Thomas Edison devised a system whereby messages could be picked up by a moving train from nearby telegraph wires. In 1864, James C. Maxwell published a mathematical analysis which proved, at least theoretically, that it was possible to produce electrical impulses which would travel through space at the velocity of light. This theory, and the formulas which resulted, opened up a new line of investigation. Although many scientists attempted t o experimentally demonstrate the validity of Maxwell's theories, it was not until 1888 that Heinrich Hertz was successful in transmitting the first radio signal. His equipment was crude — merely two loops of wire on opposite sides of a room. A battery was attached to one loop with a switch which allowed the formation of an arc. Each time an arc occurred, current was detected in the other loop, indicating a transfer of electromagnetic energy. In 1896, Guglielmo Marconi developed the first practical wireless telegraph, which operated over a distance of 2 miles. By 1898, the range had been extended to 30 miles, and in 1899, a regular wireless telegraph service across the English Channel was placed in operation. In 1901, a signal originating at the Marconi station at Poldhu, Wales, was received at St. Johns, Newfoundland, thereby spanning the Atlantic Ocean.

In this era, signals were produced by spark or arc transmitters, and the receivers consisted of electromagnets which could be energized by the weak received signal. Many more developments were necessary before the equipment could be used for the transmission of voice signals.

The beginning of voice transmission came with the invention of the telephone by Alexander Graham Bell in 1876. By 1877 an outdoor line about 2 miles long was in use. The original crude equipment has been refined, until today, with the advent of long-distance direct dialing, it is possible to pick up a home telephone and, within a few seconds, speak to any place in the country, with charges being automatically billed to the caller.

Many of these refinements would not be possible without the electron tube, which ushered in the beginning of modern radio. In 1897, an English physicist, Sir Joseph J. Thompson, discovered the electron, and later Dr. John A. Fleming invented the device which is now known as the diode. This "tube" was capable of detecting the wireless signals, but would not amplify such signals. With this in mind, Lee De Forest, known as the founder of modern radio, modified the diode by inserting a screen of wire between the two elements of the diode to control the electron flow. This tube, the *triode,* or, as it was originally known, the *audion,* revolutionized wireless communications. New methods of generating, amplifying, and rectifying electrical signals resulted from the use of the triode. In later years the tetrode, pentode, and many other multi-element tubes were developed, each making its contribution to the rapidly expanding field of electronics.

One other device which must be mentioned is the crystal detector. The crystal receiver, with its galena crystal and movable whisker, was a common sight in the early years of radio. The vacuum tube has displaced the crystal for radio communications, but the crystal and other similar devices known as semiconductors now threaten to make the vacuum tube obsolete.

Today, the radio telegraph is the chief means of long-range communications for handling routine messages of the thousands of ships at sea, and the radio is in almost every home and automobile dispensing news, music, and other entertainment at the turn of a knob. The extension of the usable radio-frequency range has made possible the present-day aircraft communications and navigation systems and the development of microwave systems.

The radio itself has evolved from the simple crystal set with its headphones, through the TRF (tuned radio frequency) to the superheterodyne receiver. The simple crystal set had a limited frequency range and was tuned by a trial and error method, while one modern aircraft communications receiver can be tuned automatically to any one of several thousand frequencies.

1-3 TERMS ASSOCIATED WITH RADIO

As with any constantly expanding science, radio engineers are continually coining new words to explain new advances. Thus, if contact with radio is lost, even for a comparatively short time, it becomes difficult to understand much of the language used. A few of the basic terms associated with radio are given here, and others will be introduced later as the need arises.

Transmission — the passage of radio waves in space between transmitting and receiving stations. The radiation of electromagnetic energy into space from a device at the transmitting station.

Reception — the interception of radiated electromagnetic energy in space and conversion of this energy to a useful form.

Antenna — a device which radiates electromagnetic energy from a transmitter into space. As was mentioned earlier, Maxwell's equations formed the theoretical basis for this phenomenon. In essence, alternating currents in the antenna form moving electric and magnetic fields at right angles to each other. The fundamental laws covered previously show that the direction of motion of these fields is perpendicular to both fields; the fields move radially out from a straight wire.

Modulation — the superimposing of intelligence on radio-frequency energy. This can be accomplished in several ways. The radio-frequency energy may be turned on and off in a coded sequence (cw), it may be varied in amplitude (amplitude modulation) or frequency (frequency modulation), or it may be broken up into a series of pulses which are coded to provide the information. The pulses may then be varied in ampli-

tude (pulse amplitude modulation), time (pulse position modulation), or duration (pulse duration modulation).

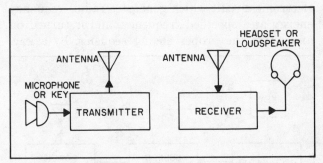

Figure 1-1. Basic Radio Communication System

1-4 A BASIC RADIO COMMUNICATION SYSTEM

Perhaps the simplest of all radio communication systems is illustrated in the block diagram of figure 1-1. The transmitter contains a source of radio-frequency energy necessary to transfer the required information. The information is superimposed on this radio frequency by the key (for telegraph signals) or the microphone (for voice signals), and the radio frequency, with its superimposed intelligence, is radiated from the antenna. At the receiver another antenna intercepts a small portion of this radiated energy and feeds it to the receiver. The receiver then amplifies this signal to a usable level, extracts the information superimposed on the radio frequency, and converts it into a form which can be used. The headset converts the electrical impulses to audible sound waves which convey the information to the listener.

This discussion has been purposely oversimplified to indicate the means of communication, rather than the devices used to achieve it. Many such devices exist, each with its own function, and a number of methods of superimposing intelligence on the radio-frequency energy are in use. Each of these will be discussed in greater detail in later sections.

Radio Transmitters

In this section are presented simplified block diagrams of the two most common types of radio transmitters — the continuous-wave, or c-w, transmitter and the amplitude-modulated, or AM, transmitter.

The c-w transmitter is the simplest type of transmitter, and is used in the transmission of radio-telegraph messages using a predetermined code to represent letters, numbers, and other symbols. A block diagram of this type of transmitter is given in figure 1-2. The oscillator is an electronic circuit which generates radio-frequency energy at a specified frequency, and is turned on and off in the proper coding sequence by a key.

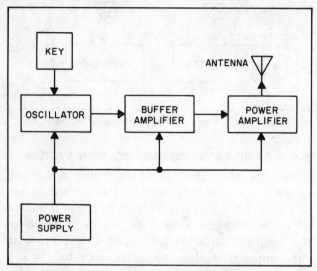

Figure 1-2. A Simple C-W Transmitter

In many cases, the oscillator contains a tuning circuit to set the basic transmitter frequency. This is followed by a buffer amplifier which amplifies these coded bursts of r-f energy. In addition, the buffer amplifier prevents the varying load effects of the power amplifier from affecting the frequency of the oscillator. The power supply provides the d-c power necessary to operate the transmitter.

The AM transmitter shown in figure 1-3 contains the same basic components, except for the key. In this transmitter, modulation is achieved by varying the amplitude of the radio-frequency energy. As before, the oscillator supplies r-f energy at a predetermined frequency, the buffer amplifier amplifies this energy and isolates the oscillator, and the power supply provides the d-c power necessary to operate the equipment. The modulation system consists of a microphone, an audio amplifier, and a modulator. The microphone converts voice sound waves to electrical signals, and the audio amplifier raises these signals to the level required by the modulator. The modulator is essentially an amplifier which contains the components necessary to apply the signals to the power amplifier. The r-f output from the buffer amplifier and the a-f signals from the modulator are both fed to the power amplifier,

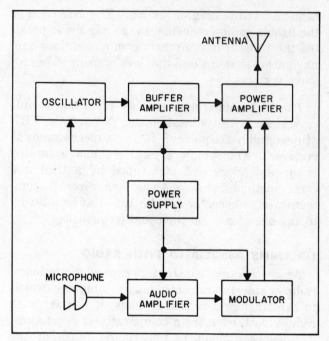

Figure 1-3. A Simple AM Transmitter

which combines them in such a manner that the audio-frequency input varies the amplitude of the rf, providing the necessary modulation. The modulated rf is then fed to the antenna to be radiated into space.

There are a number of other types of transmitters, such as FM and pulse types, which are extensions of the communications field.

Radio Receivers

There are a great many different types of radio receivers. Of these many types, only four will be discussed here. The crystal, superregenerative, and TRF receivers are of interest primarily from an historical point of view, while the superheterodyne receiver is by far the most widely used in the present age.

A block diagram of a crystal receiver is given in figure 1-4. A portion of the electromagnetic energy radiated from the transmitter station is intercepted by the antenna and converted to electric currents. The tuning circuit rejects all signals which are not of the desired frequency, and the galena crystal acts as a detector to extract the modulating signal. This signal is then converted to sound waves by the headset. Note that this receiver requires no power supply, since it contains no tubes or other components requiring power, and that no amplifying devices are used.

Crystal receivers such as this are still readily available for a few dollars.

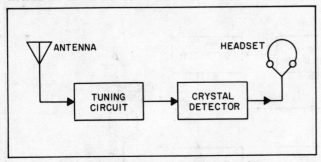

Figure 1-4. A Basic Crystal Receiver

The superregenerative receiver, illustrated in figure 1-5, made use of a special detector circuit which provided selection of the proper frequency, amplification, and detection of the received signal in a single circuit. The necessary feedback in a circuit such as this is accomplished by the use of a special type of coil which includes a feedback winding. Although the superregenerative detector gives good results, it must be operated and adjusted with care, since it has a tendency to break into uncontrollable oscillation. The detected output from the superregenerative detector is coupled to an audio amplifier which provides the signal power necessary to operate a loudspeaker.

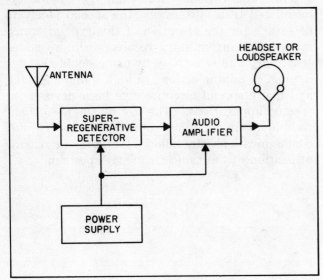

Figure 1-5. A Superregenerative Receiver

The TRF (tuned-radio-frequency) receiver was popular for many years because of its simplicity and ease of operation. In this receiver (figure 1-6), the received r-f signal is fed to one or more r-f amplifiers, each of which is tuned to pass only the desired frequencies. The amplified r-f signal,

including modulation, is then fed to a detector, which extracts the modulating signal. This signal is amplified in the audio amplifier and converted to sound waves in the loudspeaker or headset. A power supply provides the d-c power required for the operation of the various parts of the receiver.

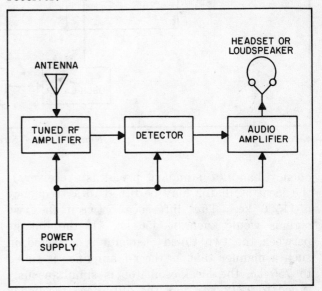

Figure 1-6. A TRF Receiver

The superheterodyne receiver, illustrated in figure 1-7, is the most commonly used type of receiver. It provides excellent stability, selectivity, and sensitivity, and for many applications is much simpler than a TRF receiver would be. For example, it is necessary in many cases to have a highly sensitive receiver. In the case of the TRF receiver, this would require as many as six or seven tunable stages. In the superheterodyne receiver, on the other hand, most of the amplification is accomplished at a fixed intermediate frequency point and only three stages must be tunable.

As with all receivers, the antenna intercepts a small portion of the transmitted energy and converts it to an electric signal. This signal is amplified by the r-f amplifier and sent to the converter. Here it is mixed with the output of the local oscillator to produce a signal at a lower frequency which varies in amplitude with the variation in the amplitude of the r-f signal. The local oscillator is tunable, and produces an r-f output of fixed amplitude. The tuning is "tracked" to the tuning of the r-f amplifier to provide a constant difference frequency. For example, if the r-f amplifier is tuned to 1050 kc (within the fre-

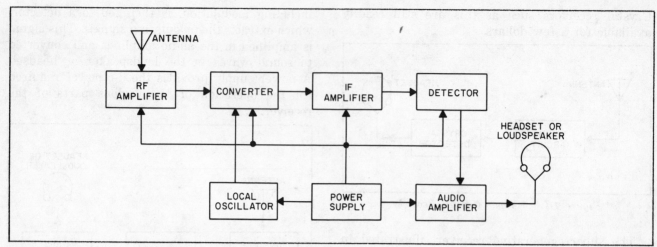

Figure 1-7. A Superheterodyne Receiver

quency band of standard broadcast receivers), the local oscillator may be tuned to a frequency of 1506 kc. The difference between the two signals would then be 456 kc. If the linkage between the two tuned elements is adjusted in such a manner that as the r-f amplifier is tuned to 756 kc, the local oscillator is simultaneously tuned to 1212 kc, then the difference frequency remains at 456 kc. It is this "tracking" feature which distinguishes the superheterodyne receiver.

The two signals (the r-f signal from the amplifier and the local oscillator signal) are mixed in the converter, and the output is fed to the i-f amplifier. It can be shown that when these frequencies are properly mixed, it is possible to obtain the difference frequency. The input portion of the i-f amplifier is therefore tuned to this fixed difference frequency. In most home receivers, the difference frequency is 456 kc. As can be seen, many i-f amplifiers could be used to increase

the sensitivity of the receiver without the necessity of making each section tunable.

The output of the i-f amplifier is fed to the detector, where the modulating signal is detected. This detected signal is fed to an audio amplifier, which amplifies the signal to the level necessary to operate the loudspeaker. The power supply again provides the power necessary for operation of the receiver.

There are many other types of receivers for specific applications; for example, frequency-modulated transmitters and the special receivers necessary for the reception of this type of transmission. Many military receivers achieve added sensitivity and selectivity by using double heterodyning, or mixing actions (a high if and a low if), and many special circuits have been devised for specific applications. The use of single-sideband techniques is another example of modern day communications to allow for the increasing utilization of the radio-frequency spectrum.

CHAPTER TWO

Power Supply Circuit Analysis

2-1 *Introduction*

The purpose of the power supply in any electronic equipment or system is to provide the proper operating voltages and currents for the vacuum tubes used in the equipment or system. In the early days of radio, batteries were used as the principal source of power for tube elements (filaments, grids, and plates). Because of the need for recharging storage batteries, and the short life of dry-cell batteries, the use of battery power supplies is undesirable and inconvenient in most present applications. However, in applications such as hearing aids, guided missiles, portable radios, and similar equipment where an a-c power source is not available, battery power supplies are desirable.

Because of the wide selection of source voltages and frequencies, and the wide variety of power requirements of electronic equipment, power supplies are constructed in a number of different ways. Power is converted from ac to dc by a motor-generator combination, more commonly called a *rotary converter*. Low-voltage d-c power is converted to high-voltage d-c power by using a dynamotor (d-c motor-generator) or a vibrator power supply. Vibrator power supplies are used extensively in automobile radio applications. Power supplies that use electronic rectifiers (vacuum-tube diodes or semiconductor diodes) to convert ac to dc are called *electronic power supplies*. When a-c power is available, the majority of power supplies used are of the electronic type.

The block diagram of a typical electronic power supply is shown in figure 2-1. Such a power supply consists of a power transformer, a rectifier, a filter, and a voltage divider. Each of these components is manufactured in a wide variety of types to meet various requirements.

In power supplies that deliver moderate voltages, all the a-c voltages are usually supplied from different secondary windings of a single transformer, called *power transformer*. This transformer supplies high a-c voltages to the plates of the rectifier tube, and low a-c voltages to the filaments of the rectifier tube and other tubes in the equipment.

The use of a power transformer allows a step-up or step-down in the a-c source voltage, thus making it possible to obtain any desired d-c output voltage. However, in some power supply circuits, where weight and cost are important considerations, the power transformer can be omitted and the rectifier connected directly to the a-c source voltage.

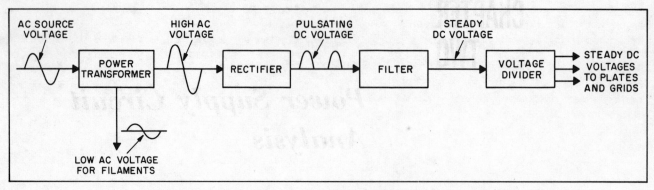

Figure 2-1. Block Diagram of a Typical Electronic Power Supply

The purpose of the rectifier in an electronic power supply is to convert the a-c source voltage that can be applied to the plates and grids of the tubes. The d-c voltage produced by the rectifier is usually in the form of pulses. This voltage, called *pulsating dc*, is applied to the filter circuit. In the filter these pulses are effectively smoothed out to produce a steady d-c voltage. From the filter the steady d-c voltage is applied to a voltage-divider circuit. The purpose of the voltage divider is to provide the proper d-c voltages for the plates and grids of the various tubes used in an equipment.

The type of electronic power supply used in a particular application (radio, TV receiver, radar set, etc) depends upon several factors, such as the voltage and current requirements of the load, the degree of voltage regulation necessary, the cost, the weight, etc. However, no matter what type of electronic power supply is used in a particular application, the power supply must meet certain basic requirements, as follows: The voltage for the plates and grids must be as nearly a steady d-c voltage as possible; the voltage regulation must be as near 0 percent as practicable; and the voltage must be correct for the equipment with which it is to be used.

2-2 PRINCIPLES OF RECTIFICATION

Rectification Using Vacuum-Tube Diodes

The fundamental principles of rectification are illustrated in figure 2-2. The a-c voltage periodically changes its polarity, as indicated by the waveform in part B of the figure. At point A the applied voltage begins its cycle, and gradually rises until a maximum positive amplitude is reached at point B. The voltage then gradually decreases until it reaches zero, at point C. During this portion of the cycle, a positive potential is applied to the plate of the diode, and conduction of the diode results in plate current.

At point C the voltage begins a gradual decrease below zero and is now on its negative swing. The voltage reaches a maximum negative amplitude at point D, then begins a gradual rise to zero, at point E, to complete the cycle. During this negative portion of the cycle (from point C to point E), a negative voltage is applied to the plate of the diode and there is no plate current. Because there is plate current only during one-half cycle of the applied ac, the ac is said to be rectified. The process is repeated for each succeeding cycle of the applied ac. The resultant output waveform thus produced is shown in point C.

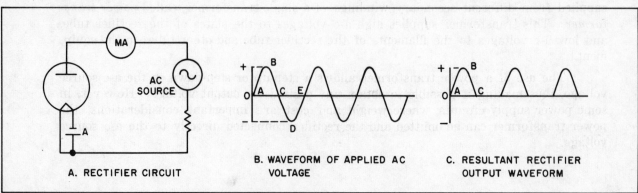

Figure 2-2. Circuit and Waveforms of a Vacuum-Tube Diode Rectifier with A-C Source

Vacuum-tube diode rectifiers are generally rated according to peak plate current, average load current, and peak inverse voltage.

The peak plate current is the maximum allowable value of instantaneous current through the diode. Peak plate current is determined by the structure of the cathode, and represents the maximum amount of emission that the cathode can supply for the normal life of the tube.

The average load current is the maximum allowable direct current that the tube can deliver to the load under continuous operating conditions. The value of average load current is less than one-half the peak plate current, since there is plate current during only one half of the a-c input cycle.

The peak inverse voltage of a rectifier is the maximum value of negative voltage that can be applied between the plate and cathode of the rectifier tube without damaging the tube. During the portion of the a-c input cycle when the plate is negative with respect to the cathode, there is no current through the diode. Because of this fact, the full a-c secondary voltage is impressed between the plate and cathode of the tube. Therefore, under normal operating conditions the peak inverse voltage is equal to the peak value of the a-c secondary voltage. The peak inverse voltage is actually limited by the spacing between the plate and the cathode, and by the electrical insulation between the plate and cathode of the tube.

Rectification Using Semiconductor Diodes

Another common type of rectifier (other than the vacuum-tube diode) is the semiconductor-diode rectifier, more commonly called a *metallic rectifier*. Semiconductors have a v e r y low resistance to current in one direction (called the *forward resistance*) and a very high resistance to current in the opposite direction (called the *back resistance*).

When used as a rectifier, the semiconductor diode is connected in series with the a-c voltage source and the load. Because of this series connection, there is current only in the forward (low-resistance) direction of the diode. The high value of back resistance of the semiconductor effectively blocks current in the back direction. Thus, the unidirectional current characteristic necessary for the operation of rectifiers is evident in semiconductor diodes.

The semiconductor substances commonly used in rectifier applications are copper oxide, copper sulphide, silicon, and selenium. Although germanium is also a good semiconductor substance, it is not used in rectifier applications since the current-handling capabilities of this substance are limited.

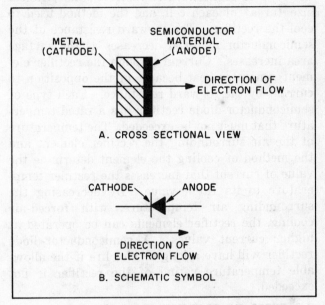

Figure 2-3. Semiconductor Diode Rectifier

The cross-sectional view and schematic symbol for a semiconductor diode are both illustrated in figure 2-3. Notice, in part A of this figure, that the semiconductor diode consists of two sections — a metal conductor, called the *cathode*, and the semiconductor substance, called the *anode*. The conductor may be iron, copper, aluminum, or a metal alloy. The semiconductor substance may be one of the substances mentioned previously. However, copper oxide and selenium are the substances generally used in the construction of semiconductor-diode rectifiers.

The direction of the current (electron flow) through a semiconductor diode is from cathode to anode. Notice, in part B of figure 2-3, that this is opposite to the direction indicated by the arrowhead of the schematic symbol of the rectifier. The direction indicated by the schematic symbol (anode to cathode) is a result of the earlier concept of the current direction. This text is based on the more recent concept of electron flow, that is, from negative (–) to positive (+) in the circuit external to the voltage source.

Similar to vacuum-tube diode rectifiers, semiconductor-diode rectifiers are also rated according to peak plate current, average load current, and peak inverse voltage. However, another important consideration when using this type of rectifier element is its temperature rating.

The amount of current that can be safely handled by a semiconductor diode is dependent upon the type of semiconductor material, the physical size (area) of each cell, and the method used to cool the rectifier. The forward resistance of the semiconductor material decreases as the surface area increases. Current through the rectifier element generates heat because of the opposition to current by the forward resistance. Each type of semiconductor-diode rectifier has a rated temperature that must not be exceeded. The temperature of the air surrounding the rectifier element and the method of cooling the element determine the value of current that increases the rectifier temperature to its rated value. By decreasing the surrounding air temperature, with forced-air cooling, the rectifier elements can be operated at higher current values. A semiconductor-diode rectifier will have a long service life if the allowable temperature rating of the rectifier is not exceeded.

2-3 TYPES OF RECTIFIER CIRCUITS

Rectifier circuits can generally be classified as either *single-phase* or *polyphase rectifiers,* depending on the power source from which they operate. Rectifiers operating from single-phase power sources are used primarily in applications requiring small or moderate power. When more than a few thousand watts of power are required, rectifiers operating from polyphase power sources are generally used.

The types of rectifier circuits to be studied will be confined to the single-phase small or moderate

power types. Some of the more common rectifiers in this group include the half-wave, full-wave, and bridge rectifiers.

Half-wave Rectifier

The schematic diagram and waveforms of a typical half-wave rectifier are shown in figure 2-4. The circuit consists of an indirectly heated cathode type of vacuum-tube diode, V1, and a load resistor, R_L, connected in series with the high-voltage secondary winding, A—B, of a power transformer, T1. A low-voltage secondary winding, C—D, of the power transformer is used to supply filament voltage for the diode tube.

Consider the operation of the half-wave rectifier circuit during the half cycles when point A is positive with respect to point B. During these periods, the plate of the diode is positive with respect to the cathode, and the diode conducts as indicated in figure 2-4. The path of the plate current is from point B through the load resistor to the cathode of the diode, from cathode to plate through the diode, and then to point A of the high-voltage secondary of the power transformer. The plate current through R_L develops a voltage across this resistor. Since the diode has very low plate resistance when it is conducting, practically all the secondary voltage appears across the load resistor, because the value of the load resistor is much higher than the resistance of the diode. The diode plate resistance and the load resistor form a voltage divider. Since the same current is present in the two resistances, and since the load resistor is larger than the diode plate resistance, the voltage across R_L exceeds the voltage across the diode. Thus, the amplitude of the voltage developed across the load resistor, which is the output voltage of the rectifier, is approxi-

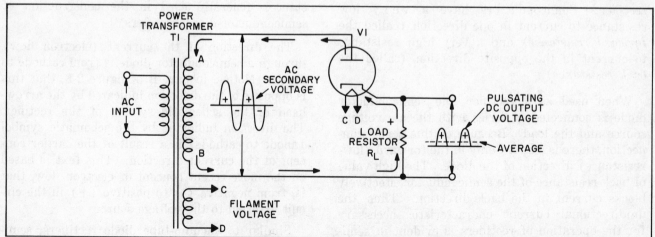

Figure 2-4. Schematic Diagram of a Typical Half-Wave Rectifier

mately equal to the amplitude of the power transformer high-voltage secondary winding voltage.

During the half cycles of transformer secondary voltage when point B is positive and point A is negative, there is no plate current. At this time the cathode of the diode is positive with respect to the plate, and the resistance of the diode is high. As a result of this high resistance (effectively an open circuit), there is no plate current through the circuit and no voltage is developed across the load resistor. Thus, by the unidirectional current characteristic of the diode, the a-c input voltage is rectified, or changed into a d-c voltage.

The d-c voltage developed across the load resistor of the half-wave rectifier is called a *pulsating d-c voltage*. This means that the dc is actually a fluctuating, or alternating, voltage of only one polarity, either positive or negative. The pulsating d-c output voltage of the half-wave rectifier shown in figure 2-4 is positive; that is, the output voltage consists of a series of alternating positive half cycles. The negative half cycles are eliminated by the action of the diode. The frequency of the pulsating d-c voltage is called the *ripple frequency*. In half-wave rectifiers the ripple frequency is equal to the frequency of the applied a-c voltage. For example, if the frequency of the a-c input voltage is 60 cps, the ripple frequency of the pulsating d-c voltage developed across the load resistor of the rectifier is also 60 cps. In the half-wave rectifier the peak inverse voltage is equal to the peak, or maximum, a-c secondary voltage.

The a-c voltage applied from the high-voltage secondary to the plate of the diode is changing continuously. The plate current of the diode can be determined at any instant by using the dynamic characteristic curve of the diode. Figure 2-5 shows the output current waveforms for a diode half-wave rectifier with different values of load resistance. In part A, the waveform obtained is that of a rectifier having a load resistance, R_L, of 100 ohms. Notice that only the positive half cycles of voltage from the high-voltage secondary winding appear in the output.

The plate current waveform obtained from a half-wave rectifier having a load resistance of 500 ohms is shown in part B. Notice now that the amplitude of the output-current waveform is reduced. This is because the value of the load resistor is increased from 100 to 500 ohms. Thus

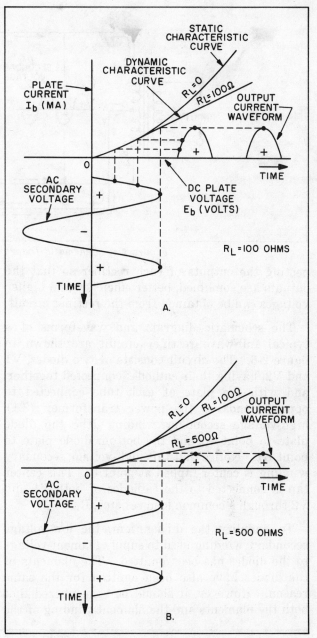

Figure 2-5. Half-Wave Rectifier Output Current Waveforms for Different Values of Load Resistance

it can be stated that as the value of the load resistor is increased, the output current from the rectifier is decreased. This, of course, is true only if the level of a-c secondary voltage remains constant.

Full-Wave Rectifier

Basically, a full-wave rectifier consists of two half-wave rectifiers so connected that one rectifier tube conducts on each half cycle of the a-c input voltage. Thus, by utilizing the complete cycle of alternating current (or full wave), and by con-

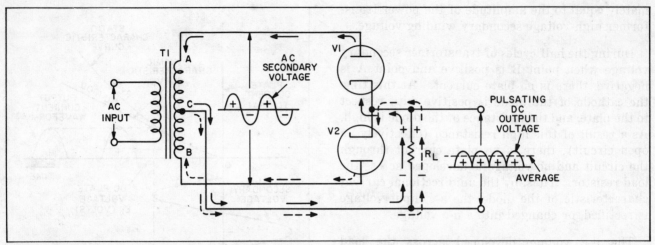

Figure 2-6. Schematic Diagram of a Typical Full-Wave Rectifier

necting the outputs of each rectifier so that the outputs are combined, better efficiency and higher voltages can be obtained from the rectifier circuit.

The schematic diagram and waveforms of a typical full-wave rectifier circuit are shown in figure 2-6. The circuit consists of two diodes, V1 and V2, having their cathodes connected together, and with the plate of each tube connected to opposite ends of the power transformer (T1) high-voltage secondary winding (the top diode plate to point A, and the bottom diode plate to point B). Notice that this high-voltage secondary winding is center-tapped at point C. This center tap is connected to the cathodes of both V1 and V2 through a common load resistor, R_L.

To simplify the diagram, the low-voltage secondary winding used to supply filament voltage to the diodes has been omitted. The filaments of the diodes have also been omitted for the same reason. However, it should be remembered that both the filaments and the filament winding of the

power transformer are essential to the operation of the circuit in actual equipment installations.

Proper operation of a full-wave rectifier depends on the polarity of the voltages developed in the center-tapped secondary of the power transformer. Figure 2-7 is a diagram of the voltages developed in this winding.

The amplitude of the voltage in each half of the secondary winding (A—C and B—C) is one-half the amplitude of the voltage across the entire secondary winding (A — B). When the voltages of windings A—C and B—C are measured in the same direction (A to C, C to B; or vice versa), their polarities are the same at every instant. When the voltages are added in the same direction, their sum is equal to the voltage that appears across the entire secondary winding.

Refer to figure 2-6 again. During the half cycles when point A is positive with respect to point C (and point B), a positive voltage is applied to the plate of diode V1 and V1 conducts.

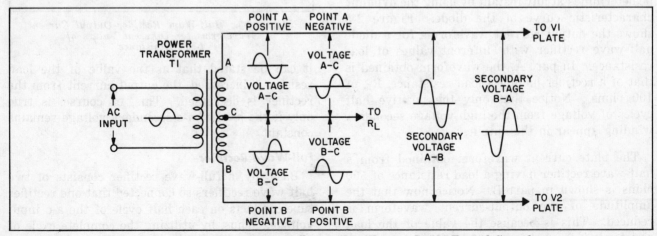

Figure 2-7. Voltage Waveforms of Power Transformer Center-Tapped Secondary

The plate current path (solid arrows) is from point C to the cathode of V1 through the load resistor, from cathode to plate through V1, and then from the plate of V1 to point A on the power transformer secondary. This plate current develops a voltage, across the load resistor, of the polarity indicated. Notice that there is no plate current through diode V2 at this time since point B on the transformer is at a negative potential. This effectively applies a negative potential to the plate of V2, thus preventing V2 from conducting.

However, when the polarity of the applied ac reverses, and point B is positive with respect to points C and A, plate current passes through V2 but none is allowed through V1. The plate current path (dotted arrows) is from point C through the load resistor to the junction between the cathodes, from cathode to plate through V2 and then from the plate of V2 to point B on the transformer secondary. Since point A is negative at this time, the plate of V1 is also negative and no plate current can pass through this diode.

Notice that the plate current of V2 passes through the load resistor in the same direction as the plate current of V1. Because of this, the polarity of the voltage developed across the load resistor (the output voltage) is the same for both half cycles of the a-c secondary voltage.

Compare the output voltage waveform of the full-wave rectifier in figure 2-6 with the output voltage waveform of the half-wave rectifier in figure 2-4. Notice that the output of the full-wave rectifier has twice as many pulses (positive half cycles) as t h a t of the half-wave rectifier.

Assuming no voltage drop in the secondary winding or the rectifier tubes, and with the same value of a-c voltage on the plates, the output voltage (average value) of the full-wave rectifier is twice that of the half-wave rectifier. This is true because the full-wave rectifier supplies current and voltage to the load for the full cycle of a-c input voltage, while the half-wave rectifier supplies current and voltage to the load for only one half of the a-c input cycle. The peak inverse voltage of one diode in the full-wave rectifier is equal to the full a-c secondary voltage when the other diode is conducting.

Also, compare the ripple frequencies of the full-wave and the half-wave rectifiers. Since the full-wave rectifier conducts on each half cycle of the a-c input voltage, its ripple frequency is twice the frequency of the a-c input. For example, if the frequency of the applied a-c voltage is 60 cps, the frequency of the rectifier output voltage is 120 cps. Remember that the ripple frequency in the half-wave rectifier is equal to the frequency of the applied a-c voltage because the half-wave rectifier conducts only on the positive half cycles of the input voltage.

Vacuum-Tube Bridge Rectifier

A type of full-wave rectifier that does not require a center-tapped high-voltage winding is shown in figure 2-8. Since the vacuum-tube diodes in this circuit are arranged in the familiar bridge configuration, the circuit is usually called a *bridge rectifier*. In the operation of this circuit, two tubes conduct in series, and produce one d-c pulse in the output, during each half cycle of the a-c input voltage.

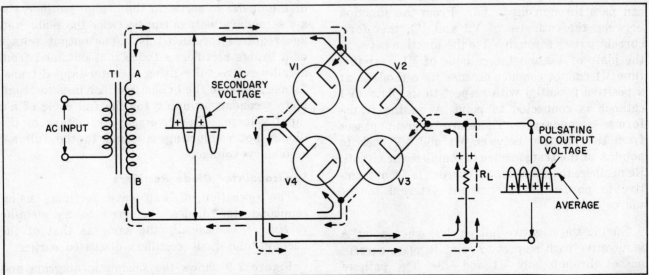

Figure 2-8. Schematic Diagram of a Vacuum-Tube Bridge Rectifier

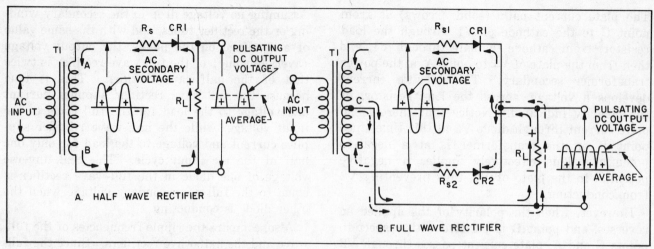

Figure 2-9. Half-Wave and Full-Wave Metallic-Rectifier Circuits

During the positive half cycles of the a-c input voltage, when point A is positive with respect to point B, plate current passes through only V2 and V4. The path of this current flow (solid arrows) is from point B on the high-voltage secondary winding to the junction between the plate of V3 and the cathode of V4. Because of the unidirectional current characteristic of a diode (from cathode to plate), V3 does not conduct. The current path, therefore, is through V4 to the junction between the plates of V1 and V4. V1 does not conduct at this time for the same reason that V3 did not conduct previously. Current from the plate of V4 then passes through the load resistor, developing a voltage across this resistor (as indicated), to the junction between the cathodes of V2 and V3. Since the plate of V3 is connected to point B on the high-voltage secondary, and since point B is at a negative potential at this time, no current can pass through diode V3. From the junction between the cathodes of V2 and V3, therefore, current passes through V2 to the junction between the plate of V2 and the cathode of V1. At this time V1 cannot conduct because its cathode is at a positive potential with respect to its plate (V1 cathode is connected to point A on the transformer secondary). Therefore, current passes from the junction between V1 and V2 back to point A of the transformer to complete the circuit. Remember, the direction of current is from negative to positive in the circuit external to the source voltage.

During the negative half cycles, when point A is negative with respect to point B, plate current passes through only V1 and V3. The path of this current (dotted arrows) is from point A on

the high-voltage secondary to the junction between V1 and V2, through V1 to the junction between V1 and V4, through the load resistor to the junction between V2 and V3, through V3 to the junction between V3 and V4, and finally back to the high-voltage secondary at point B to complete the circuit. During these negative half cycles of a-c secondary voltage, diodes V2 and V4 do not conduct for the same reasons that V1 and V3 did not conduct during the positive half cycles of voltage.

Notice that plate current through the load resistor is in the same direction during both half cycles of the a-c secondary voltage. Because of this, full-wave rectification occurs in the bridge rectifier, and the output waveform is similar to that of the conventional full-wave rectifier.

Since the secondary voltage is applied to two of the diodes in series in the bridge rectifier, the a-c secondary voltage can be twice the plate voltage required for each tube. The output voltage of a bridge rectifier is twice that obtained from a full-wave rectifier using a center-tapped transformer, because the bridge rectifier uses the complete secondary winding for the full cycle of a-c input voltage. The inverse peak voltage of the diodes not conducting is equal to the full a-c secondary voltage.

Semiconductor Diode Rectifiers

The operation of half-wave rectifiers using semiconductor diodes (referred to as *metallic rectifiers*) is basically the same as that of the vacuum-tube diode rectifiers discussed earlier.

Figure 2-9 shows the schematic diagram and waveforms of a metallic half-wave rectifier circuit.

A surge resistor, R_s, is placed in series with the rectifier element and the power transformer secondary winding to limit the peak current through the rectifier. If no surge resistor were present in the circuit, possible damage to the rectifier element could result from large surges of current when power is first applied to the circuit. This problem is not present in the vacuum-tube circuits discussed previously because of the time required to heat the cathode of the tube. The value of R_s depends on the peak current rating of the rectifier element.

The operation of a metallic full-wave rectifier (figure 2-9) is similar to that of a vacuum-tube diode full-wave rectifier. Notice that the circuit in figure 2-9 is similar to the circuit shown in figure 2-6, except that metallic rectifiers are used in place of the vacuum-tube diodes, and surge resistors (R_{s1} and R_{s2}) are included in the metallic-rectifier circuit.

The metallic bridge rectifier, similar to the vacuum-tube bridge rectifier, does not require a center-tapped high-voltage secondary winding.

In fact, the operation of the metallic bridge rectifier is similar in all respects to that of the vacuum-tube bridge rectifier.

The advantages of bridge rectifiers, mentioned earlier under vacuum-tube bridge rectifiers, also apply to metallic bridge rectifiers.

Voltage-Doubler Circuits

Half-Wave Voltage Doubler

A voltage doubler is a rectifier circuit whose maximum d-c output voltage (for all practical purposes) is equal to twice the peak value of the a-c secondary voltage. The circuit diagram of a half-wave voltage doubler is shown in part A of figure 2-10. By adding more rectifiers and capacitor networks to the basic doubler circuit, voltage-multiplier circuits that produce output voltages many times larger than the peak a-c secondary voltage can be obtained. Voltage-doubler circuits produce high voltages at low currents; hence, their use is restricted to applications with these needs.

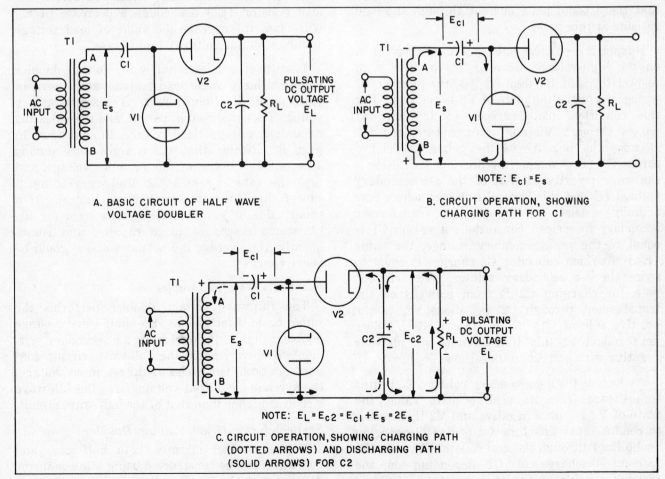

A. BASIC CIRCUIT OF HALF WAVE VOLTAGE DOUBLER

B. CIRCUIT OPERATION, SHOWING CHARGING PATH FOR C1

NOTE: $E_{c1} = E_s$

C. CIRCUIT OPERATION, SHOWING CHARGING PATH (DOTTED ARROWS) AND DISCHARGING PATH (SOLID ARROWS) FOR C2

NOTE: $E_L = E_{c2} = E_{c1} + E_s = 2E_s$

Figure 2-10. Schematic Diagram and Circuit Operation of a Half-Wave Voltage Doubler

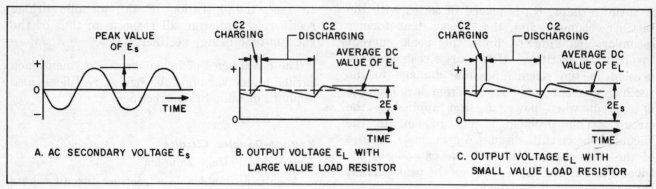

Figure 2-11. Waveforms of Half-Wave Voltage Doubler

To understand the circuit operation of the half-wave voltage doubler, first refer to part B of figure 2-10. During the negative half cycles of a-c secondary voltage (E_s), when point A is negative with respect to point B, the plate of V1 is positive with respect to its cathode while the plate of V2 is negative with respect to its cathode. As a result, plate current passes through V1, and charges capacitor C1 to a value (E_{c1}) equal to the peak value of the a-c secondary voltage. Notice that there is no plate current through the load resistor at this time.

During the positive half cycles, when point A on the high-voltage secondary is positive with respect to point B (figure 2-10), the plate of V1 is negative while the plate of V2 is positive. For this condition, plate current (dotted arrows) passes through V2 and charges capacitor C2. Because the polarity of the voltage developed across C1 (E_{c1}) during the previous half cycle is the same polarity as that of the a-c secondary voltage (E_s) at this time, the voltage source now actually consists of C1 and the transformer secondary in series. Since the voltage on C1 is equal to the peak secondary voltage, the value (E_{c2}) to which capacitor C2 charges is equal to twice the a-c secondary voltage. The current path for charging C2 is from point B on the transformer, through C2 and diode V2, to the positive side of C1. Notice that diode V1 does not conduct at this time because its plate is negative with respect to its cathode.

As soon as the a-c secondary voltage, E_s, begins to decrease from its peak positive value, the plate of V2 becomes negative and V2 then ceases to conduct. At this time C2 begins discharging (solid line) through the load resistor, R_L, with the rate of discharge of C2 depending on the resistance value of the load resistor. If R_L is large, a small current passes through the load resistor and C2 discharges slowly. This causes the voltage of capacitor C2 to be very nearly equal to twice the value of the a-c secondary voltage. If R_L is small, a large current passes through the load resistor, causing C2 to discharge more rapidly, which, in turn, causes the voltage of C2 to decrease to a lower voltage at the end of each discharge cycle. Because the voltage of capacitor C2 (E_{c2}) and the voltage developed across the load resistor (E_L) are equal, a decrease in E_{c2} will cause the average d-c value of load voltage (doubler output voltage) to decrease.

The waveforms of a half-wave voltage doubler having a large value load resistor are shown in parts A and B of figure 2-11. The a-c secondary voltage (E_s) is shown in part A, and the pulsating d-c output voltage (load voltage, E_L) is shown in part B. Notice that C2 charges only during alternate half cycles of the a-c input voltage, and that the rate at which C2 discharges is much slower than the rate at which it charges. If a small value of load resistance were used for R_L, C2 would discharge more rapidly, and consequently, the average d-c output voltage would be lower (part C).

Full-Wave Voltage Doubler

The full-wave voltage doubler performs the same basic function as the half-wave voltage doubler; that is, it doubles the a-c secondary voltage. However, since the full-wave circuit conducts on both half cycles of the a-c input voltage, the average d-c output voltage from the full-wave circuit is higher than that of the half-wave circuit.

Semiconductor-Diode Voltage Doubler

Voltage-doubler circuits, both half-wave and full-wave, can be constructed using semiconductor diodes (metallic rectifiers), as well as vacuum-tube diodes. The operation of these types of circuits is similar to that of the vacuum-tube circuits just discussed.

Transformerless Power Supply Circuits

The a-c source voltage can be rectified in a type of power supply that does not use a power transformer. In such a circuit, the a-c input voltage is connected directly to the rectifier tube. The average d-c output voltage of this type of rectifier is approximately equal to the a-c input voltage. To obtain a higher output voltage, a voltage multiplier (doubler, tripler, etc) can be used. This type of rectifier circuit can be operated from either an a-c power source or a d-c power source, since the power transformer is eliminated. An advantage of the transformerless power supply, or *line rectifier as* it is commonly called, is its compactness. This makes the unit easily adaptable for small a-c/d-c portable radios, test equipment, and other electronic equipment applications where space is limited. A disadvantage of this circuit is its low output current.

A few of the more common line-rectifier circuits are shown in figure 2-12. Notice the similarity (excluding the power transformer) of these circuits to the equivalent transformer circuits discussed earlier.

Notice that the negative output terminal (B–) of the rectifier is connected directly to one side of the power line. If this negative terminal were connected directly to the chassis of the equipment, as is commonly done with power transformer type circuits, possible dangers of fire hazard and electrical shock would be introduced. These dangers are present when one side of the power line is grounded, which is usually done in most sections of the United States. Depending on the direction in which the equipment power plug is inserted into the power outlet, either side of the power line (grounded or ungrounded) may be connected to the chassis. If the ungrounded side were connected to the chassis, touching any part of the equipment could result in an electrical shock. The possibility of fire is present since an accidental short circuit of the power leads may cause a short circuit of the power lines.

The dangers of electrical shock and fire can be eliminated by using a *bus bar* or other insulated conductor (insulated from the chassis) for the B– line. In cases such as this, the B– line is connected to the chassis of the equipment through a 0.1-microfarad (or smaller) capacitor. Such a

capacitor, called the *buffer capacitor*, provides a low-impedance path for rf, but presents high impedance to the a-c input frequency (usually 60 cps).

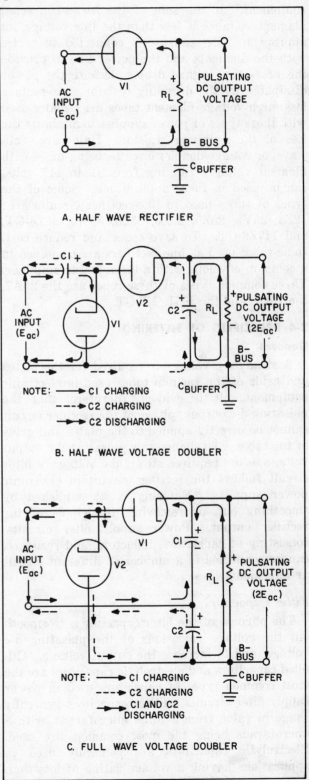

A. HALF WAVE RECTIFIER

NOTE: → C1 CHARGING
      --→ C2 CHARGING
      ⇢ C2 DISCHARGING

B. HALF WAVE VOLTAGE DOUBLER

NOTE: → C1 CHARGING
      --→ C2 CHARGING
      ⇢ C1 AND C2 DISCHARGING

C. FULL WAVE VOLTAGE DOUBLER

Figure 2-12. Transformerless Power Supply Circuits (Line Rectifiers)

Since the power transformer is eliminated in line-rectifier circuits, the filament of the rectifier tube is usually connected in series with the power line and the filaments of the other tubes in the equipment. If the sum of the series-connected filament voltages is less than the line voltage, an appropriate size resistor is connected in series with the filaments and the power line to provide the necessary voltage drop. Because the power dissipated by the dropping resistor represents a loss, high-voltage filament tubes are usually used with these types of power supplies to minimize the loss of the dropping resistor. Half-wave, full-wave, or voltage-doubler circuits, using tubes with filament voltages ranging from 12 to 117 volts, can be used in these applications. Some of the types of tubes used in line-rectifier circuits are: 12Z3, 25Y5, 25Z5, 25Z6, 35Z5, 35W4, 45Z5-GT, and 117Z6-GT. To save space and reduce cost, some tubes used as line rectifiers are combined in a common envelope with a beam-power amplifier. Three common types of these tubes are the 25A7, the 70L7, and the 117L/M7-GT.

2-4 PRINCIPLES OF FILTERING
General

A steady d-c voltage is required for the plates and grids of the vacuum tubes used in electronic equipment. It is evident, therefore, that the pulsating d-c output voltage of the rectifier circuit cannot be directly applied to the plates and grids of the tubes. To change this pulsating d-c output voltage to the required steady d-c voltage, a filter circuit follows the rectifier circuit in electronic power supplies. Filtering is accomplished by smoothing out, or removing, the ripple of the rectifier output. Power supply filter circuits, consisting of capacitors, inductors, and resistors, can be connected in a number of different circuit arrangements.

Filter Capacitors

The purpose of the filter capacitor is to smooth out the voltage variations of the pulsating d-c voltage, and to increase the output voltage. Oil-filled capacitors and electrolytic capacitors are the most common types of capacitors used in power supply filter circuits. Filter capacitors generally range in value from 2 to 50 microfarads, with 8 microfarads being the most common size used. Electrolytic capacitors are generally used in applications having a voltage rating of less than 800 volts. For higher voltage ratings, oil-filled capacitors or oil-impregnated paper capacitors are generally employed. Because electrolytic capacitors are polarized, the positive (+) terminal of the capacitor must be connected to the most positive side of the voltage source. This is a very important characteristic of electrolytic capacitors. When oil-filled capacitors are used, however, either terminal can be connected to the positive side of the voltage source because oil-filled capacitors are not polarized.

Capacitors are usually rated in terms of the d-c working voltage and the peak voltage. The d-c working voltage is the maximum d-c voltage that the capacitor can safely withstand under continuous operating conditions. The peak voltage is the d-c voltage plus the peak a-c ripple voltage that the capacitor can safely withstand under continuous operating conditions. In a filter circuit using a capacitor as the first element of the filter (capacitor-input filter), the peak voltage rating of the capacitor is very critical.

Filter Inductors

The primary purpose of the inductor used in a power supply filter circuit is to smooth out the current variations of the rectifier output. Inductors used in power supplies are usually referred to as *filter chokes*, since the action of the inductor opposes, or chokes, any variation of current through it. Filter chokes generally range in value from 5 to 30 henrys, with 15 henrys being the most common value used.

Filter chokes designed to have a specified value of inductance at full-load current and a different value of inductance at no-load current are called *swinging chokes*. A swinging choke provides a means of preventing the ratio of peak to average plate current from becoming excessive as the load current varies over a wide range. The usual way of rating swinging chokes is by specifying minimum and maximum values of inductance for full-load and no-load currents, respectively. Values of inductance ranging from 5 henrys at full-load current to 25 henrys at no-load current are typical for swinging chokes.

Three factors that determine the rating of a filter choke are: inductance, direct current rating, and d-c resistance. The inductance of a choke coil varies inversely with the value of direct current passing through it. For this reason the inductance of a choke is specified for the rated full-load current. The d-c resistance of the choke is important because of its effect on voltage regulation.

Voltage Regulation

The variation in d-c output voltage of the rectifier from no-load voltage to full-load voltage is called the voltage regulation. Voltage regulation is usually expressed as a percentage of the d-c output voltage at full load by the following formula:

$$\% \text{ of Voltage Regulation} = \frac{E_{NL} - E_{FL}}{E_{FL}} \times 100$$

$$(2\text{-}1)$$

where:

E_{NL} = no-load voltage
E_{FL} = full-load voltage

Ripple Voltage

The pulsating d-c output voltage of the rectifier may be considered as a steady voltage having an alternating voltage component superimposed on it. The alternating component is called the *ripple voltage*. The frequency of this ripple voltage depends upon the frequency of the input voltage and the type of rectifier circuit (half-wave, full-wave, etc). The ripple voltage does not vary in the same manner as does a perfect sine wave. For this reason the ripple voltage may be considered to consist of a fundamental frequency and its harmonics. Since the effects of the harmonics is negligible, compared to that of the fundamental, the harmonics are usually ignored. The fundamental frequency of the ripple voltage is equal to the frequency of the a-c input signal for half-wave rectifiers. For full-wave rectifiers the ripple voltage fundamental frequency is twice the a-c input frequency.

The effectiveness of a filter can be measured by a ratio called the *ripple factor*. The ripple factor is the ratio of the effective (r-m-s) value of the fundamental component of the ripple voltage to the average value of the d-c output voltage. The ripple factor is usually expressed by the formula:

$$k_r = \frac{E_r}{E_{dc}}$$

$$(2\text{-}2)$$

where:

k_r = ripple factor
E_r = r-m-s value of fundamental component of ripple voltage, in volts
E_{dc} = average value of output voltage, in volts

When the ripple voltage is expressed in terms of percentage of the output voltage, the following formula is used:

$$\% \text{ of Ripple Voltage} = \frac{E_r}{E_{dc}} \times 100$$

$$(2\text{-}3)$$

where:

E_r and E_{dc} are as defined for formula (2-2).

Types of Filter Circuits

Power supply filter circuits are primarily in the low-pass filter group. These filters are designed to pass all frequencies below a predetermined cutoff frequency, and satisfactorily suppress all frequencies above this cutoff frequency. Since the output of the power supply filter is a d-c voltage, the cutoff frequency is usually between zero frequency and the expected ripple frequency. The cutoff frequency is chosen so that the lowest value of expected ripple frequency is adequately suppressed.

Power supply filter circuits are generally classified as capacitor-input or choke-input filters, depending on whether the first element in the filter is a capacitor or choke. Examples of typical capacitor-input and choke-input filters are illus-

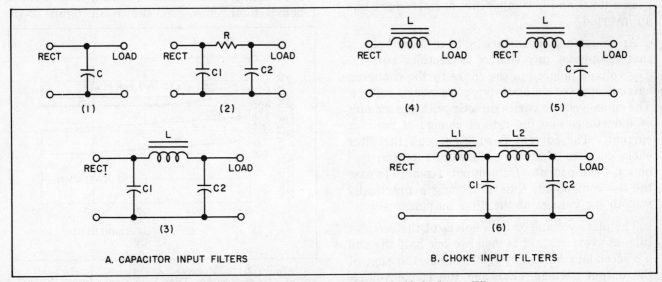

Figure 2-13. Typical Capacitor-Input and Choke-Input Filters

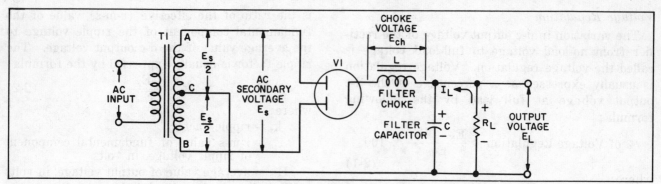

Figure 2-14. Schematic Diagram of Full-Wave Rectifier with Choke-Input Filter

trated in figure 2-13. These filter circuits can be further classified as e i t h e r single-section or double-section filters. Single-section filters are represented by (1), (4), and (5) in figure 2-13, and double-section filters are represented by (2), (3), and (6).

Notice that the capacitor is across the load in all the filter circuits shown. As the ripple frequency increases, the reactance of the capacitor decreases. This causes the ripple frequency to be bypassed, eliminating these variations from the output voltage. If the capacitors were placed in series with the load, the capacitor would block the direct current flow and there would be no output from the filter.

Choke-Input Filter

Filters consisting of combinations of capacitors and inductors (chokes) provide better filtering action than single-capacitor filters. A full-wave rectifier having a single-section, choke-input filter is shown in figure 2-14. This type of filter is also called an *L-type filter* because on schematic diagrams its L and C components are arranged like an inverted L.

An important characteristic of a filter choke is that it opposes any change in rectifier current. The voltage induced in the choke by the changing current opposes changes in a-c secondary voltage. The choke voltage varies directly with the amount of inductance and the rate of change of rectifier current. The current flowing through the filter choke consists of an a-c component superimposed on a d-c component. Capacitor C tends to bypass the a-c component, thus producing a practically smooth d-c voltage at the filter output.

The plate voltage of both halves of the rectifier tube at every instant is equal to one-half the full a-c secondary voltage ($E_s/2$), minus the sum of the output voltage (E_1) and the choke voltage

(E_{ch}). Because the choke voltage opposes any change in a-c secondary voltage, the plate voltage of each half of the rectifier tube is maintained positive during alternate half cycles of secondary voltage, and conduction occurs over the entire cycle of a-c secondary voltage. Although the output voltage never reaches the peak value of the secondary voltage, the average value of d-c output voltage of a choke-input filter is approximately equal to the average value of the secondary voltage. The output voltage of a power supply with a choke-input filter is less than that of a power supply with a single-capacitor filter. However, the voltage regulation of the power supply with a choke-input filter is better than that of a power supply using a capacitance filter.

Tube manuals usually include graphs that show the rectifier d-c output voltage at the input to the filter plotted against the load current (d-c output current) for various types of rectifier tubes used with choke-input filters. A graph showing the voltage-regulation characteristics of a 5U4-G full-wave rectifier tube, used in conjunction with a 3-henry filter choke, is shown in figure 2-15.

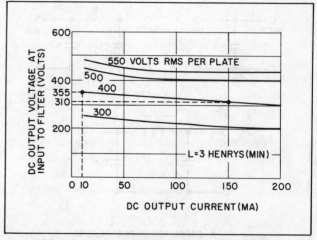

Figure 2-15. Voltage-Regulation Characteristics of 5U4-G Rectifier Tube with Choke-Input Filter

Notice that the rectifier d-c output voltage at the input to the filter (vertical axis) is less than the r-m-s voltage applied to each plate. Also notice that there is little change in the rectifier d-c output voltage as the load current (horizontal axis) increases. The vertical axis represents only the d-c output voltage of the rectifier tube, and does not include the d-c voltage drop in the filter choke. Thus, to find the d-c voltage at the output of the filter, subtract the d-c voltage drop in the choke from the voltages shown by the graph.

When a choke-input filter is operated at practically zero load current, the voltages induced in the choke decrease to a very small value, and the choke ceases to be effective. In this case, the choke-input filter acts like a simple capacitance filter, and the rectifier tube conducts in short pulses. When this occurs, the filter capacitor charges to a voltage practically equal to the peak value of the a-c secondary voltage ($E_s/2$), and the d-c output voltage increases.

To improve voltage regulation at light loads, a swinging choke is sometimes used. Filter chokes are usually designed with an air gap in the iron core to prevent magnetic saturation of the iron core when the choke is operating at its rated d-c load current. The swinging choke has a very small air gap so that decreasing the d-c load current to a small value causes a large increase in inductance. The swinging choke provides greater smoothing action at light loads, thereby increasing the useful operating range of the filter.

The output voltage and peak plate current of the rectifier depend on the input choke inductance and the d-c load resistance. The minimum value of inductance that is required to keep the output voltage at the average value of the a-c voltage being rectified is called the *critical inductance*. The choke-input filter tends to act like a capacitor-input filter if the inductance of the choke is less than the critical value, because under these conditions the choke presents a relatively small impedance to the a-c component of the rectified output. Increasing the choke inductance to more than its critical value further decreases the ratio of peak to average plate current. This maintains a more nearly constant flow of current through the choke. If the value of choke inductance is increased to more than twice its critical value, the operating characteristic of the filter is not appreciably improved. Thus, the optimum value of choke inductance is equal to twice the critical value of inductance.

The percentage of ripple voltage for a single-section, choke-input filter can be approximated by using the following formula:

$$\% \text{ of } E_r \cong \frac{144 \times 10^4}{(f_r)^2 \, LC} \qquad (2\text{-}4)$$

where:

   f_r = ripple frequency, in cps
   L = filter inductance, in henrys
   C = filter capacitance, in microfarads

When a single-section, choke-input filter does not provide adequate filtering, another identical section is usually connected in series with it. See filter (6) in part B of figure 2-13. The first inductor is called the *input choke* and the second is called the *smoothing choke*. For double-section filters, the total percentage of ripple voltage is approximately equal to the product of the individual percentages of ripple voltage (of each section) divided by 100.

Capacitor-Input Filter

A basic capacitor-input filter is shown at (3) in part A of figure 2-13. This type of filter is often called a *pi-section filter* because its schematic arrangement resembles the Greek letter π (pi). Capacitor C1 operates as a single-section capacitance filter and produces a higher output voltage than can be obtained with a choke-input filter. Filter choke L and capacitor C2 provide additional filtering action. The capacitor-input filter is used in applications where inexpensive power supplies are required, since it allows the maximum d-c output voltage with a minimum of ripple for a given transformer secondary voltage. Thus, a smaller power transformer can be used with a capacitor-input filter. The capacitor-input filter is undesirable for applications that require a large current, because the peak current that must flow in the tubes to charge the input capacitor may damage the tubes. Since the capacitor-input filter has poor voltage regulation, it is almost always used in applications where the load current is practically constant.

Tube manuals usually include graphs that show the rectifier d-c output voltage at the input to the filter plotted against the load current (d-c output current) for various types of rectifier tubes used with capacitor-input filters. A graph showing the voltage-regulation characteristics of a 5U4-G full-wave rectifier tube, used in conjunction with a 4-microfarad input capacitor, is shown in figure 2-16. Notice that the d-c output voltage of the rectifier decreases rapidly as the load current

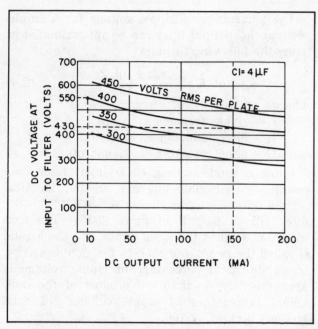

*Figure 2-16. Voltage-Regulation Characteristics
of 5U4-G Rectifier Tube with
Capacitor-Input Filter*

increases. To find the d-c output voltages of the filter, subtract the voltage drop in the filter choke from the voltage values plotted on the graph.

The percentage of ripple voltage at the output of a pi-section filter, similar to circuit (3) in figure 2-13, can be approximated by using the following formula:

$$\% \text{ of } E_{r2} \cong \frac{2.245 \times 10^7}{R_L \, C_1 \, f_r \, [\, (3.984 \times 10^{-5} \, L \, C_2 \, f_r^2) - 1\,]}$$

$$(2-5)$$

where:

E_{r2} = ripple voltage at capacitor C2, in volts
f_r = frequency of ripple voltage, in cps
R_L = resistance of load, in ohms
L = inductance of choke, in henrys
C_1 = capacitance of C1, in microfarads
C_2 = capacitance of C2, in microfarads

In comparison to the choke-input filter, the capacitor-input filter delivers voltages at lighter loads. Although the filtering characteristics are better than those of a choke-input filter, the capacitor-input filter has poorer voltage regulation. The ratio of peak rectifier current to average current is higher in the capacitor-input filter, because the rectifier current in this type of filter flows in pulses rather than at a uniform rate. The d-c working voltage rating of the input capacitor should never be less than the peak transformer voltage. In fact, as a safety precaution, the working voltage of the input capacitor

is usually selected to be higher than this value. Capacitor-input filters are generally used in applications requiring relatively small amounts of power, such as test equipment, radio receivers, and public-address systems.

Resistance-Capacitance Filter

A resistance-capacitance filter (R-C filter) is formed by placing a resistor in series with the load, with the filter capacitor connected across the load. The resistor R, in such a circuit is used in place of a choke (replacing L in circuit (5) of figure 2-13) when the load current of a power supply is very small. Filter action is obtained when the resistance of the series resistor, R, is high compared with the capacitive reactance of the filter capacitor, C. The R-C time of this filter must be large compared with the time of one cycle of the cutoff frequency. The d-c resistance of the R-C filter is comparatively high, making the voltage drop, heat dissipation, and voltage regulation high.

The percentage of ripple voltage in the output of a single-section R-C filter may be determined by using the following formula:

$$\% \text{ of } E_r \cong \frac{100}{2\pi \, f_r \, RC} \qquad (2-6)$$

where:

f_r = ripple frequency, in cps
R = filter resistance, in ohms
C = filter capacitance, in farads

The ripple voltage in an R-C filter, or a single-section capacitance filter, can be reduced to an acceptable value if additional filter sections are provided. A double-section filter, consisting of a single-section capacitor filter and a single-section R-C filter, is shown at (2) in figure 2-13. Such a filter is actually a form of capacitor-input filter. An approximation of the percentage of ripple voltage of this double-section filter can be found by using the formula:

$$\% \text{ of } E_{r2} \cong \frac{3.573 \times 10^{12}}{f_r^2 \, C_1 \, C_2 \, R \, R_L} \qquad (2-7)$$

where:

E_{r2} = ripple voltage at capacitor C2, in volts
f_r = frequency of ripple voltage, in cps
C_1 = capacitance of C1, in microfarads
C_2 = capacitance of C2, in microfarads
R_L = resistance of load, in ohms
R = resistance of R, in ohms

The percentages of ripple voltage obtained with this formula are not extremely accurate, but fairly close results are obtained for long time constants of R and C2.

2-5 VOLTAGE DIVIDERS

A voltage divider is generally connected in the output of a power supply (between the filter and the load) to provide a selection of different values of d-c output voltages. In most instances, the voltage divider consists of either a single resistor with a sliding tap (variable resistor) or a combination of fixed-value resistors in series. A voltage divider is required in every power supply that delivers power to a load having a variety of voltage and current requirements.

When connected in the output of a power supply, the voltage divider also acts as a bleeder resistor. The purpose of a bleeder resistor is to serve as a temporary light load for the rectifier immediately after the equipment is turned on. Rectifier tube filaments are usually of the directly heated type and deliver current very soon after the application of power, while the tubes in the load generally employ indirectly heated cathodes and require some time to begin operating. The bleeder resistor prevents any high-voltage surge from being applied to the load during the initial warm-up period.

It is particularly important that a bleeder resistor be used with a choke-input filter. When the load is removed from a power supply with a choke-input filter, the choke action is no longer present (an inductor must have a changing current to produce a counter emf). Hence, the filter effectively becomes a capacitor-input filter, and causes the output voltage to rise to the peak value. The use of a bleeder resistor prevents this effect by providing a light load, which allows the passage of sufficient current to maintain the action of the choke. Because the bleeder resistor draws a fixed amount of current from the power supply (usually 10 to 20 percent of full-load current) at all times, it reduces the no-load output voltage of the power supply. Thus, the bleeder resistor improves the voltage regulation of the power supply by reducing the voltage difference between that obtained at no-load and at full-load.

Another important function of the bleeder resistor is to supply a path for discharging the filter capacitors after the equipment is turned off. This function is most important in high-voltage power supplies, where the filter capacitors can store a lethal quantity of energy. It is also important in low voltage power supply circuits, where the filter capacitors often store enough energy to damage test instruments.

Bias Voltages

If the location of the zero reference point is properly selected, both positive and negative voltages can be obtained from the same voltage divider. The negative voltages developed in a voltage divider are called *bias voltages*. These bias voltages are usually applied to the control grids of the vacuum tubes (where such voltages are required) in the equipment.

Some types of equipment use separate power supplies to produce the required positive and negative voltages. When used to produce the negative voltages, the power supply is commonly called a *bias supply*. A bias supply circuit, consisting of a metallic half-wave rectifier, an R-C filter, and a variable-resistor voltage divider, is shown in figure 2-17. The operation of the rectifier is similar to that of the half-wave rectifier discussed under Semiconductor-Diode Rectifiers. Notice that the zero reference point (ground) is at the positive end (top) of the variable resistor. Therefore, any voltage selected by the sliding tap of the resistor is negative with respect to ground.

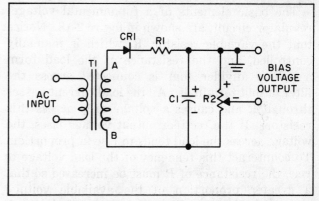

Figure 2-17. Schematic Diagram of Metallic-Rectifier Bias Supply

2-6 VOLTAGE REGULATORS

Most electronic equipment can operate satisfactorily with a certain amount of variation in the supply voltage without suffering any operational deficiency. However, some circuits are very critical, and even slight deviations from the normal supply voltage cause unsatisfactory operation. These circuits require the use of some type of voltage-regulating device. The voltage-regulating device may be inserted in the circuit either between the rectifier and its load, or at the power source that supplies electrical energy to the rectifier. The regulators that are used within the power supply are generally electronic, while those in the power source itself are generally mechanical. Only the electronic regulators are covered in the following discussion.

Fundamental Voltage Regulator

A regulator used to stabilize the output voltage of a rectifier usually takes the form of a variable resistance in series with the output. Thus the variable resistance and load resistance form a voltage divider. The variable element is controllable so that the voltage across the load can be held constant.

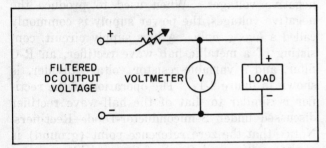

Figure 2-18. Simplified Diagram of Fundamental Voltage Regulator

The basic elements of a fundamental voltage-regulator circuit, are shown in figure 2-18. Notice that the variable resistor, R, which is manually controlled, and the resistance of the load form a voltage divider that is connected across the filter output terminals. All the load current passes through R and causes a voltage drop across this resistor. If the rectifier output voltage rises, the voltage across the load tends to rise in proportion. To counteract this tendency of the load voltage to rise, the resistance of R must be increased so that a greater proportion of the available voltage appears across R. The voltage across the load, therefore, is held constant if the resistance of R is increased sufficiently to counteract the increase of the rectifier output voltage. If the resistance of the load increases, a greater portion of the available rectifier voltage tends to appear across the load. When this occurs, the resistance of R must be increased in order to hold the load voltage constant.

In this fundamental voltage regulator, the variable resistor, R, must be adjusted manually in order to keep the voltage across the load constant. The same basic action must take place in all voltage regulators. However, in actual practice, automatic voltage regulators are used because they respond more quickly and are more accurate than the manually operated regulator.

Ballast-Tube Voltage Regulator

One type of automatic voltage regulator is the ballast-tube regulator. The regulator tube consists of an iron wire enclosed in a hydrogen-filled envelope. The resistance of the iron wire in the tube varies as the current through it varies. If the rectifier output voltage tends to increase, more current passes through the ballast tube. The resistance of the tube then increases and more of the output voltage is dropped across the tube. The voltage across the load, therefore, remains nearly constant.

The ballast-tube regulator does not regulate the rectifier output voltage if the load changes. If the load current increases, more current is drawn from the power supply and the load voltage decreases. In addition, the greater current drawn by the load causes the resistance of the ballast tube to increase, and the load voltage is made even lower by this additional drop in the ballast tube.

Although a ballast-tube regulator may be used to compensate for line voltage variations, it is generally inserted in series with several additional elements through which it is desired to maintain a constant current flow. In such applications, the resistance of the ballast tube changes to counteract the effect of changing voltage across the circuit.

VR Tube Voltage Regulators
VR Tube Characteristics

The voltage-regulator tube (VR tube) is one of the simplest means for keeping the output voltage of a rectifier constant. Four of the most widely used types of VR tubes are the OA3/VR-75, OB3/VR-90, OC3/VR-105, and OD3/VR-150. The first three identifying characters (OA3, OB3, OC3, and OD3) are often omitted, and the tubes are referred to simply as VR-75, VR-90, VR-105, and VR-150, respectively. The numbers 75, 90, 105, and 150 indicate the operating voltages of the tubes. The minimum plate current for these voltage-regulator tubes is approximately 5 ma, and the maximum plate current is usually between 30 and 40 ma. Besides being rated according to voltage drop (operating voltage), VR tubes are also rated according to the maximum current that can be allowed to flow through them. For example, a VR-105/40 maintains a 105-volt output, and has a maximum current rating of 40 ma. All of the aforementioned VR tubes are of the cold-cathode, glow-discharge, gas-filled type.

The characteristics curve of a VR-105 tube is shown in figure 2-19. Notice that the plate voltage is essentially constant over a wide range of plate current. For a gas tube to conduct when a voltage is applied, the voltage must exceed the ionizing potential, which is the potential required to ionize the gas in the tube. For example, the ionization potential of the VR-105 is 115 volts. When the applied voltage exceeds this value, the gas in the tube breaks down (ionizes) and the plate voltage drops to 105 volts. For positive firing of the VR-105, a minimum striking potential of 133 volts is required. The plate voltage remains essentially constant (only a 4-volt change) at 105 volts over a plate current range of 5 to 40 ma. To maintain ionization of the gas, the plate current must be kept larger than 5 ma, but to prevent damage to the tube, the current must not be allowed to exceed 40 ma.

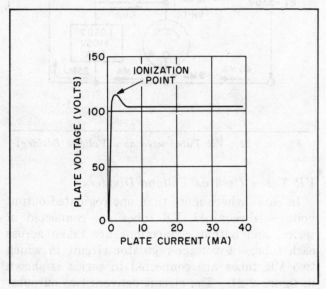

Figure 2-19. Characteristics Curve of VR-105 Tube

The characteristics curves of VR-75, VR-90, and VR-150 tubes are similar to the characteristics curve of the VR-105. The principal differences are the value of ionization potential and the value of constant output voltage maintained across each tube; also, the maximum current rating of the VR-90 is 30 ma instead of 40 ma. The ionization potential of a VR tube is usually 10 to 20 percent higher than the voltage rating of the tube. For this reason, the minimum d-c starting voltage (striking potential) of a VR tube is usually 30 percent higher than the voltage rating of the tube.

VR Tube Regulator Circuit Operation

The circuit diagram of a VR tube voltage regulator is shown in figure 2-20. A current-limiting resistor, R, and a VR-75 tube are connected between the output of the power supply filter and the load resistor, R_L. The current-limiting resistor and the load resistor form a single voltage divider. The voltage appearing across the load resistor before the VR tube begins to operate (ionizes) can be determined by the formula:

$$E_L = E_f \frac{R_L}{R_L + R} \qquad (2-8)$$

where:

E_L = voltage across R_L, in volts

E_f = d-c output voltage of filter, in volts

R = current-limiting resistance, in ohms

R_L = load resistance, in ohms

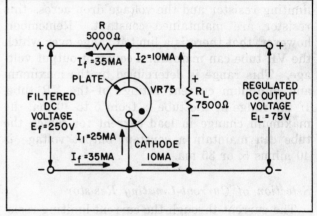

Figure 2-20. Schematic Diagram of VR-Tube Voltage Regulator

The VR-75 tube draws just enough current to maintain its plate voltage constant at 75 volts. To determine the current through the current-limiting resistor required to maintain an output voltage of 75 volts, use the formula:

$$I_f = \frac{E_f - E_r}{R} \qquad (2-9)$$

where:

I_f = d-c current from filter, in amperes

E_f = d-c output voltage of filter, in volts

E_r = regulated d-c output voltage, in volts

R = current-limiting resistance, in ohms

If the power supply voltage rises above 250 volts, the VR tube draws more current. This increases the voltage drop across the limiting resistor, R, and thereby maintains the plate voltage (and load voltage) at 75 volts. On the other hand, if the power supply voltage decreases, the VR tube draws less current, the voltage drop across the limiting resistor decreases, and the load voltage is maintained at 75 volts. Thus, regardless of an increase or decrease in the power supply voltage, the voltage across the VR tube (and the load resistor) is held constant.

The VR tube regulator can also regulate the output voltage in the event that the load current (I_2) changes. For example, consider the case where the load current is increased by decreasing the load resistance. As soon as the load current starts to increase, the current through the current limiting resistor also begins to increase, and the load voltage starts to decrease. For this condition, the current drawn by the VR tube decreases by the same amount that the load current increases. Thus, both the current through the limiting resistor and the voltage drop across this resistor are maintained constant. Remember, however, that there is a limited range over which the VR tube can maintain a constant output voltage. This range is determined by the maximum and minimum current ratings of the VR tube. If the range of the tube is from 5 to 40 ma, the maximum change in load current for which the tube can maintain a constant output voltage is 40 minus 5, or 35 ma.

Selection of Current-Limiting Resistor

The current through the current-limiting resistor is equal to the sum of the VR-tube current and the load current. In a properly designed voltage-regulator circuit, the current through the limiting resistor is limited to a value that the VR tube can pass safely. If this is not done, disconnecting the load resistance will cause an overload that will damage the VR tube. The maximum plate-current rating of VR-75, VR-105, and VR-150 tubes is 40 ma, while that of the VR-90 is 30 ma. The value of resistance for the limiting resistor required to limit the plate current of the VR tube to the maximum allowable value can be determined by using the formula:

$$R = \frac{E_f - E_r}{I_{max}} \qquad (2\text{-}10)$$

where:

R = minimum value of current-limiting resistance, in ohms

E_f = d-c output voltage of filter, in volts

E_r = regulated d-c output voltage, in volts

I_{max} = maximum rated VR-tube current, in amperes

In practical applications it is common practice to select a resistance value slightly larger than the calculated value of R. However, the use of too high a resistance value must be avoided, because an excessive amount of resistance will restrict the load current to a very low value.

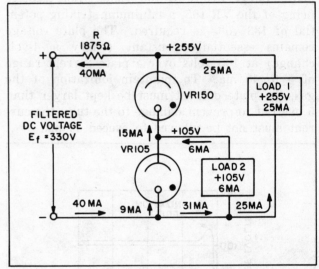

Figure 2-21. VR Tubes used as a Voltage Divider

VR Tubes Used as Voltage Dividers

In cases where more than one regulated output voltage is required, VR tubes are connected in series, and output connections are taken across each tube. A voltage-regulator circuit in which two VR tubes are connected in series is shown in figure 2-21. The circuit delivers two outputs: load 1, 255 volts at 25 ma; and load 2, 105 volts at 6 ma. VR tubes generally are not connected in parallel. If one of the tubes in a parallel-connected circuit is defective, the other tube may be forced to draw more current than its maximum rated value and thus be damaged.

Notice (in figure 2-21) that the voltage across load 1 is the sum of the operating voltages of the series VR tubes. If additional regulated voltages (at low current drains) are required, three or more VR tubes can be connected in series. However, the minimum and maximum current ratings of the VR tubes must be observed if proper circuit operation is to be expected.

In some cases, the changes in load voltage may be too rapid for the VR tube to operate properly.

Under these conditions, a capacitor is sometimes connected in parallel with the VR tube. The purpose of the capacitor is to shunt the rapid changes (pulses) until the VR tube can regain control of the circuit. The size of the shunt capacitor used should be limited to the values indicated in the tube manual for a particular type of tube. The maximum value of capacitance used is usually less than 1 microfarad.

2-7 SUMMARY

Electronic power supplies are used to provide the d-c voltages necessary for the operation of electronic equipment. The type of circuit arrangement of a power supply depends upon the particular application in the equipment.

A power supply is basically composed of a rectifier device and an associated filter network. Power supply rectifiers can be arranged to form half-wave, full-wave, or bridge type circuits. The pulsating d-c current develops a voltage across the load connected to the supply. In order to provide a steady source of d-c voltage, a filter network is inserted between the rectifier and the load. The circuit arrangement of the filter — either capacitor or choke input — is dependent upon whether the supply is required to deliver a high voltage at a low current or a lower voltage at a higher current.

If it is desired that a power supply be capable of producing a higher-voltage output than that supplied by the alternating input voltage, a voltage-doubler circuit can be employed, if the current requirement is not too great.

The voltage regulation and the amount of ripple are important in some applications. To improve the voltage regulation of a power supply, ballast or VR tubes can be employed. The action of these devices is to automatically adjust the voltage and current output to maintain a constant output to the equipment load. By careful choice of filter circuit arrangement and values, the amount of ripple present on the output voltage can be minimized.

REVIEW QUESTIONS

1. Name three sources of power for electronic equipment.

2. What is the polarity relationship between the cathode and plate of a vacuum-tube diode when conducting? When cutoff?

3. What is meant by the term *peak plate current*?

4. What is meant by the term *peak inverse voltage*?

5. What limits the peak inverse voltage?

6. What is a metallic rectifier?

7. Describe the operation of the half-wave rectifier.

8. Why are greater d-c output voltages obtained from a full-wave rectifier than from a half-wave rectifier?

9. What is the frequency of the ripple voltage in a half-wave rectifier? In a full-wave rectifier?

10. What advantages does the bridge rectifier have over the half-wave and full-wave rectifiers?

11. Explain the operation of the voltage doubler.

12. Why is filtering required in a power supply?

13. Describe some of the characteristics of the capacitor-input filter.

14. Describe some of the characteristics of the choke-input filter.

15. What is meant by the term *percentage of voltage regulation*?

16. What is a swinging choke?

17. Why are voltage dividers generally required in a power supply?

18. Describe the action of the ballast-tube regulator.

19. What is a VR tube?

20. What is meant by the term *VR striking voltage*?

CHAPTER THREE

Basic Amplifiers

3-1 Introduction

The term *amplifier*, in the sense here used, refers to an individual circuit or group of circuits consisting of one or more vacuum tubes with associated components, whose purpose is to increase the strength of an applied input signal. The output signals of many control devices and detection circuits are small voltage variations which must be increased in amplitude to provide usable operating voltages. Such a small input voltage, when applied between the grid and cathode of a triode or pentode vacuum tube, is very effective in controlling the current from a d-c voltage source in the plate circuit. From a study of vacuum tube characteristics, it is known that varying the grid voltage a small amount causes a greater variation in plate voltage, thereby effectively increasing the amplitude of the input signal.

3-2 CLASSIFICATION OF AMPLIFIER CIRCUITS

Amplifier circuits or systems are classified according to the type of service provided, the type of biasing arrangement employed, and the frequency handling capabilities. Amplifiers are also classified as to the method of transferring, or coupling, the signal between vacuum tube stages.

Classification by Type of Service

Basically, the purpose of an amplifier is to increase either the voltage or the power level of the input signal. When classed according to the type of service they provide, amplifiers are divided into two broad groups: voltage amplifiers and power amplifiers.

A voltage amplifier is designed primarily to produce a large value of fluctuating output voltage across the load impedance in the plate circuit. The load impedance must be as high as practicable in order to produce t h e largest usable voltage. A power amplifier is designed primarily to deliver power to the load in the plate circuit. The ratio of a-c output power to a-c power consumed in the grid circuit is known as the power amplification of the circuit. Voltage amplification in a power amplifier is incidental. The load impedance for a power amplifier is selected either to give maximum power with minimum distortion or to give a desired value of plate efficiency. Plate efficiency is the ratio of output power to d-c plate power.

Classification by Bias

Amplifiers may also be divided into various classes according to the selection of the tube operating point and the amplitude of the input signal; these two factors determine the length of time the tube conducts during each cycle of the input signal. These classes are discussed in the following paragraphs:

Class A

In class A_1 operation, the value of grid bias and the amplitude of the signal (grid-drive) voltage are such that they allow plate current at all times. In this class of operation, the total grid voltage (bias plus negative peak signal voltage) is not great enough to drive the tube into cutoff. The tube is biased about midway on the linear portion of the E_g-I_p curve. With this type of operation, the distortion is low, the voltage amplification is high, and the power output and efficiency are relatively low.

In class A_2 operation, the grid is driven positive on the positive signal peaks, thus making it draw current.

Class B

Class B amplifiers are operated so that there is plate current for approximately half of the a-c input cycle. Ordinarily, such amplifiers are operated class B_2, which means that the grid is driven positive during part of the a-c input cycle. For high-power class B operation a value of bias is established usually near cutoff, to prevent the plate dissipation rating of the tube from being exceeded. Class B operation is characterized by high distortion, power consumption in the grid circuit, and good efficiency.

Class AB

As the name implies, class AB operation is a compromise between class A and class B operation in that the bias and driving requirements are intermediate between those of these two classes. There is plate current for more than 180 degrees, but less than 360 degrees, of the a-c input cycle. The tube is driven into cutoff for a portion of the negative half-cycle of the grid signal. In class AB_1 there is no grid current and the operation is nearly class A; but in class AB_2 there is grid current and the operation approaches class B. The bias for class AB is about halfway between the values for class A and cutoff. The power output and efficiency are higher than with class A, but at the expense of more distortion. Class AB audio amplifiers are operated push-pull, in which case the efficiency is much greater than that of class A; the distortion is about equal.

Class AB_2 amplifiers require low-impedance grid-drive sources, and therefore are often transformer-coupled to power drivers. Class AB_2 operation provides p o w e r output and efficiency ratings more nearly equal to those provided by class B operation.

Class C

Class C amplifiers are operated with the grid bias value two or three times greater than that required to cause plate-current cutoff. The signal voltage applied to the grid must have sufficient amplitude to overcome this bias and produce pulses of current in the plate circuit. The efficiency of the circuit increases as the duration of the plate-current pulses is decreased, and can be made to approach 100 percent. Shortening the duration of these pulses, however, also reduces the input power and therefore the output power. As a compromise between power output and efficiency, class C amplifiers are usually operated so that there is plate current for about 120 to 170 degrees of the input cycle. Under these conditions a circuit efficiency of between 60 and 80 percent is obtained.

Since the distortion is extremely high, class C operation is never used in audio amplifiers, but it is quite often used in tuned r-f amplifiers. The flywheel effect of the tuned r-f amplifier tank circuit serves to smooth the intermittent pulses of plate current into sine-wave oscillations in the tank circuit.

Classification By Frequency

Another frequently used basis for amplifier classification is the frequency range of the signal to be amplified. The signal frequencies used in radio communication range from 20 cycles per second to far beyond 30,000 megacycles per second, and a variety of amplifiers have been designed to amplify these signal frequencies.

Audio Amplifiers

Stages that amplify frequencies within the range of human hearing and somewhat higher are called audio amplifiers. They are either voltage or power amplifiers. Since power is needed to actuate a loudspeaker, the output stage of an audio amplifier must be a power amplifier. For the power stage to operate satisfactorily, enough signal input voltage must be applied to ensure operation over the entire useful portion of the tube characteristics curve. The voltage obtained from the detector stage of a receiver, or from such a device as a phonograph pickup or microphone, is not sufficient to drive a power tube. Voltage amplifiers are needed for this reason. If grid current is drawn by the final output stage, so that power is consumed, an intermediate power amplifier called a *driver* must provide this power. Class A operation is always used in single-ended audio amplifiers.

Audio amplifying systems are frequently classified according to the quality of their performance. For example, an amplifier with a flat frequency response from approximately 20 to 20,000 cps is usually called a *high-fidelity amplifier*. Equally important are such characteristics as an extremely high signal-to-noise ratio, low harmonic and intermodulation distortion, linear phase response, and the ability to damp out transient oscillations

of the speaker. As these characteristics become poorer, an amplifier falls into the medium-fidelity and the low-fidelity categories. It should be recognized that a wide frequency response alone does not necessarily mean that an amplifier is capable of faithful reproduction.

R-F Amplifiers

Radio frequencies range from approximately 20,000 cycles per second to 30,000 megacycles per second, and the amplifiers used to amplify these signals are known as radio-frequency amplifiers. In this type of amplifier, usually only one given frequency is amplified. However, r-f amplifiers frequently are tunable so that they can operate over a range of frequencies. A typical r-f voltage amplifier is that used as the first stage in a radio receiver. The input and output circuits of this stage both employ transformer coupling, usually with the secondary of each transformer being tunable over the entire broadcast frequency range.

The stage following a transmitter oscillator is usually an r-f buffer amplifier. The primary purposes of such a stage are to isolate the oscillator from the final transmitter stages in order to prevent changes in loading of the oscillator, and to amplify the output in order to provide greater drive for succeeding stages. In low-power transmitters the buffer amplifier is sometimes used for frequency-doubling, the plate tank circuit being tuned to twice the frequency of the input signal.

In radio transmitting equipment, class C amplifiers are used extensively for the final r-f power amplifier. The principal advantage of a class C final amplifier is its ability to deliver a large amount of r-f power at high efficiency.

Video Amplifiers

Uniform gain over a very wide range of frequencies is required in many electronic equipments which must amplify nonsinusoidal signals. An amplifier having such a wide frequency range is known as a video amplifier. Video circuits are used in the amplification of the nonsinusoidal waves found in radar, television, oscilloscopes, telemetering, and communication applications.

A video amplifier is similar to an audio-frequency, R-C coupled voltage amplifier. Certain modifications of the circuit are necessary, however, to broaden the frequency response. The gain of an ordinary amplifier circuit falls off at high frequencies because t h e stray capacitance to ground acts as a plate-circuit bypass capacitor.

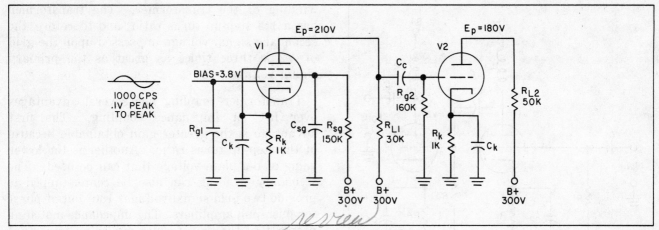

Figure 3-1. R-C Coupled Amplifier Circuit

This stray capacitance is made up of the tube, socket, component, and wiring capacitances to ground. At the frequency where the reactance of the stray capacitance equals the value of the plate load impedance, the gain is only 70% of the mid-frequency gain. At progressively higher frequencies, the gain decreases, until a frequency is reached where the circuit produces no amplification. It can be seen from this relationship that if the value of the plate load impedance were decreased, the stray shunt capacitance would not have so great an effect. Of course, a great deal of gain is lost, but this loss is tolerated in favor of the greater bandwidth. The addition of a peaking coil aids in extending the high-frequency response. If the coil is chosen so that its reactance cancels the reactance of the stray capacitance at the frequency where the response is ordinarily down to 70%, the gain will be increased at this frequency, and the response will be extended.

The problem of obtaining wide frequency response in an amplifier is somewhat simplified by using low-capacitance tubes and special wiring techniques, while the disadvantage of low gain is partially offset by using special high-gain tubes; however, the problem is still very complex.

Classification by Method of Coupling

A single-stage amplifier is usually not sufficient for most applications. Greater gain can be accomplished by connecting several amplifier stages together. The output of one stage becomes the input to the next. This method is known as *cascading*, and is used extensively in electronic circuitry. Various coupling networks are used to transfer the signal energy from one circuit to the next.

Resistance-Capacitance Coupling

Resistance-capacitance coupling, illustrated in figure 3-1, is the most common type employed in audio amplifiers. In this form of coupling, the capacitance of capacitor C_c must be high, so that the capacitor approximates a short-circuit at the lower frequencies. As the frequency decreases toward zero, however, the capacitor and resistor R2 act as a voltage-dividing network and the input voltage applied to the second tube declines rapidly. This condition determines the low-frequency limit of the stage. The value of load resistor R2 is made as great as the maximum allowable tube direct-voltage drop will permit. The factor limiting the maximum value of R2 varies according to the tube used, and may not exceed the value at which the grid starts collecting positive ions contained within the envelope. Shunting the load resistance are the tube and stray capacitances. The effective input capacitance is increased by an amount depending on the gain of the stage. At the high frequencies, the shunt reactance becomes low enough to decrease the net impedance in the output and input circuits of the tube. This condition determines the upper frequency limit of the system.

Impedance Coupling

If the plate-load resistor of the R-C coupled amplifier is replaced with an inductor, the amplifier is said to be impedance-coupled. Since the plate-load reactance will be very high for the high-frequency a-c components of the plate current, a greater degree of amplification can be obtained in the high-frequency range by this method. Because the d-c resistance of plate-load inductor L1 in figure 3-2 may be very low, a higher

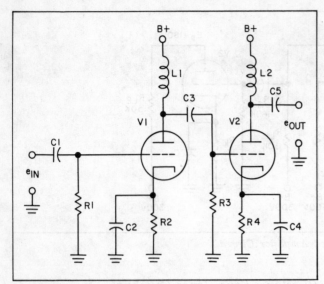

Figure 3-2. Impedance-Coupled Amplifier Circuit

d-c voltage may be obtained at the plate than is possible with a resistive load. One undesirable feature is that the reactance of the inductor varies with frequency, and therefore the amount of amplification for various frequencies is not uniform. Generally, it is possible to obtain a fairly uniform r e s p o n s e characteristic from the impedance-coupled amplifier over a limited frequency range only.

Transformer Coupling

Another method of coupling amplifier stages in cascade is transformer coupling. A typical transformer-coupled amplifier is illustrated in figure 3-3. The input signal voltage to the grid of V1 varies the plate current in the primary winding of T1. This varying current in the primary of T1 induces a voltage in the secondary

winding of the transformer. The transformer has a 1:3 step-up turns ratio; and therefore, the secondary signal voltage impressed upon the grid of V2 is three times as great as the primary signal voltage.

Transformer coupling has several advantages over R-C or impedance coupling. The first advantage is the greater gain obtainable because of the step-up turns ratio. Another is the lower value of d-c plate voltage that can be used. The secondary winding can also be center-tapped to provide two grid-signal voltages 180° out of phase for push-pull amplifiers. The impedance-matching property of the transformer is also an important advantage.

Some of the disadvantages of transformer coupling are the high cost of transformers, their size and weight, and the stray electromagnetic field they produce.

Direct Coupling

Only the a-c signal voltages in the plate circuit have been coupled to the following grid circuit in the coupling methods discussed in the previous paragraphs. However, in the direct-coupled amplifier shown in figure 3-4, the plate of V1 is connected directly to the grid of the next stage. Since the direct-coupled amplifier does not use capacitors or transformers as coupling devices, direct current and low-frequency a-c signal voltages may be amplified. The voltage-divider network, R1 through R4, provides the necessary operating voltages. Tracing the d-c voltage drops through this divider will show that each plate is positive with respect to its cathode and each grid is negative with respect to its cathode. One major

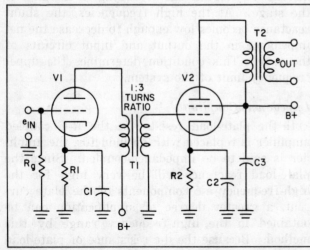

Figure 3-3. Transformer-Coupled Amplifier Circuit

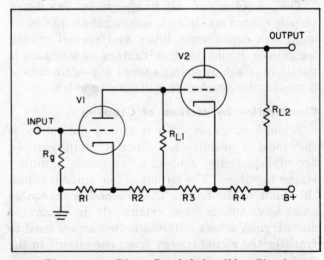

Figure 3-4. Direct-Coupled Amplifier Circuit

disadvantage of the direct-coupled amplifier is the large value of supply voltage which must be provided for a multistage d-c amplifier.

3-3 DISTORTION

The amplified output signal from an ideal amplifier would be an exact replica of the input signal. However, all amplifiers introduce some distortion. The three types of distortion found in vacuum-tube amplifiers are amplitude, frequency, and phase.

Amplitude or nonlinear distortion occurs when the amplifier tube is operated on the nonlinear portion of the dynamic characteristics curve. Operation on this portion of the curve generates unwanted harmonics of the fundamental frequency being amplified. These unwanted harmonics are combined in the plate circuit with the fundamental frequency and the resultant is a distorted output signal. Figure 3-5 is an example of amplitude distortion.

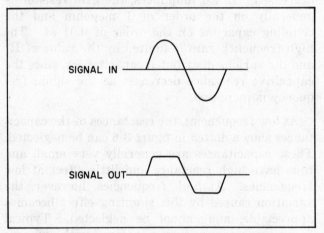

SIGNAL IN

SIGNAL OUT

Figure 3-5. Example of Amplitude Distortion

Frequency distortion occurs when certain frequencies are amplified more than others. Frequency distortion generally is due to the inductive and capacitive elements in the circuit, because their impedance varies with frequency. Frequency distortion occurs at low frequencies if the coupling capacitor is too small, and therefore presents a high series impedance to the low-frequency signal. Distortion also occurs at high frequencies as a result of the shunting effect of the stray capacitance in the circuit.

Phase distortion results when one frequency component of a complex input signal takes a longer time to pass through the amplifier than another. Although both frequency components are amplified, one has suffered a time delay and

the output signal is considerably distorted from the input signal.

3-4 AUDIO-FREQUENCY AMPLIFIERS

The audio-frequency amplifier is a vacuum-tube circuit designed to increase the level of a signal in the frequency range below 20,000 cycles per second. Although the primary use is the amplification of sound signals in such applications as speech amplifiers, public-address systems, and the audio section of radio receivers, the same circuits are often used in other applications that utilize signal frequencies in the audio range. Examples of such applications may be found in systems used to control radar antennas.

The specific types of a-f amplifiers discussed in the following paragraphs are divided by purpose (voltage or power) and type of coupling. Most a-f amplifiers use cathode bias provided by a bypassed cathode resistor. This resistor sets the quiescent value of plate current (the value of plate current with the grid at ground potential). The d-c cathode voltage is therefore positive, and is the bias on the tube. The cathode voltage is dependent upon the choice of tube and the available supply voltage. The bypass capacitor provides an a-c ground for the cathode, and the a-c signal is therefore effectively applied between grid and cathode. The b y p a s s capacitor is generally large, on the order of 10 to 50 μf, and is usually of the electrolytic type.

Voltage Amplifiers

The voltage amplifier is, as its name implies, used to amplify a signal voltage. Both triode and pentode type tubes are found in such circuits, the particular choice being largely dependent upon the required gain. Triodes are generally used in low-gain applications and provide gain values of approximately 5 to 50, while pentodes can give gain v a l u e s up to about 370 in conventional circuits. R-C coupling is used when the gain must be reasonably uniform over the entire frequency range, or when weight and economy are important factors. Transformer and impedance coupling are generally used in applications where plate-supply voltages are low. The gain with these two types of coupling is not uniform over the entire range of frequencies because of resonance characteristics. Since the gain is high at the resonant frequency, transformer or impedance coupling is often used where only a single frequency or narrow band of frequencies is to be amplified.

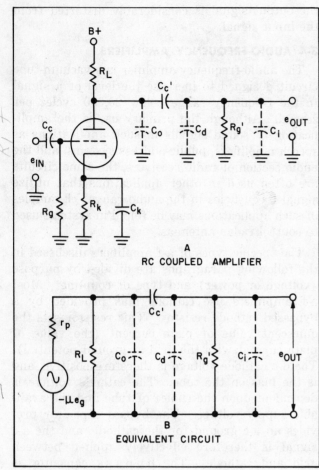

*Figure 3-6.   R-C Coupled Amplifier and
Its Equivalent Circuit*

R-C Coupled Amplifier

An a-f voltage amplifier employing R-C coupling is shown in part A of figure 3-6. It can be seen that a resistance is used as the plate load, and that the output is capacitively coupled to the following stage. The input signal is coupled through the input capacitor C_{c1}, to the control grid. For proper operation, the amplitude of this signal must be such that the tube operates as a class A amplifier (that is, such that the grid is not driven positive with respect to the cathode on the positive alternation or below cutoff on the negative alternation). The variation in the signal applied to the control grid results in a variation in plate current through the tube. This variation in plate current produces a change in the voltage across the plate load resistor that is 180 degrees out of phase with the variation across the input. The a-c component of the voltage across R_L is an amplified version of the input signal, and is capacitively coupled to the next stage.

The capacitors shown in dotted form represent the distributed wiring capacitance (C_d), the output capacitance (C_o), and the input capacitance of the following stage (C_i). The application of the signal voltage to the control grid causes a variation in plate current which is the same as would be produced by using, in place of the tube, a generator having an internal impedance of Y_p and developing a voltage of $-\mu e_g$. The minus sign indicates that the polarity of the output variation is opposite to that of the input signal. Thus the equivalent circuit can be drawn as shown in part B of figure 3-6.

As mentioned previously, R-C coupling allows uniform gain over a fairly wide range of frequencies. The low-frequency gain is limited by the values of the grid resistor and coupling capacitor, since the capacitive reactance and resistance act as a voltage divider and the reactance of the coupling capacitor increases as the frequency is decreased. In a-f amplifiers, the grid resistor is generally on the order of 1 megohm and the coupling capacitor on the order of 0.01 μf. The high-frequency gain is limited by the value of R_L and the various distributed capacitances, since the capacitive reactance decreases as the signal frequency is increased.

At low frequencies, the reactances of the capacitances shown dotted in figure 3-6 can be neglected. These capacitances are generally very small and thus have high reactance and little effect at low frequencies. At high frequencies, however, the variation caused by this shunting effect becomes appreciable, and cannot be neglected. Typical frequency response curves obtained with different values of R_L are shown in figure 3-7. Note that increasing the value of R_L will increase the gain of the stage, but will d e c r e a s e the frequency response. The actual size of R_L is dependent upon the application as well as on the particular tube characteristics. For example, high-fidelity amplifiers use many stages, each having extremely broad frequency response but comparatively low gain, while intercom equipments, which require only that understandable voice communications be available, generally consist of fewer stages, each having higher gain, to meet weight and size limitations.

As an example of poor low-frequency response, assume a grid resistor of 1 megohm and a coupling capacitor of 0.001 μf. (This value is too small, and w i l l give p o o r low frequency responses.) The reactance of the coupling capacitor is given by:

$$X_c = \frac{1}{2\pi fC} \qquad (3\text{-}1)$$

At $f = 3000$ cps (a voice frequency),
$$X_c = 0.052 \text{ megohm}$$
While at $f = 100$ cps (a low audio frequency),
$X_c = 1.6$ megohms.

X_c and R_G form a voltage-divider network, and the voltage appearing at the grid of the tube can therefore be calculated from the formula:

$$V_g = V_a \frac{R_g}{\sqrt{R_g^2 + X_c^2}} \qquad (3\text{-}2)$$

where:

V_g = voltage appearing at grid
V_a = applied voltage
R_g = value of grid resistor (1 megohm)
X_c = capacitive reactance

It can be seen that for a frequency of 3000 cps, the capacitive reactance (X_c) is negligible in comparison with the grid resistance (0.052 megohm compared to 1 megohm); therefore, $V_g = V_a$. However, this is not the case at a frequency of 100 cps.

At $f = 100$ cps,

$$V_g = V_a \frac{1 \times 10^6}{\sqrt{(1 \times 10^6)^2 + (1.6 \times 10^6)^2}}$$

$$= V_a \frac{1 \times 10^6}{\sqrt{3.56 \times 10^{12}}}$$

$$= V_a \frac{10^6}{1.89 \times 10^6}$$

$$= 0.53 \, V_a$$

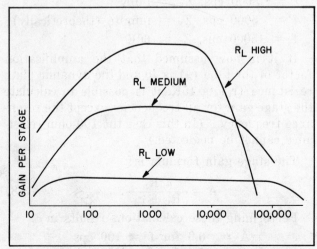

Figure 3-7. The Effect of Load Resistor Valve on Frequency Response

Only a little over half the applied signal will appear at the grid. Therefore, if the uniform response must extend downward to 100 cps, a larger coupling capacitor is necessary.

For high-frequency response calculations, assume a plate load resistor of 500K and a distributed capacitance of 200 $\mu\mu$f.

At a frequency of 3000 cps, $X_c = 2.7$ megohms; while at a frequency of 15,000 cps (a high audio frequency), $X_c = 530$K

The plate load resistance and the shunting capacitance form a parallel R-C circuit (R_g' can be neglected, since it is high). This type of circuit has been discussed previously under a-c circuits, and it should be recalled that the total impedance is given by:

$$Z_T = \frac{RX_c}{\sqrt{R^2 + X_c^2}} \qquad (3\text{-}3)$$

Inserting the correct values for R and X_c, the total impedance is calculated for frequencies of 3000 cps and 15,000 cps.

For $f = 3000$ cps, $Z_T = 492$K
$f = 15,000$ cps, $Z_T = 367$K

The stage amplification is, it will be recalled, given by the formula:

$$A = \frac{\mu R_L}{R_L + r_p} \qquad (3\text{-}4)$$

where:

A = stage gain
μ = amplification factor of tube
R_L = plate load resistance
r_p = dynamic plate resistance of the tube

If it is assumed that the tube has a μ of 45 and a dynamic plate resistance of 15K (reasonable values for a triode), then:

for $f = 3,000$ cps, $A = 43.7$
for $f = 15,000$ cps, $A = 43.3$

Thus, for the values chosen, the stage gain does not deteriorate very badly. This is in fact the case with most triode audio amplifiers, since the distributed capacitance is generally small enough to make little difference in the high-frequency response.

Impedance-Coupled Amplifier

An impedance-coupled a-f voltage amplifier is shown in part A of figure 3-8. This circuit employs an inductor (L_L) as the plate load impedance rather than the resistor of the R-C coupled amplifier, and in general, the operation is

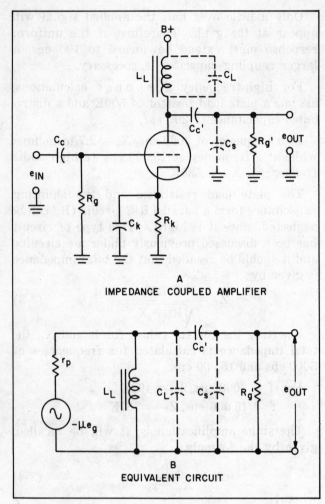

Figure 3-8. Impedance-Coupled Amplifier and Its Equivalent Circuit

quite similar to that of the R-C coupled amplifier. Note that the output voltage is developed across inductor L_L. The inductive reactance, and therefore the amplifier gain, increases as the signal frequency is increased. However, the inductance and the various shunting capacitances (including the inter-winding capacitance C_L of the inductor) resonate at some frequency, causing the amplifier to have maximum gain at this frequency. Gain decreases as the signal frequency is increased or decreased from this value.

The impedance-coupled amplifier is often used where the available supply voltage is low, since the d-c resistance of the inductor is low. It is also found where the circuit is required to amplify only a narrow band of frequencies.

As an example of the performance of the impedance-coupled amplifier, assume that the value of the inductor is 5 henrys. Since the

resistance of such an inductor is only about 100 ohms, it will be neglected in order to simplify the calculations. The total shunting capacitance is assumed to be 200 $\mu\mu f$, and the inductor is therefore resonant at a frequency of 5000 cps.

It will be recalled that the formula for the line current in a parallel circuit is:

$$I_{line} = \sqrt{I_R^2 + (I_{X_L} - I_{X_c})^2} \qquad (3-5)$$

In this example, R (which is R_g', the grid resistor of the following stage), is assumed to be very large and therefore I_R is very nearly zero. In this case formula (3-5) reduces to:

$$I_{line} = I_{X_L} - I_{X_c} \qquad (3-6)$$

It will be recalled from a-c theory that Ohm's law for a-c circuits is:

$$I = \frac{E}{Z}$$

Substituting this in equation (3-6) and solving for the total impedance gives:

$$Z_T = \frac{\dfrac{L}{C}}{X_L - X_c} \qquad (3-7)$$

The ratio L/C is calculated to be 2.5 x 10^{10}, while at:

f = 100 cps, X_L = 3140, and X_c = 8 megohms
f = 3000 cps, X_L = 94.2K, and X_c = 265K
f = 5000 cps, X_L = 157K, and X_c = 159K (the approximate resonance condition)
f = 15,000 cps, X_L = 471K, and X_c = 53K

Therefore at:
f =   100 cps, Z_T = 3100 ohms
f =   3000 cps, Z_T = 146K
f =   5000 cps, Z_T = infinite (theoretically)
f = 15000 cps, Z_T = 60K

If it is now assumed that the amplification factor of the tube (μ) is 40 and the dynamic plate resistance (r_p) is 15K, it is possible to calculate the stage gain for all frequencies except the resonance frequency. (In this case the 100-ohm resistance cannot be neglected.)

The stage gain formula is:

$$A = \frac{\mu\, R_L}{R_L + r_p} \qquad (3-8)$$

Performing these calculations results in
A =   6.9 for f =   100 cps
A = 36.2 for f =   3000 cps
A = 32.0 for f = 15000 cps

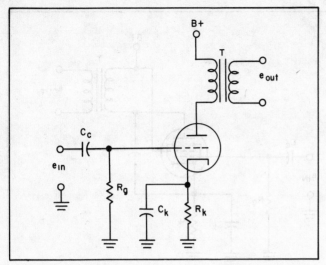

Figure 3-9. Transformer-Coupled Amplifier Circuit

The reasonant condition and t h e extreme decrease in gain at low frequencies are obvious from this example, and clearly indicate the problem encountered with the use of impedance coupling.

Transformer-Coupled Amplifier

A transformer-coupled a-f amplifier is shown in figure 3-9. As can be seen, the plate load impedance consists of the primary winding of a transformer. As with the impedance-coupled amplifier, the transformer-coupled amplifier suffers from the problem of frequency response. However, if a step-up transformer is used, an additional voltage gain can be obtained.

In applications where an extremely high gain is desirable, a pentode vacuum tube is often used

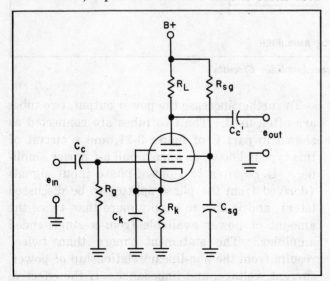

Figure 3-10. R-C Coupled Pentode Amplifier Circuit

in place of the triode discussed thus far. Usually, pentode a-f amplifiers are of the R-C coupled type shown in figure 3-10. As in the case of the triode amplifier, the output is developed across the plate load resistance (R_L) and capacitively coupled to the following stage by C_c'. T h e screen-grid circuit contains a bypass capacitor, C_{sg}, whose function is to provide a low-reactance path to ground for all a-c components of the screen-grid voltage. This keeps the screen-grid voltage constant and prevents degeneration. Since, in general, the dynamic plate resistance of the pentode vacuum tube is high, the plate load resistor, R_L, should be as large as the power supply voltage and tube characteristics will allow.

Power Amplifiers

An a-f power amplifier is used, as its name implies, to amplify or increase the power of an input a-f signal. It differs from a voltage amplifier in that current more so than voltage is amplified; for this reason power amplifiers are often referred to as current amplifiers. Practically all a-f power amplifiers make use of transformer coupling at the output. It will be recalled that maximum power transfer from a generator to its load occurs when the load impedance is equal to the generator impedance. Similarly, for maximum power transfer in a power amplifier, the load impedance (in general, the impedance of the primary of the output transformer) should be made equal to the dynamic plate resistance of the tube. However, an exact impedance match often results in distortion, and a small amount of power is then usually sacrificed in order to limit the distortion to low values. One further advantage of transformer coupling lies in impedance matching. The impedance of the load driven by a power amplifier seldom matches the output impedance of the amplifier, and some type of impedance-matching network is necessary. A properly designed transformer offers a very convenient method of providing an impedance match, since by selecting the proper turns ratio, almost any load can be made to reflect the correct impedance to the plate circuit of the tube.

An a-f power amplifier circuit using a single triode tube is shown in part A of figure 3-11. It should be noted that the diagram of this circuit is identical to that of the transformer-coupled a-f voltage amplifier shown in figure 3-9. The difference between the two amplifiers lies in the type of tube used and the power ratings of the

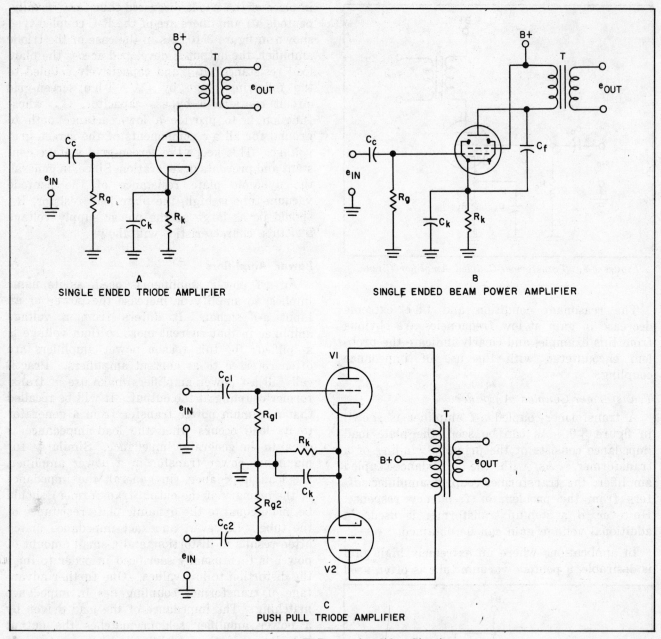

Figure 3-11.   A-F Power Amplifier Circuits

various components. This type of power amplifier is known as a single-ended amplifier and is usually operated class A, giving good fidelity but requiring a large input signal amplitude.

A beam-power type of tube is often used in place of the triode in the single-ended power amplifier, as shown in part B of figure 3-11. The beam-power tube requires less input signal in the form of grid drive, but there is also a loss in fidelity and a tendency towards oscillation. To overcome this tendency, inverse feedback, provided by capacitor C_f, is frequently used.

To further increase the power output, two tubes are often used. The two tubes are connected as shown in part C of figure 3-11, and a circuit of this type is known as a push-pull a-f power amplifier. It requires two out-of-phase input signals (derived from the phase splitter to be discussed later), and is able to supply more than twice the amount of power available from a single-ended amplifier. The statement "more than twice" results from the non-linear relationship of power, current, voltage, and impedance. If the effective a-c component of voltage across the transformer is doubled, as is the case when out-of-phase a-c signals are applied to opposite ends of the primary winding, the effective power increases by a factor of four (assuming no added losses). This theoretical increase is not obtained in practice, but the available power is more than doubled. One other factor which enters into the problem of power transfer in the power amplifier is harmonic distortion. Any distortion produces both even and odd harmonics in the output circuit. In the push-pull amplifier, the even harmonics produce magnetic fluxes in the transformers w h i c h are theoretically equal in magnitude and opposite in direction. The resultant cancellation of even harmonics reduces the harmonic distortion, and permits closer matching of the plate load impedance to the dynamic plate resistance of the tubes, thus increasing the power delivered to the load.

The push-pull a-f power amplifier is often operated as a class A amplifier, with self-bias

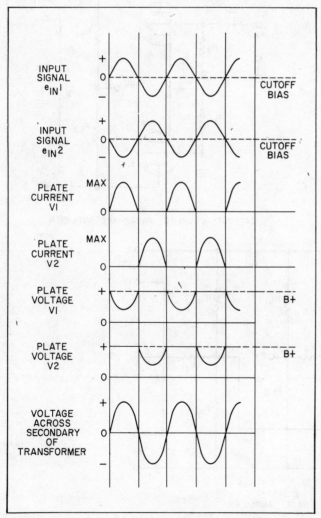

Figure 3-12. Waveforms of Push-Pull Amplifier Biased at Cutoff

being supplied by the bypassed common cathode resistor, but it may also be operated class AB or class B. Little distortion is introduced in class AB or B operation, since fluxes resulting from the plate current pulses add to produce a complete a-c cycle in the output, as illustrated in figure 3-12. In fact, with class A operation, bypass capacitor C_k can be omitted with no appreciable ill effect.

Pentodes and beam-power tubes are frequently used in push-pull circuits, but use of these types of tubes results in odd harmonics of the input signal appearing at the output. These harmonics are not eliminated by cancellation as are the even harmonics, and the plate load impedance cannot be increased beyond the point where such distortion becomes objectionable.

Further advantages of the push-pull circuit include more efficient design possibilities for the transformer and the cancellation of power supply ripple voltages. Since the fluxes caused by the d-c components of plate current in the tubes cancel, the transformer core does not need to carry a residual d-c field, and can therefore be made smaller. The power supply ripple voltages cancel, thus reducing the power supply filter requirements.

In general, the push-pull circuit is used whenever possible in a-f power amplifier circuits because of the advantages it has over other types of a-f power amplifier circuits. Considerable effort has been devoted to improving the frequency response of such circuits for high-fidelity reproduction, and many complex arrangements have been developed. However, for most purposes, the basic circuits shown here are sufficient.

Phase Splitter

As was mentioned in the previous discussion of the push-pull a-f power amplifier, two signals of opposite phase are required at its input. Since the a-f voltage amplifier which provides the input signal is generally of the single-ended type, it is necessary to include a circuit which will convert the single-ended output signal from the a-f voltage amplifier into the two signals required by the push-pull a-f power amplifier. A number of circuits which will accomplish this are illustrated in figure 3-13; they are known as phase splitters. (Other names used are phase inverter and paraphase amplifier.) Strictly speaking, the phase splitter is not generally an amplifier, since in most cases the output signals are actually somewhat lower in amplitude than the input signal (a stage

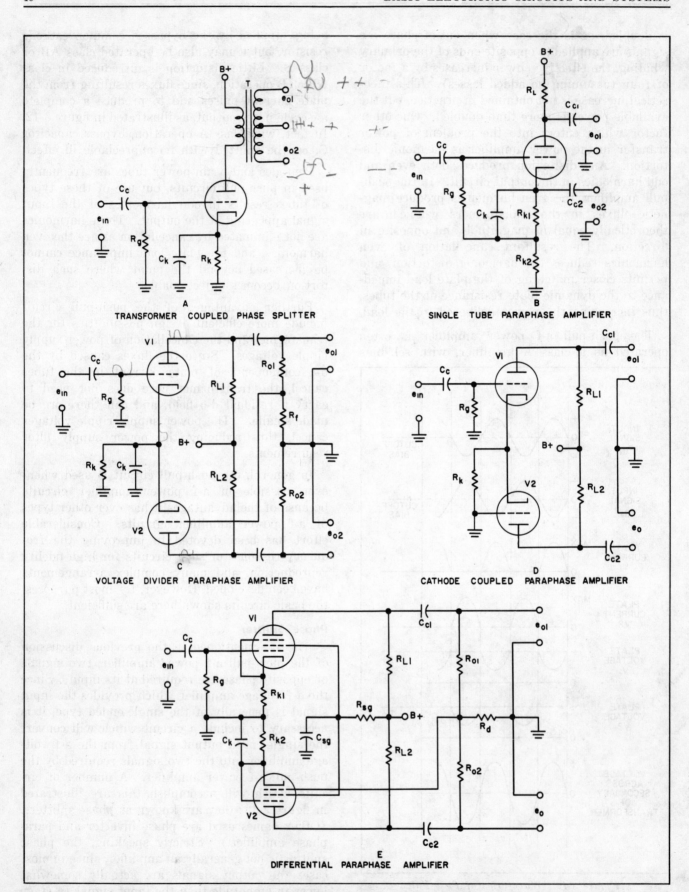

Figure 3-13.   Transformer-Coupled Phase Splitter and Paraphase Amplifier Circuits

gain of less than one). However, because of its application, the discussion of the phase splitter is included in the material on amplifiers.

The transformer-type phase inverter, illustrated in part A of figure 3-13, is nearly identical to the transformer-coupled a-f voltage amplifier (figure 3-9). The difference is that a transformer having a center-tapped secondary is used. If the center tap is grounded, the secondary winding produces two signal outputs which are equal in amplitude and opposite in phase. This is the costliest type of phase splitter, but has the advantages of smaller power loss in the interstage coupling and less distortion.

The simplest and least expensive type of phase splitter is the single-tube circuit shown in part B of figure 3-13, to which the term *paraphase amplifier* is applied. Since the plate current through the tube is also the current through R_{k_2} and R_L (R_{k_1} is bypassed by C_k and therefore presents negligible reactance to the a-c component of plate current), the output signals are of equal amplitude if these two resistors are equal in value. It will be recalled that signal phase inversion takes place between the grid and the plate, but not between the grid and cathode. The two output signals are therefore opposite in phase.

This type of phase splitter is frequently used because of its simplicity and low cost. However, it has the disadvantage of a stage gain of less than one (that is, the amplitude of the output signal is less than that of the input signal).

Part C of figure 3-13 shows a paraphase amplifier which uses a voltage-divider network and can provide amplification of the input signal besides performing its phase-splitter function. The tube V1 is a conventional R-C coupled amplifier, with the output signal appearing across the series combination of R_{o_1} and R_f. These resistors act as a conventional voltage divider, and the portion of the signal appearing across R_f appears at the grid of V2. If resistors R_{o_1} and R_f are of the proper values, the signal appearing at the grid of V2 will have the same amplitude as the input signal. If the two stages are identical, then the two outputs will be equal in amplitude and opposite in phase.

The phase splitter shown in part D of figure 3-13 is quite similar to that of part C, the difference being in the method of coupling. In this circuit, V1 is an R-C coupled amplifier in which the cathode is unbypassed. Thus, if the value of

R_k is properly chosen, the signal appearing across it is one-half the value of the input signal. In this case, the grid-to-cathode variation which is amplified by tube V1 is actually one half the amplitude of the applied signal. This grid-to-cathode variation is amplified and inverted by V1 and becomes one of the two outputs. The circuit of tube V2 is a cathode-fed grounded-grid amplifier. It will be recalled from the previous discussion of this type of circuit, that, although the signal input to the cathode is amplified, no phase inversion takes place. This output is therefore in phase with the applied signal. With this configuration, therefore, the two output signals are equal in amplitude and opposite in phase.

Part E of figure 3-13 shows a differential paraphase amplifier which utilizes two pentode tubes. V1 is a conventional R-C coupled voltage amplifier with the exception of the unbypassed cathode resistor, R_{k_1}. The output appears across the series combination of R_{o_1} and R_d. The output of V2 is opposite in phase to that of V1 and appears across the series combination of R_{o_2} and R_d. The resultant voltage across R_d is thus the difference of the two voltages. It can be seen that if the two outputs were of exactly equal amplitude, where R_{o_1} and R_{o_2} are of equal value, there would be no grid excitation of V2. In order to provide grid excitation for V2, it is necessary that the amplitude of the output from V1 be slightly higher than that from V2. Although the use of pentodes, with resulting high gain, minimizes this difference, the circuit is not frequently used.

3-5 CATHODE FOLLOWER

The schematic diagram of a cathode follower is shown in part A of figure 3-14. By way of review, the cathode follower is a circuit in which the unbypassed cathode resistor provides degenerative feedback. The output signal is taken across this same resistor, and the plate of the vacuum tube is at a-c ground potential. The circuit therefore operates as a grounded-plate amplifier, and the input and output are of the same polarity.

Because of the unbypassed cathode resistor the voltage gain is always less than one, and is given by the formula:

$$A = \frac{\mu R_K}{r_p + R_k (\mu + 1)} \qquad (3-9)$$

Part B of figure 3-14 shows the equivalent circuit of the cathode follower. It can be seen that the voltage gain formula above follows from a calculation of e_{out}/e_{in}.

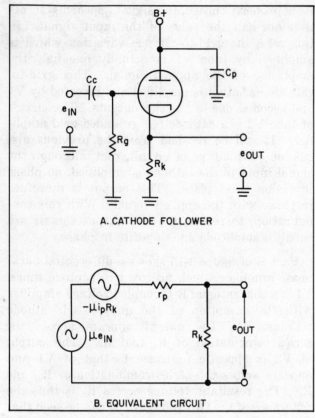

A. CATHODE FOLLOWER

B. EQUIVALENT CIRCUIT

Figure 3-14. Cathode Follower and Its Equivalent Current

The major use of the cathode follower circuit is in impedance-matching applications where the output signal is fed to a transmission line or other low-impedance device. It is also frequently used to isolate critical circuits from the loading effects of low impedances.

The input impedance of a cathode follower is high. The grid is negative with respect to the cathode, and, because of the degenerative effect of the unbypassed cathode resistor, a high-amplitude pulse may be applied between grid and ground without causing grid current.

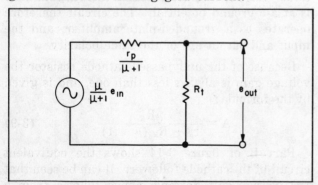

Figure 3-15. Equivalent Output Circuit of Cathode Follower

On the other hand, the output impedance of the cathode follower is low. The equivalent output circuit shown in figure 3-15 is obtained from the expression below for plate current in the circuit of figure 3-14.

$$i_p = \frac{\mu e_{in}}{r_p + R_k(\mu+1)} \tag{3-10}$$

Dividing both the numerator and denominator by the factor $\mu + 1$ results in:

$$i_p = \frac{\frac{\mu}{\mu+1}e_{in}}{R_k + \frac{r_p}{\mu+1}} = \frac{\mu' e_{in}}{R_k + r'_p} \tag{3-11}$$

It can be seen that this expression is that of an amplifier in which the tube gain is μ' (or $\frac{\mu}{\mu+1}$) and the a-c plate resistance is r_p' (or $\frac{r_p}{\mu+1}$).

Since the plate is at a-c ground potential, the output impedance is the parallel combination of the cathode resistance and the equivalent a-c plate resistance, and is therefore given by:

$$Z_{out} = \frac{R_k \frac{r_p}{(\mu+1)}}{R_k + \frac{r_p}{\mu+1}}$$
$$= \frac{R_k r_p}{r_p + R_k(\mu+1)} \tag{3-12}$$

This impedance is low when compared to that of a conventional amplifier stage, and proper choice of the tube (selection of r_p and μ) and the value of cathode resistor will permit matching to any load impedance.

The high input impedance is essentially constant, and the cathode follower makes possible the isolation of a critical circuit from the effects of variations in load impedance. The low output impedance makes it possible to match the load impedance, and thus avoid effects which result in distortion or loss of power. It should be noted that in this application, the gain of the stage is generally of secondary importance.

3-6 BELS AND DECIBELS

The terms *bel* and *decibel* are used in electronics to express the ratio of two power values, voltage values, or current values. Primarily, the bel and decibel are used to relate the ratio of two power levels. As originally expressed, the bel represented a power ratio of 10 to 1 between the strength of two sounds. To get a better under-

$$60 = \log_{10} \frac{P_2}{P_1} = .001$$

standing of the concept of the bel, consider three sounds of the s a m e frequency but unequal intensity (power level). If the intensity of the second sound is 10 times the intensity of the first, its power level is said to be 1 bel above that of the first. If the third sound has an intensity which is 10 times that of the second, its level is 1 bel above that of the second. But, since the third sound is 100 times as intense as the first, its level is 2 bels above that of the first.

Thus a power ratio of 100 to 1 is represented by 2 bels; a power ratio of 1000 to 1 by 3 bels; a power ratio of 10,000 to 1 by 4 bels; etc. From these relationships it should be noted that the concept of bels represents a logarithmic relationship, since the logarithm of 100 to the base 10 equals 2 (corresponding to 2 bels), the logarithm of 1000 equals 3 (corresponding to 3 bels), etc. The exact relationship is given by the formula:

$$\text{bels} = \log_{10} \frac{P_2}{P_1} \qquad (3\text{-}13)$$

where:

$$\frac{P_2}{P_1} = \text{the ratio of the two powers}$$

This logarithmic characteristic of the bel makes it a very convenient means for expressing power ratios. The bel is a rather large unit, and its use as such in expressing the power ratios of two audio signals or radio-frequency signals is rather impractical. Usually, therefore, a smaller unit, the decibel, is used. Ten decibels equal 1 bel. A 10 to 1 power ratio, which can be represented by 1 bel, can also be represented by 10 decibels (10db), a 100 to 1 ratio (2 bels) can be represented by 20 db, a 1000 to 1 ratio (3 bels) by 30 db, etc. The previous formula for bels may be rewritten to give a result in decibels merely by multiplying by 10. This resultant f o r m u l a becomes:

$$\text{decibels (db)} = 10 \log_{10} \frac{P_2}{P_1} \qquad (3\text{-}14)$$

As an example of the use of this formula, consider the case where two audio amplifier systems are involved. The first audio amplifier is capable of delivering a maximum of 10 watts of power to a given load, while the second is capable of supplying 100 watts of power to an identical load. Inserting these values in formula (3-14) and solving, yields:

$$\begin{aligned} \text{db} &= 10 \ \log_{10} \frac{P_2}{P_1} \\ &= 10 \ \log_{10} \frac{100}{10} \\ &= 10 \ \log_{10} \ 10 \\ &= 10 \end{aligned}$$

Thus the output capability of the second amplifier is 10 db above the first. It should be clearly understood that the term *decibel* does not in itself indicate power, but rather a ratio or comparison between the two power values. In the testing of audio amplifier systems and communications and radar transmitters and receivers, it is often found that performance measurements are presented in terms of decibels. These comparisons can be accomplished by using a fixed power level as the reference.

The decibel may be used as an absolute level by agreeing to specify the ratio always with respect to a fixed reference value, called the *zero level*, and to indicate the absolute unit by its number of decibels above or below the fixed reference value. As an example, assume that it is desired to specify the value in decibels of the output from a 20-watt amplifier. Further assume that 0.001 watt (1 milliwatt) is the reference level. This is equivalent to a power ratio of $\frac{20}{0.001}$ or 20,000, which can be expressed in terms of db as follows:

$$\begin{aligned} \text{db} &= 10 \ \log_{10} \frac{20}{0.001} \\ &= 10 \ \log_{10} \ 20,000 \end{aligned}$$
(Note: $\log_{10} 20,000 = 4.3$)
$$\begin{aligned} \text{db} &= 10 \times 4.3 \\ &= 43 \end{aligned}$$

A "zero level" of 1 milliwatt (with decibels above or below this level being stated commonly as ± dbm) has gained considerable acceptance in the electronics industry, although 6 milliwatts and other values are also widely used as reference levels. It is therefore very important, when the decibel is being used as an absolute unit in this way, that the reference value be clearly understood.

Voltage and current r a t i o s may also be expressed in terms of decibels, provided the resistance into which the current is fed or across which the voltage is dropped remains constant.

TABLE 3-1. DECIBELS AND POWER, VOLTAGE, OR CURRENT RATIOS

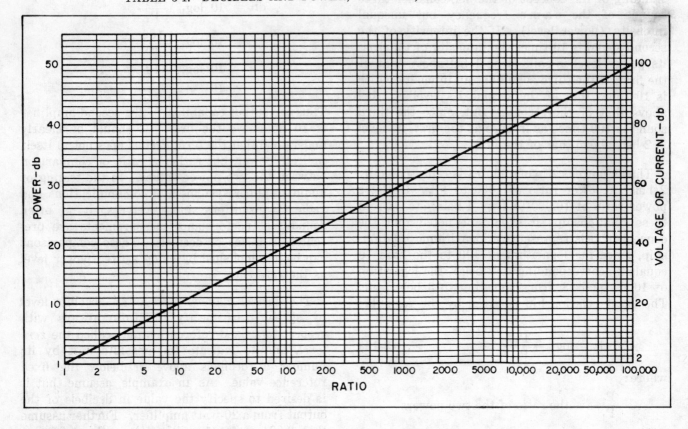

For equal resistances, the formulas are:

$$db = 20 \; \log_{10} \; \frac{E_2}{E_1}$$

$$db = 20 \; \log_{10} \; \frac{I_2}{I_1} \tag{3-15}$$

The difference in the multiplying factor in these formulas (20 rather than 10, as in the case of power ratios) arises from the fact that power is proportional to the square of voltage or current, and when a number is squared, the logarithm of that number is doubled. For power ratios, the db value is 10 times the logarithm of the ratio. For voltage or current ratios, the db value is 20 times the logarithm of the ratio. Table 3-1 presents a graphical means of determining power, voltage, or current ratios expressed in terms of db; it will be found that the graph is a useful tool for quickly obtaining decibel relationships of audio- or radio-frequency signals.

In order to further help convey the meaning of sound intensity, as expressed in decibels, the following table (table 3-2) illustrates the approximate noise intensities, in db, associated with common sound levels.

TABLE 3-2. SOUND LEVEL CHART

Level* in DB	Relative Sound Condition
0	Average threshold of hearing
10	Rustle of leaves in a gentle breeze
20	Whisper at 5 feet
30	Quiet country residence
40	Average residence
50	Average office
60	Residential street
65	Average conversation
70	Busy city street
80	Average motor truck at 15 feet
90	Very heavy street traffic at 15 feet
100	Subway
110	Boiler factory
120	Discomfort
130	Average threshold of pain

*Based on 0 db as 10^{-10} microwatts per cm^2

Decibel Meter Scales

Many combination test instruments, particularly volt-ohm-milliammeters and vacuum-tube voltmeters, are equipped with scales calibrated in decibels. Such meters are of great value in making many types of measurements where direct indication in decibels is desirable. When improperly used, however, the indication obtained may be so inaccurate as to be utterly meaningless. In most cases the calibration of these instruments is based upon an impedance of 600 ohms and a zero level of 1 milliwatt. Therefore, when a meter is connected across an impedance having a value different from 600 ohms, the calibration will not be correct. The correction factor which must be applied is determined as follows:

$$\text{Correction factor (db)} = 10 \log_{10} \frac{\text{meter } Z}{\text{circuit } Z}$$

(3-16)

When the impedance of the circuit under measurement is greater than the meter impedance, the correction factor is subtracted from the meter indication; when the value of the impedance is less than the meter impedance, the correction factor is added to the meter indication. Most of the better meters employed in the testing of electronic circuits have the calibration impedance for the db scale imprinted somewhere on the face of the meter scale plate.

3-7 SUMMARY

The short discussion on types of amplifiers and their differences should provide an insight into the broad requirements placed on a vacuum tube in the amplification of signal voltages.

Amplifier circuits are classified according to application and circuit characteristics. The most general means of identifying amplifier circuits is by the major output requirement, voltage or power. Further classifications of amplifiers include the operating point of the vacuum tube and the frequencies of the signal the circuit must amplify.

So far as circuit application is concerned amplifiers are used as audio-frequency, radio-frequency, and video-frequency amplifying devices. In order to perform properly for the desired application an appropriate type of coupling must be used. The two most common means of connecting one amplifier output to the input of another is by means of resistance-capacitance or transformer coupling.

The ability of amplifier circuits to provide an increased signal voltage which is identical to the input is sometimes hampered by the choice of circuit component values, thus producing a distorted output signal. The types of distortion which can occur in amplifier circuits are amplitude, frequency and phase distortion, all of which are undesirable in most applications.

Audio-frequency amplifiers may be used for a number of purposes, and the specific application determines the selection of one or a combination of the various circuits. The voltage amplifier is used to increase the voltage level of an input signal, and a number of different types of coupling have been shown. The p o w e r amplifier is generally used to drive a loudspeaker or similar device, while the phase splitter, or paraphase amplifier, is used to provide the two out-of-phase inputs required by the push-pull power amplifier. The cathode follower is generally used as an impedance-matching circuit, and is also frequently used to isolate a critical circuit from the effects of load variation. The audio section of a typical military communications receiver makes use of many of these circuits. There are, generally, several stages of voltage amplification, followed by a phase splitter and a push-pull amplifier.

It is important to note that many of these circuits are also used where audio-frequency information other than sound communication is to be amplified. One example of such usage is in the field of radio navigation, where the push-pull amplifier is often used as a phase-amplitude comparison device.

The use of the bel and decibel as a means of easily expressing the relationship between two power or voltage levels, and less commonly, the ratio between two current levels, has been widely adopted in radio, sound amplification, and other branches of electronics. The decibel is by far the most common term employed to express the logarithmic relation of power, voltage, and current values. The dbm, which indicates the "zero reference level," is used as the basis for comparison with respect to some specified milliwatt standard.

$$A = \log_{10} B$$
$$10^A = B$$

$$db = 10 \log \frac{P_{out}}{P_{in}}$$
$$60 = 10 \log \frac{X}{.001}$$
$$6 = \log \frac{X}{.001}$$

$$10^6 = \frac{X}{.001}$$

REVIEW QUESTIONS

1. What is the main difference between a voltage amplifier and a current amplifier?

2. The ratio of output power to d-c plate power is known as what?

3. Is the amplifier tube ever cut off during class A operation? *Page 29*

4. What class of amplifier is biased at a value two or three times as great as that required to produce cutoff? *Page 29*

5. Which class of amplifier operation produces the least distortion? Which produces the most? *C*

6. What type of amplifier would be used to amplify a frequency of 400 cycles? 400 kilocycles? 400 megacycles? *audio*

7. What is meant by the term *fidelity*?

8. In what way is a video amplifier different from either an audio or r-f amplifier? *Page 30*

9. What is the factor in an R-C coupled amplifier which determines the upper frequency limit? *RL*

10. What is one major disadvantage of the direct-coupled amplifier? *supply voltage, has to have a large*

11. What are the three types of distortion which may be found in vacuum-tube amplifiers? *Phase frequency amplitude*

12. What is the purpose of the cathode bypass capacitor in self-biased amplifiers? *a C ground for cathode*

13. Under what condition is transformer coupling or impedance coupling better than R-C coupling? *High gain*

14. Why is R-C coupling desirable? *high frequency responce*

15. Explain the reason for decrease in gain at high frequencies in an R-C coupled amplifier. *Page 34*

16. Why does the R-C coupled amplifier have poor response at very low frequencies? *Page 34*

17. Explain the reason for poor frequency response in an impedance-coupled amplifier. *Page 36*

18. Why are even harmonics of the input signal not present in the output from a push-pull amplifier? *Page 39*

19. What is the output from the phase splitter? *two signals out of phase*

20. What is the purpose of the unbypassed cathode resistor in the phase splitter shown in part D of figure 3-13? *Page 41*

21. What are the two major uses of the cathode follower?

22. Define the *bel* and *decibel*. *Page 42*

23. Compute the db relationship between two amplifiers, one having an output of 1500 watts, the other 15 watts.

24. Compute the db relationship for an audio amplifier having an output power of 50 watts, based upon the standard "zero reference level."

25. State the nominal impedance value for the db portion of a volt-ohm-milliammeter.

$3db = .707 \text{ of max power}$

$\text{or } \frac{1}{2} \text{ power}$

$P = \frac{E^2}{R}$

$db = 10 Log \frac{E^2}{E_n}$

$db = 20 Log \frac{E_{out}}{E_{in}}$

$60 = 20 Log E_0$

$10^3 = \frac{E_0}{.001} = .001$

$\frac{}{.001} = 1. v \, dt$

CHAPTER FOUR

Loudspeakers

4-1 Introduction

The loudspeaker is a device which converts electrical energy to sound energy. For this reason, it is frequently called an electro-acoustic transducer. As was previously mentioned, the headset used with early crystal receivers and still in use today in many applications is one type of electro-acoustic transducer. However, in most applications, the headset has the obvious disadvantage that it must be he held close to the ears. With the average home radio, for example, the headset is highly inconvenient. A loudspeaker is required in these applications because the transducer must be able to produce sound waves that are sufficiently intense to be easily heard and distinguished in a room of ordinary size. In a few applications, such as public address systems, the sound waves must be heard and distinguished anywhere in a much larger area, and must be sufficiently intense to overcome the normal background noise in such places as auditoriums and theaters. Loudspeakers of various types and with many different design characteristics are available for a wide variety of applications.

In general, a loudspeaker should produce a wave of sound pressure which at any instant corresponds to the electrical voltage applied across it. It should have a reasonably uniform response to all audio frequencies. (This requirement is dependent upon the application. For example, loudspeakers of the public address system installed on an aircraft carrier are required to reproduce voice information, while the loudspeakers for high-fidelity music reproduction must operate over a far greater frequency range.) Finally, the loudspeaker should respond properly to an increase in the amplitude of the applied electrical signal. As the signal is increased, the strength of the sound waves (or volume) should also increase, and such an increase should be linear.

All practical loudspeakers are a compromise, being something less than ideal in one or more respects. However, it is often possible to compensate for distortion or nonlinearity introduced by the loudspeaker by deliberately distorting the electrical signal applied to it, or by using more than one s p e a k e r, each having different characteristics.

Actually, the efficiency with which the loudspeaker converts an electrical signal to sound waves is very low. Practically all loudspeakers have an efficiency of less than 10 percent, and the efficiency of the average loudspeaker (such as the speaker in a home radio) is less than 5 percent. The efficiency of even the best speakers does not exceed approximately 35 percent.

4-2 HEADSETS

Before studying actual types of loudspeakers, it will be helpful first to consider the basic operation of the headset, which was the forerunner of the loudspeaker.

The headset (or earphones) used in radio work is very similar to the listening device in an ordinary telephone. In general, the headset consists of two earphones connected in series. Each of the phones comprises a horseshoe-shaped permanent magnet with two pole pieces as shown in part A of figure 4-1, two coils, a vibrating metal diaphragm, and an enclosure. A cross-sectional view of an earphone is shown in part B of figure 4-1.

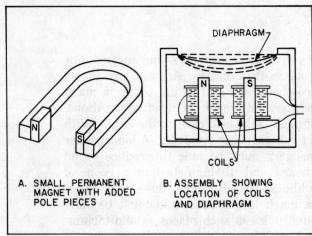

Figure 4-1. Construction of an Earphone

With no current in the coils wound around the pole pieces, the magnetic field between the poles holds the metal diaphragm in the position shown by the solid line. Note that the magnetic field between the magnetic poles tends to exert tension on the diaphragm and pull it away from a normally flat plane. When current passes through the coils, it generates a magnetic flux. This flux aids or opposes the magnetic flux of the permanent magnet, and thus increases or decreases the total magnetic field, depending upon the direction of current. Thus the tension on the diaphragm is increased or decreased. An alternating current applied to the coils causes the diaphragm to vibrate at the frequency of the applied current, and if this frequency is in the correct range, the vibrating diaphragm will generate audible sound waves.

Since the current generated by radio receivers is small, the coils in good earphones usually consist of several thousand turns of fine enameled copper wire and have a total resistance of 2000 to 5000 ohms. The connections are extremely small

and easily broken; therefore, extreme care should be exercised in cleaning or repairing earphones. In addition, the diaphragm must be handled carefully, since a bent or loose diaphragm will considerably increase the distortion which occurs.

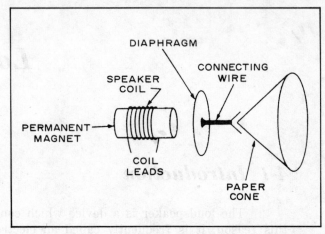

Figure 4-2. Construction of Early-Type Speaker

4-3 THE DYNAMIC SPEAKER

The speaker most commonly used in present-day radio receivers and phonographs is the dynamic (or moving-coil) speaker. The dynamic speaker is subdivided into two general classes, the permanent-magnet dynamic speaker and the electromagnetic dynamic speaker, more often referred to as the PM and EM speakers, respectively.

Very early speakers consisted of a paper cone fastened to a diaphragm as shown in figure 4-2. This speaker did not prove very satisfactory; with strong-current signals being fed to the speaker coil the diaphragm was pulled against the magnet, resulting in speaker rattle with accompanying sound distortion.

The modern dynamic speaker, which incorporates a voice coil, overcomes this and other problems presented by this construction. (See figure 4-3.) The voice coil is a small coil wound on a tube of bakelite or fiber material, and is so mounted that the tube can move back and forth along the permanent magnet. The voice-coil tube is held in place by a very flexible, springy material called a *spider*, and is also attached directly to the paper cone. Variations of current passing through the voice coil produce a varying magnetic field which interacts with the stable magnetic field of the speaker magnet. The interaction of magnetic fields causes motion of the voice-coil form and the cone to which it is attached, producing sound waves.

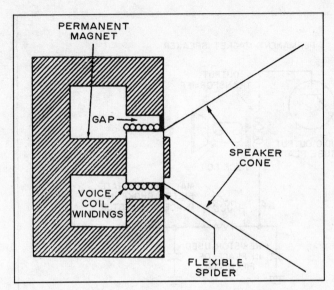

Figure 4-3. Construction of Permanent-Magnet Dynamic Speaker

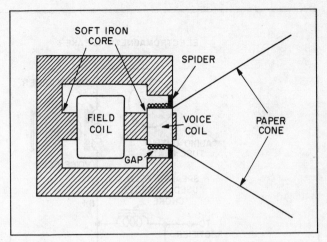

Figure 4-4. Construction of Electromagnetic Dynamic Speaker

When the fluctuating plate current (audio signal) from the audio output stage is fed to the voice coil through the output transformer, a varying magnetic field is set up around the coil. This varying magnetic field reacts with the fixed magnetic field around the permanent magnet, causing the voice coil to move back and forth along the length of the permanent magnet within design limits. The movement of the voice coil is directly proportional to the current through its windings, a higher current producing a greater movement of the coil, and vice versa. Because of the flexibility of the spider, the voice coil is in motion along the magnet while there is signal current, but returns to its original position when the current ceases.

Since the speaker cone is directly connected to the voice coil, its motion corresponds to that of the voice coil, in accordance with the audio signal. This movement, or vibration, will disturb the air and produce sound waves directly related to the variations of the audio signal. This, then, is the manner in which the permanent-magnet dynamic speaker converts the audio electrical energy into audio acoustical energy.

The basic design of the electromagnetic dynamic speaker shown in figure 4-4 is very similar, with respect to the voice coil, cone, and spider suspension, to that of the PM dynamic speaker. The electromagnetic type differs, however, in that an electromagnet, formed by a field coil consisting of a considerable number of turns of wire around a soft iron core, replaces the permanent magnet.

In the electromagnetic dynamic speaker a direct current is passed through the field coil. The current through the field coil causes the iron core to become magnetized, while the varying current through the voice coil produces the same action with this electromagnet as occurs with the permanent magnet of a PM speaker, and the audio electrical energy is converted to acoustical energy.

It should be noted that the electromagnet employs a soft iron core, while the permanent magnet is a hard metal. From the study of basic magnetism, it may be remembered that the soft iron will lose its magnetism as soon as the current through the field coil is removed, while the hard steel employed in the permanent magnet speaker will retain its magnetic properties for an indefinite period. The choice of speaker magnet type is primarily governed by cost factors and space requirements since, for comparable design characteristics, the difference in performance between the two types is negligible. The electromagnetic-type speaker requires extra power to activate the field coil, while the permanent magnet type requires only the power applied to the voice coil. This problem is, of course, taken into consideration in the design of modern receivers. The circuits of the two types of speakers are illustrated in figure 4-5. In electromagnetic speaker applications, the field coil is commonly utilized as a filter choke in the power supply filter system. In permanent-magnet speaker applications, a resistor is ordinarily used in the filter circuit, although a separate choke may be used to improve the filtering action.

Filtering of the B plus supply in an electromagnetic speaker circuit must be given careful con-

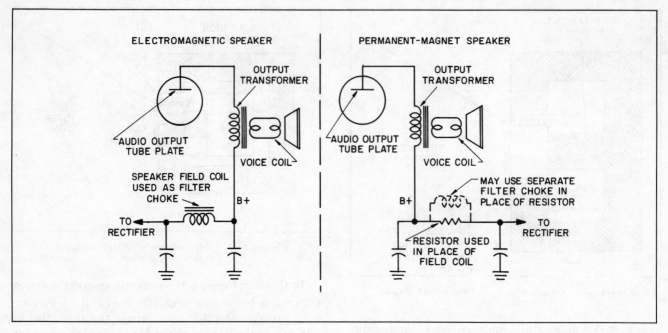

Figure 4-5. Methods of Connecting Electromagnetic and Permanent-Magnet Speakers

sideration in view of the possibility of a-c hum problems. However, this means of supplying the power to the field coil is commonly used.

Two factors must therefore be kept in mind in the design of the electromagnetic speaker. The field coil must be able to handle the power requirements of the receiver and also to provide sufficient magnetism for the proper speaker performance. In general, the field coil is designed for a dissipation approximately equal to the electrical power output of the receiver. Factors to be considered are the number of ampere-turns in the field, which is governed by the wire size and available current, and the temperature rise in the windings. The temperature factor is ordinarily checked under actual operation.

It is necessary when designing a dynamic speaker to provide sufficient flux in the air gap; otherwise, the low-frequency resonance of the cone may be overpronounced. A certain amount of over-emphasis in low-frequency response is desirable in some cases and, consequently, may be deliberately incorporated into the speaker design. A small air gap would of course improve the sensitivity of the speaker. However, there are limitations to the decrease in gap size; otherwise, mechanical problems are encountered which tend to introduce distortion.

The voice coil must provide a field which will interact with the field of the magnet and thus cause the voice coil to move a desired distance along the magnet. Therefore, the physical requirements of the voice coil demand that it be small, both in wire size and in over-all size. Because of the one-half inch to one-inch diameter of the magnet pole piece employed in the average radio and television speaker, the voice-coil impedance is usually 3.2 ohms. A higher impedance is ordinarily employed in speakers designed for heavy output wattage; however, a 3.2-ohm voice coil has been employed in speakers capable of handling 12 to 15 watts.

The actual operation of the voice coil, as previously described, depends upon the interaction of the voice-coil varying magnetic field with the constant magnetic field of the speaker magnet. This is illustrated in figure 4-6. From a previous study of basic physics and magnetism, it will be recalled that like poles repel and opposite poles attract. Remember that the position of the voice coil is directly over one of the poles on the speaker magnet, as shown in figure 4-7. Further, it is known that by applying the left-hand rule to the current in the voice coil, it is possible to determine the polarity of the magnetic field formed by the current passing through the coil. Regardless of the direction of the voice-coil current, there are two magnetic fields, that produced by the coil and that

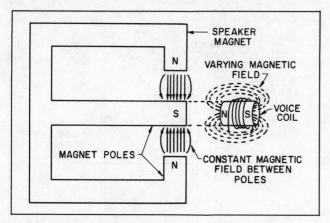

Figure 4-6. Operation of Voice Coil, Showing Action of Magnetic Fields

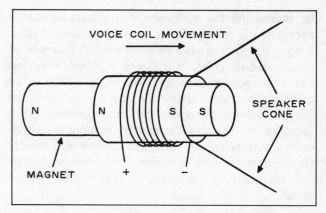

Figure 4-8. Alignment of Magnetic Fields to Produce Forward Voice-Coil Motion

of the speaker magnet. If the voice-coil field is such that its north pole is in the same direction as the north pole of the magnet, the magnetic lines of force will have a tendency to cause a repelling action, and attempt to push the voice coil off the magnet entirely, which in this case is in a forward direction on the speaker's axis (see figure 4-8).

If the poles of either the magnet or the voice coil are reversed, so that the opposite poles are adjacent, north to south, the voice-coil direction will be backward. This action is due to the tendency of the magnetic lines of force to cause the magnets to align or center their poles as closely as possible. Movement of the voice coil in either direction will naturally cause a corresponding movement of the cone, which moves (or disturbs) the air mass and produces the resulting sound waves.

The ability of the cone to move the surrounding air mass is relative to the amount of electrical

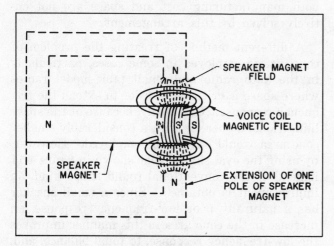

Figure 4-7. Relative Positions of Constant and Variable Magnetic Fields

power applied to the voice coil, and determines the efficiency of the speaker. Loudspeaker efficiency is defined, therefore, as the amount of acoustical output obtained for a given amount of audio signal input. It is measured in decibels.

To obtain good efficiency, the various speaker components — the speaker magnet, the voice coil, and the cone — must be properly matched. The speaker magnet and the voice coil must both be of sufficient size, weight, and power to move the cone mass in the desired proportion to the applied audio signal power. At the same time, the voice-coil size and weight must not be too great, or distortion of the acoustical output may result.

The proper design of the cone is of great importance in achieving proper tonal balance with respect to fidelity and range. In this connection, it should be noted that the design engineer's goal is tonal balance in the speaker with respect to the over-all audio system. A loudspeaker may have excellent low-frequency response but, because of the inability of the speaker to reproduce satisfactorily, it may have a noticeable "booming" sound. In other words, the reproduced sound may contain too much bass response. Again, the speaker may have excellent high-frequency response, yet, because of the absence of sufficient low frequencies, sound very thin, or "tinny." However, if a balance is achieved between the amount of low-frequency response and high-frequency response, even though both may be somewhat limited, the loudspeaker can provide an over-all sound range with enough naturalness to be satisfactory to the ear.

The factors which affect the frequency response of the cone are its size, material, and shape. The low-frequency range of the cone can be extended by increasing the cone size, but this results in a sacrifice of some of the high-frequency range. Primarily, this is due to a necessary increase in the voice-coil mass, which has a direct effect on the high-frequency range. By going in the other direction and decreasing the size of the cone, the high-frequency response can be increased at a sacrifice in the low-frequency response. Obviously, it is necessary to select a cone size which, in conjunction with the amplifier system and cabinet enclosure to be used, will give the desired result.

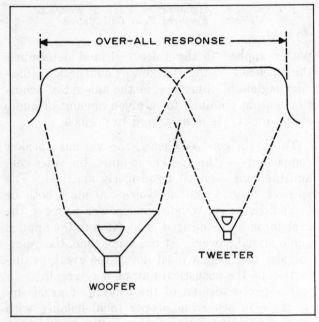

Figure 4-9. Use of Separate Large- and Small-Cone Speakers for Extended Frequency Response

A partial solution is to use two speakers, a small speaker designed to cover a specific range of high frequencies and properly matched with a large speaker which is designed for a specific range of low frequencies. As illustrated in figure 4-9 the over-all range of frequencies is thus extended to provide the desired response.

This arrangement, however, has its limitations. In view of the space required for two speakers of this type, the cabinet enclosure, into which the speakers will be installed, must be relatively large; this would eliminate many small console and practically all table-model receivers. A further consideration might be the cost of the two speakers as compared to the cost of the receiver into which they will be installed, which in some cases, would be prohibitive.

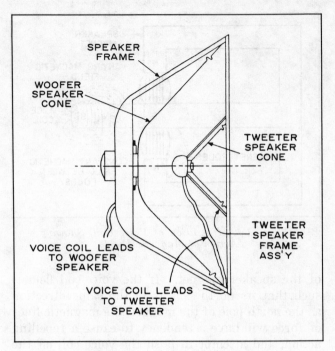

Figure 4-10. Construction of Coaxial Speaker

Space limitations inside the cabinet enclosure resulted in the development of the co-axial speaker, which consists of a speaker with a small cone area mounted within a speaker on the same axis having a large cone area, as shown in figure 4-10. The name *co-axial* means having coincident axes. In some instances the term *woofer-tweeter* is given to these dual-speaker arrangements, whether they are two separate speakers or the co-axial type. The term *woofer* is applied to the large speaker and the small speaker is referred to as the *tweeter*. The type and size of the receiver model is still a factor which will determine the use of the co-axial speaker since the problems of both manufacturing cost and space are not entirely solved by this arrangement.

A different method of treating the problem of cone size is employed in some cases, particularly in the auto radio and small table-model radios where space is critical, in order to extend the frequency response. Ordinarily, because of the space limitations, a speaker with a considerably smaller cone area would have to be employed. However, by using the oval-shaped cone shown in figure 4-11 instead of the conventional round shape kind, an improvement is obtained. Since a small speaker has a naturally poor low-frequency response, an increase in the cone area in this manner improves the low-frequency response, to tonal balance, and, to some degree, the efficiency of the speaker.

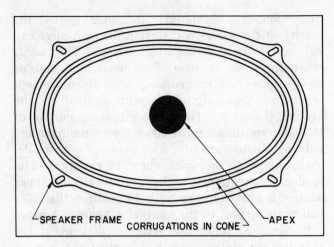

Figure 4-11. Oval-Shaped Speaker

At this point the limitations of the input signal to the audio system should be considered, since they will directly affect the design considerations of the audio system and its components, including the speaker. For example, the standard AM broadcast radio station, with the possible exception of some "high fidelity" stations, is limited to a bandwidth of 10 kilocycles, 5 kilocycles on either side of the carrier frequency, for the audio modulation. "High fidelity" stations are those which are located in such position on the broadcast band of frequencies that their sideband frequencies can be extended beyond the 5-kilocycle limit, as authorized, without interfering with adjacent radio station transmission.

The majority of AM broadcast stations in the United States are of the type limited to a 5-kilocycle sideband and, therefore, the maximum possible audio modulation signal transmitted would be 5 kc or less. However, as illustrated in figure 4-12, the FM radio and television stations are ca-

pable of transmitting audio signals which have considerably greater audio-frequency range. In many cases, because of technical problems, the stations are unable to utilize their full audio-modulation capabilities. Network programs may also suffer a loss of frequency response due to limitations of the cable transmission equipment. These factors are mentioned only to point out the possible sources of loss of response. The maximum audio-modulated signal, therefore, that a standard AM broadcast r a d i o would ordinarily receive would be 5000 cycles or less, provided that it does not incorporate an FM radio section or a phonograph.

Another signal source is the phonograph which may be incorporated in the unit. The signal from such a source may contain frequencies up to the very highest limit of human hearing.

These, then, are some of the factors which govern the design of the audio system and, consequently, the speaker size and design.

The speaker should exhibit certain characteristics such as uniformity of response, good transient response, and negligible amplitude distortion and self-resonant effects. Very often, when one of these effects is present in the speaker, one or more of the others may also be present, since they are somewhat inter-related.

The frequency response of the speaker should be relatively uniform, whether its range is extended or limited, so that each frequency reproduced by the speaker has approximately the same intensity; otherwise, the naturalness of the reproduced sound will be affected. Non-uniform

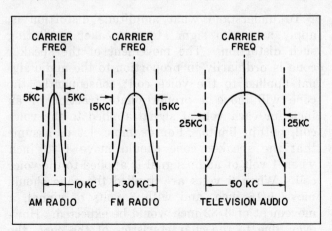

*Figure 4-12. Comparison of AM, FM, and
Television Audio-Modulation Limitations*

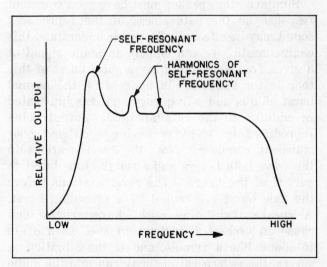

*Figure 4-13. Effects of Self-Resonance on
Over-all Speaker Response Curve*

speaker response is due mainly to the self-resonant characteristics of the speaker (see figure
4-13).

Compensation must be made for any self-resonant characteristics; otherwise, a note from a certain m u s i c a l instrument, reproduced by the
speaker and occurring at this resonant frequency,
may be many decibels higher in intensity than a
higher or lower note. Harmonics of the resonant
frequency may also occur producing a similar
effect.

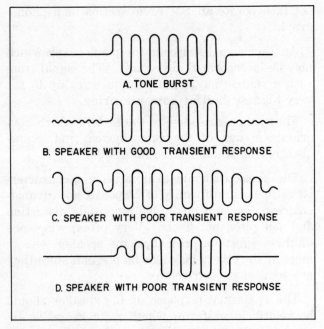

*Figure 4-14. Comparison of Good and
Poor Transient Response with Tone Burst
Applied to Speaker*

Similarly, the speaker must have good transient
response or the naturalness of the reproduced
sound may be affected. To better understand this
characteristic, we can employ an audio signal of
a given frequency and apply a short burst of this
tone to the speaker. In figure 4-14, the normal
burst of this audio-frequency signal is illustrated
in addition to the resultant audio output being
reproduced by speakers having good and poor
transient response. Note the reverberations in
the wave both before and after the tone burst in
part C of the figure. The reverberations before
the tone burst are caused by a preceding burst.
A speaker exhibiting such characteristics can
cause an orchestral instrument such as a drum
to sound like a rumble, and if the situation is
severe, the reverberations may run into the audio
signals which follow, thus causing considerable

distortion of the signal. In other words, the
clarity of the sound is distorted through mechanical imperfections of the speaker cone. They occur
when the cone, because of its mass, material, or
design, does not immediately stop its movement
when the audio-signal current applied to the
voice coil ceases. Thus, the vibrating motion of
the cone continues until other forces dampen and
subdue the movement. The spider, to some degree, helps to dampen such vibrations. The
spider, as mentioned earlier, is actually an inner
suspension whose purpose is to position the voice
coil with respect to the speaker magnet. A properly designed inner suspension will prevent the
side motion of the voice coil against the magnet
while permitting freedom of movement backwards and forwards over the magnet, and will
return the voice coil to its original position after
current through it ceases.

Poor transient response may be due to another,
different effect. The speaker cone may resist the
natural motion stimulated by the audio-signal
current through the voice coil, so that the cone
does not begin to move as soon as current is
applied to the coil, as shown in part D of figure
4-14. Note how the forepart of the burst is suppressed and must build up gradually. The resultant sound lacks crispness, and it is very possible
for low-intensity audio signals to be lost entirely.
It is very often the case that a speaker having
poor transient response will also have poor response uniformity, which is another indication
of the interrelation of these undesirable characteristics.

Amplitude distortion may be present due to
the design characteristics of the cone material,
cone mass, or general design of the speaker.

To understand what amplitude distortion is,
apply an audio signal to a speaker exhibiting
such distortion. The movement of the speaker
cone is ordinarily in proportion to the audio signal applied to the voice coil; consequently, the
cone will move a proportionate fraction of an
inch for each volt of signal applied to the voice
coil, within limits. For example, let us assume
that the speaker cone should move 1/32 inch
when 1 volt of audio signal is applied to the voice
coil. When 2 volts are applied the cone should
move 1/16 inch, and with 3 volts of signal, a
movement of 3/32 inch would be expected. However, due to the characteristics of the cone, the
cone movement may be less than 3/32 inch at 3

volts. Furthermore, since the movement of the cone is greatest at low audio frequencies, such distortion is ordinarily more pronounced at low frequencies than in the middle- or high-frequency range.

The movement of the cone varies throughout the frequency range. At the low audio frequencies the entire cone is in action as a single unit (all parts in motion in unison), and the action is therefore somewhat like that of a piston. However, as the frequency increases, the movement of the cone is by sections, with the greatest cone activity centered around the apex. Therefore, care must be taken to select the proper material for the apex part of the cone, the apex shape, and the dust cover over the apex to achieve the desired high-frequency response.

The preceding paragraphs have discussed the major problems which may be encountered in designing the loudspeaker. As was mentioned before, proper selection of the magnet and voice coil is important to the design, and also in reducing undesirable characteristics.

Various methods are also employed in the design of the cone to help overcome these problems. Alterations can be made in the cone to help overcome the problems of tonal balance, response uniformity, self-resonant characteristics, transient response, amplitude distortion, and efficiency. Since the cone movement varies at different frequencies, the material used in the cone can be changed to either accentuate or suppress the particular frequency or frequencies. The material selected for the cone may be either soft or hard, fiber or paper, and the thickness of the material, which affects the cone mass, may be varied.

In some instances, a combination of hard and soft materials may be employed in the cone construction. The hard or rigid material is employed in the center cone section, while the outer section is made of the soft or nonrigid material. The purpose of employing two materials of varying rigidity is to reduce or eliminate cone resonance effects.

A very effective and widely used method of improving the response uniformity, which, of course, helps to reduce cone resonance effects, is to corrugate or wrinkle the cone material at specific points as shown in figure 4-15. The corrugations serve to break up the resonant wave effect that may be present due either to the cone

mass or the rigidity of the material. The shallowness or angle between the sides of the cone will to some degree affect the rigidity and, in turn, the efficiency and response. The shallowness, therefore, should be in proportion to the speaker size.

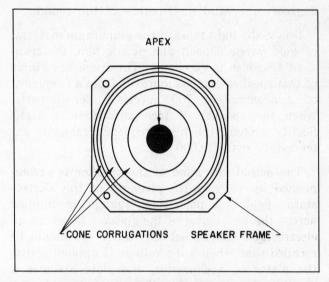

Figure 4-15. Speaker-Cone Corrugations To Improve Uniformity of Frequency Response

4-4 THE ELECTROSTATIC SPEAKER

A new type of tweeter speaker is employed with some high-fidelity equipment. It is known as an *electrostatic* speaker and its construction is similar to that of a capacitor. Consequently, it is sometimes known as a *capacitor* speaker. The high-frequency range of the speaker is outstanding and extends considerably above the previous limitations of most high-fidelity systems.

As already mentioned, its construction is not unlike that of a capacitor, since it consists of two metallic plates separated by a thin insulating film acting as a dielectric. One plate is made of rigid aluminum, of semicircular shape. The surface, however, is not smooth but is formed into small flat segments, while the entire surface area is perforated. The perforations prevent pressure on the diaphragm that would result from the vibrating movement of the front plate and which, of course, would introduce mechanical distortion problems.

The front plate consists of a pure gold vapor deposit upon a polyester plastic film which forms the dielectric. The characteristics of the plastic film are such that it will not shrink or stretch and has almost no mass. It is fitted across the segmented rigid plate and held in place by a spring-loaded metal bar located at the back of the rigid plate.

The result of this mechanical construction is equivalent to many tweeter speakers arranged to form a semicircle, thus providing almost 180 degrees of spatial distribution of the sound.

Due to the light mass of the diaphragm material or gold vapor deposit and plastic film, the transient response is excellent. The frequency range of this speaker extends upwards from a frequency of approximately 7000 cycles. Consequently, when the speaker is incorporated in a high-fidelity system, the high-frequency range is extended to over 20,000 cps.

The actual operation of the speaker is accomplished by varying the strength of the electrostatic field. A polarizing voltage is applied across the two plates of the speaker to set up an electrostatic charge between them. It should be recalled that when a d-c voltage is applied across the plates of a capacitor, one plate assumes a positive charge and the other a negative charge, depending upon the direction of current. The charges set up a stress between the two plates, so that they are attracted to one another (figure 4-16).

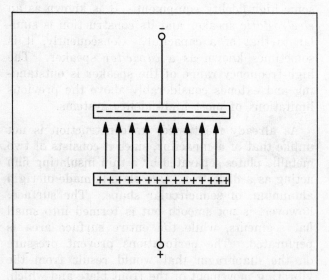

Figure 4-16. Stress Between Two Plates of a Capacitor with Opposite Charges

A polarizing voltage for the speaker is obtained from the plate of one of the tubes in the push-pull audio output stage. This voltage passes through a high-value resistor (R₂ in figure 4-17) to the terminal on the speaker attached to the

diaphragm. The rigid frame of the speaker is connected to ground, and since capacitance exists between the two plates, they form a capacitor. The resistor and the capacitance of the speaker form an integration network that filters the fluctuations in the plate voltage, causing it to appear across the speaker as a constant value of d-c voltage. This polarizing voltage sets up the required stress, or tension, between the two speaker elements so that a change in the electrostatic field will cause the diaphragm to move back and forth.

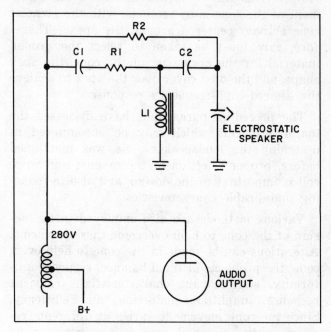

Figure 4-17. Electrostatic Speaker and Associated Circuit

An audio voltage is then needed which will vary the electrostatic charge between the two plates in direct proportion to the frequencies to be reproduced. This voltage is obtained from the same audio output tube plate that supplies the polarizing voltage, and is applied through a resistance-capacitance-inductance network to the speaker diaphragm terminal, along with the polarizing voltage. The R-C-L network forms a high-pass filter which passes only those frequencies above approximately 7000 cps. The purpose of the filter is to eliminate frequencies below 7000 cps, since these frequencies, due to the design of this speaker, would not be faithfully reproduced.

As the varying audio voltage is impressed across the speaker, which already has applied to it the polarizing voltage (see figure 4-18), the strength of the electrostatic force between the two plates also changes in direct proportion to the variations of the audio voltage. This, in turn, causes a greater or lesser attracting force between the two speaker elements, and consequently the movable plate (diaphragm) is set in motion, reproducing audible vibrations of the electrical modulation energy being applied to the speaker. The frequencies below 7000 cps are adequately handled by the bass or woofer speaker which has been previously discussed. The electrostatic speaker is mounted in an aperture in the cabinet front in order to fully utilize its spatial distribution characteristics.

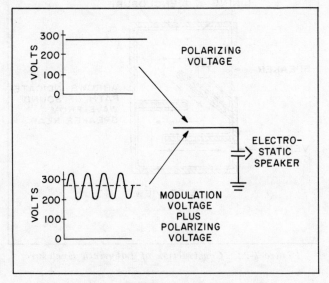

Figure 4-18. Polarizing Voltage and Modulation (Audio) Voltage Applied to Electrostatic Speaker

4-5 DESIGN OF THE SPEAKER ENCLOSURE

The design of the cabinet enclosure in which the loudspeaker will be installed is of equal importance to the over-all audio speaker system design. The cabinet can be designed to help suppress certain undesirable characteristics of the speaker system which, for various reasons, could not be entirely handled by the basic design of the speaker. More often, however, the cabinet enclosure is designed to supplement and add to the desirable characteristics of the speaker and thus improve the response of the over-all system. The enclosure is ordinarily considered a baffle. One of the characteristics of a loudspeaker is that the sound emanating from the rear of the speaker is 180 degrees out of phase with the sound emanating from the front, and results in cancellation as shown in figure 4-19. This effect is most pronounced at the lower frequencies because of their longer wavelengths. The length

of the sound path or air path of the waves is also important, since a shorter air path for the front and back waves to travel and meet will cause a greater cancellation. Such a situation would exist with a speaker without any baffling.

If the length of the air path from front to back of the speaker is increased, the cancellation effect is reduced. The simplest method of accomplishing this, of course, is to add to the surface area at the top, bottom, and sides of the speaker frame, or by mounting the speaker behind an opening in a flat baffle board. A flat baffle of this type, however, must have considerable size in order to satisfactorily accomplish its purpose.

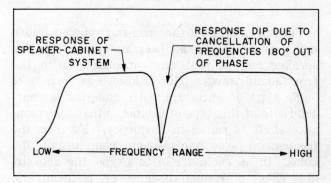

Figure 4-19. Effect of Cancellation of Frequencies When Sound from Rear of Speaker Cabinet Is 180 Degrees Out of Phase with Sound at Front

The problem, therefore, is to reduce the size of the baffle, but at the same time achieve the desired results. One method of reducing the comparative size is to fold back the edges to form a box shape, with one end open. Actually, this design forms what might be considered a resonant open-ended chamber. The resonance of an enclosure or baffle of this design causes a sharp rise in the response. The frequency at which this occurs depends upon the construction of the baffle enclosure, and is usually in the low-frequency range. This causes a very booming effect in the reproduced sound and, of course, an undesirable effect on the naturalness. In figure 4-20, the transition from a flat baffle type to the open-ended baffle enclosure is illustrated. The open-end baffle enclosure is very commonly employed because of its ease of manufacture.

The resonance effect can be reduced by the design of the speaker. Placement of the speaker to one side or off the center axis of the cabinet is commonly employed as a means of reducing the cancellation effect further.

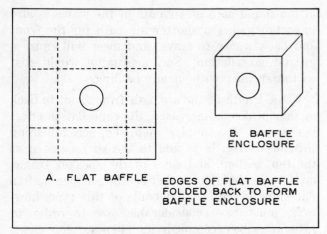

Figure 4-20. Folded-Baffle Enclosure

Placing a back on the open-end type enclosure will reduce entirely all back radiation from the speaker and prevent any cancellation with the front sound waves. This is known as an *infinite baffle* type of enclosure. An undesirable characteristic of this type of cabinet is that the resonance effect is raised in frequency. Further, the frequencies below the resonant point usually decline. In an enclosure of this type, the undesirable effect of resonance, however, is taken into consideration by designing the speaker to compensate for this effect. Acoustic padding on the inner walls also is employed in the infinite baffle.

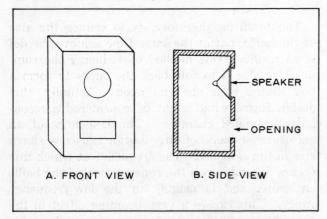

Figure 4-21. Bass-Reflex Baffle Enclosure

Certain types of cabinet enclosures are designed so that at low frequencies the back wave from the speaker is used to augment the front wave, as in the *bass-reflex* type enclosure shown in figure 4-21. In the bass-reflex enclosure, the back wave from the speaker, at low frequencies, is inverted in phase and then added to the forward sound wave in phase. This arrangement effectively increases the efficiency of the speaker at low fre-

quencies. Such an enclosure must be carefully designed to match the speaker in order to function properly — a properly designed system of speaker and bass-reflex enclosure provides a relatively smooth and extended low-frequency response. There is some distortion of the mid-frequency response. However, this can usually be corrected by proper use of damping or sound-absorbing material.

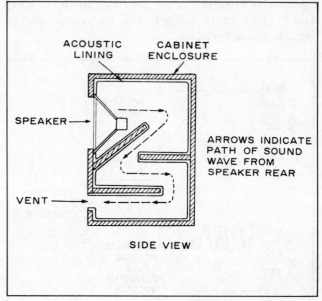

Figure 4-22. Construction of Labyrinth Enclosure

There are variations of this type enclosure wherein the back wave of the loudspeaker is inverted in phase and used to augment the forward sound wave. One type is the *labyrinth* enclosure, figure 4-22, which contains a resonant tube whose length is one-quarter wavelength long at the resonant frequency of the speaker. Essentially, the quarter-wave tube, which is folded in this design in order to conserve space, presents a high impedance to the rear of the speaker at its resonant frequency and a low impedance to the sound at the open end or cabinet vent. Therefore, the resonant frequency is damped. The response is increased, however, at twice the resonant frequency, since the tube is effectively a half wavelength long, causing a phase inversion of the sound at the cabinet opening which then adds to the forward speaker wave. An acoustic lining or sound-absorbent lining used on the tube suppresses any resonance effects at the higher frequencies.

Another type of baffle enclosure is the *folded-horn* baffle shown in figure 4-23. In this arrangement, high-frequency sound is radiated from the front of the speaker, while the low frequencies are radiated by the horn-shaped arrangement of the enclosure. Actually, the addition of a horn to the speaker effectively increases its efficiency, or ability to move the air mass, at the lower frequencies. Variations of this arrangement may be found where the general shape or design of the horn is altered. However, the foregoing paragraphs deal with some of the basic types of baffle enclosures.

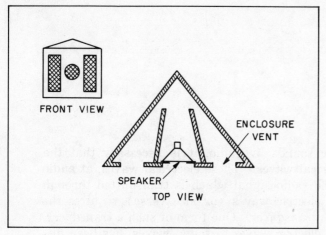

Figure 4-23. Folded-Horn Baffle

In summarizing, the primary purpose of the baffle is to reduce or eliminate the cancellation of sound waves which occur because of their out-of-phase relationship at the front and rear of the speaker. The baffle, however, can be designed to serve a further purpose of effectively extending and smoothing the frequency response, and thus improve the over-all response which is important to the tonal balance of the system.

4-6 SUMMARY

The loudspeaker and its enclosure convert the electrical voltages and currents from the audio amplifier into audible sound waves. There are many different types of loudspeakers and enclosures, each having its own characteristics which determine the selection for specific applications. In such applications as home radios, a compromise between uniform response over a wide frequency range and size and weight is usually required. In high-fidelity equipments, the primary requirement is uniform frequency response over a wide frequency range, with size and weight generally secondary. In applications such as auditorium public address systems, the loudspeaker must be capable of delivering a large volume of sound with reasonable fidelity in the voice-frequency range of approximately 100 to 4000 cps (as compared with the audio-frequency range of 20-20,000 cps).

REVIEW QUESTIONS

1. Explain the operation of the earphone.

2. What is a loudspeaker? ~Page 47~

3. What is the function of each of these elements?

4. Explain what causes the voice coil of a dynamic loudspeaker to vibrate.

5. Name two types of dynamic loudspeaker and describe the difference between them.

6. Why are two or more loudspeakers generally used in high-fidelity systems, and what is the function of each? ~woofer tweeter woofer used for bass tweeter used for high~

7. What is the principle of operation of the ~frequency~ electrostatic speaker?

8. Why is some type of enclosure desirable?

9. Describe the principle of operation of the labyrinth enclosure.

10. What is the bass-reflex enclosure, and why is an acoustic lining necessary?

~Page 58~

CHAPTER FIVE

Microphones and Phonograph Pickups

5-1 Introduction

In order to transmit voice or music sounds by radio, it is necessary that the audible sound waves be converted to electrical waves. These electrical waves, at audio frequencies, are then superimposed upon the radio signal which is transmitted through space. The conversion of sound waves to electric waves (or vice versa) requires the use of a device known as an *electro-acoustic transducer*. One form of such a transducer, the loudspeaker, which ordinarily converts electric waves to sound waves, has been discussed previously. The microphone is another type of electro-acoustic transducer, and is used to convert sound waves to electrical waves. Thus it is essentially the opposite of the loudspeaker. In many cases, the microphone and loudspeaker are actually the same device. For example, in many home and office intercommunications systems, the "push-to-talk" lever converts the loudspeaker to a microphone merely by switching the connections of certain circuit components. In most cases, however, the microphone has been especially designed to perform its function of converting sound waves to electrical waves, and will not function properly as a loudspeaker.

Although there are many different types of microphones, practically all of them have certain characteristics in common. They must be able to convert sound energy into electrical energy efficiently in order to provide the greatest possible electrical signal for a given sound intensity. In general, they must have as wide a frequency response as possible, and should convert a given sound frequency into the same electrical signal frequency in order to faithfully reproduce the actual s o u n d s. Finally, microphone response to variations in sound energy should be linear; that is, doubling the energy contained in the sound wave should double the energy contained in the generated electric wave.

Other desirable microphone characteristics depend upon the particular application. For example, a microphone designed for recording music should have a high sensitivity over a wide range of frequencies, because proper reproduction demands that the smallest sounds occurring at comparatively long distances be converted to electric waves. On the other hand, a microphone designed for use in an aircraft, where the background noise level is generally high, should be relatively insensitive and respond only to high-intensity sounds, such as voice sounds when the microphone is held only a few inches from the mouth.

Directivity, or the ability of the microphone to pick up sounds from various directions, also depends upon the particular application. A microphone used to pick up orchestral music in a hall, for example, should ideally be omnidirectional (able to pick up sounds from all directions equally well), because much of the effect is created by the acoustic qualities of the room itself. On the other hand, a microphone used by a speaker in an auditorium should be highly directional in order to minimize unwanted background noises.

5-2 CARBON MICROPHONES

There are a number of different types of microphones, each with different characteristics. Of all types, perhaps the most common is the single-button carbon microphone, which is usually found in telephones. Although the carbon microphone does not have the most desirable reproduction characteristics, it is inexpensive, rugged, and highly reliable. These characteristics are important in the telephone, which is generally used by persons who are unaccustomed to handling sensitive instruments. The single-button carbon microphone, shown in part A of figure 5-1, operates on the principle of varying the resistance between granules of powdered carbon by varying the pressure, and thus the distance between the granules. The sound waves strike a metal diaphragm, causing it to vibrate. The metal pin attached to the center of the diaphragm, and the metal button attached to the pin vibrate in accordance with the diaphragm motion. As the button vibrates, it alternately forces the carbon granules closer together and farther apart. When the granules are compressed, the electrical resistance decreases, and when the granules move farther apart, the electrical resistance increases. If this varying

resistance is connected across a battery or other direct-current source, the circuit current will vary in the opposite sense; that is, the current will decrease when the resistance increases and vice versa. Thus, the sound waves are converted to a mechanical motion by the diaphragm, the motion is converted to a varying resistance by the effects of pressure on the carbon granules, and finally, the varying resistance is converted to a varying current by the connection to a direct-current source.

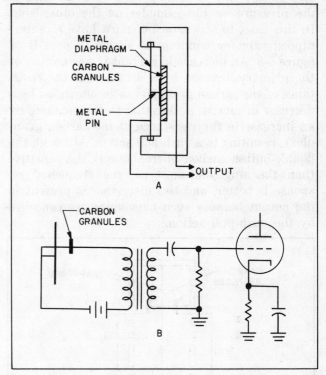

Figure 5-1. Single-Button Carbon Microphone

In order to make use of this current variation, the primary of a transformer is connected in series with the carbon granules and the direct-current source. The current variations induce voltage variations in the transformer secondary, which is coupled, as shown in part B of figure 5-1, to the grid of an audio-frequency amplifier.

The electrical output from the carbon microphone is comparatively large (about 0.1 to 0.3 volt across 50 to 75 ohms in the transformer primary), and it can be increased by using a step-up transformer. However, the frequency response is poor. The telephone microphone response is sufficiently broad for reasonably good reproduction of sound waves in the voice-frequency band (about 100 to 4000 cps), but it is too limited for good reproduction of music. Frequency response can be increased by making the diaphragm lighter and stretching it more tightly, but at the cost of reduced sensitivity.

The double-button carbon microphone, shown in part A of figure 5-2, is a variation of the single-button carbon microphone. It operates in a manner analagous to the operation of the push-pull amplifier. The buttons are located on opposite sides of the diaphragm, and as the diaphragm vibrates, an increase in the pressure on the granules on one side is accompanied by a decrease in the pressure on the granules on the other side. In this case, the transformer must have a center-tapped primary winding, as shown in part B of figure 5-2. An increase in current in one section of the primary (caused by a decrease in the resistance of the carbon granules) is accompanied by a decrease in current in the other section (caused by an increase in the resistance of the carbon granules), resulting in a push-pull action. Although the double-button carbon microphone is less sensitive than the single-button type, the frequency response is better, and less distortion is present in the output because even harmonics are cancelled by the push-pull action.

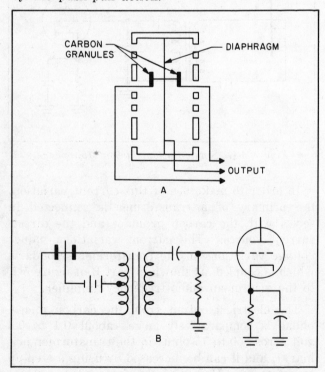

Figure 5-2. Double-Button Carbon Microphone

As previously mentioned, the carbon microphone is used in telephones. It is also often found in aircraft and other applications where ruggedness and reliability are the main requirements.

The disadvantage of poor frequency response has already b e e n mentioned. In addition, carbon microphone can easily develop packing troubles, in which the carbon granules tend to stick together and reduce the sensitivity; also, a large current will produce tiny arcs between the granules, thus generating microphone noise.

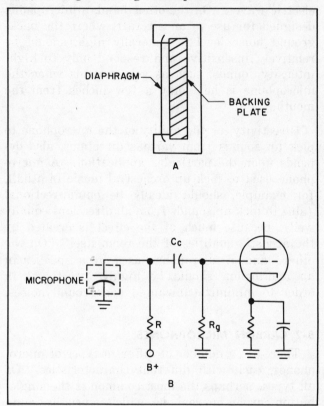

Figure 5-3. Capacitance Microphone

Capacitor

In contrast to the carbon microphone, the capacitor microphone has excellent frequency response and gives high-quality reproduction of speech or music. Also in contrast, it is an extremely delicate instrument and can easily be damaged by mechanical shock or high-intensity sound waves.

The capacitor microphone consists of a thick metal plate, with a thin metal diaphragm set close to it, as shown in part A of figure 5-3. In general, the distance between the two plates is on the order of 0.001 inch, and the thickness of the metal diaphragm is also on the order of 0.001 inch. The separation at the edges is provided by an insulating ring, which also prevents accumulation of dust or moisture between the plates.

In use, the microphone is connected across a high-voltage source, as shown in part B of figure 5-3, and the backing plate and diaphragm act as the plates of a capacitor. Sound waves cause the diaphragm to vibrate, v a r y i n g the spacing between it and the back plate. These changes in spacing cause changes in the capacitance, and, if the microphone is connected as shown in part B of figure 5-3, these capacitance changes produce variations in the current through the resistor, R. These variations are coupled through the large coupling capacitor, C_c, to the grid of an audio amplifier.

The capacitor microphone has a wide frequency response but low sensitivity. Since long leads increase the over-all capacitance, the amplifier must be located close to the microphone to obtain maximum sensitivity, and more stages of amplification are needed than with the carbon microphone. Because of its high quality reproduction, the capacitance microphone is frequently used in laboratory w o r k and in high-fidelity sound recording.

Crystal

A third type of microphone, the crystal microphone, makes use of the piezoelectric effect. By way of review, certain t y p e s of crystalline structures, such as quartz and Rochelle salts, generate an electric potential when mechanically deformed. The polarity and amount of electric potential for a specific crystal depend upon the direction and amount of mechanical pressure, respectively, and the crystal microphone utilizes this potential.

The basis of the crystal microphone is a pair of crystal slabs with foil bonded to each side. These are clamped together as shown in part A of figure 5-4, and with the proper crystals, form what is known as a *bimorph*. The bimorph essentially consists of two crystals in series. If the crystals are properly cut, the potentials will have the same polarity, and thus will add to give twice the output of a single crystal. Part B of figure 5-4 shows two bimorphs mounted in series, with a light membrane which excludes dust and moisture. In this type, the crystals are clamped along two edges, and sound waves cause them to vibrate as shown by the dotted lines in the figure. The mechanical deformation generates an electric potential. To generate a usable potential, the crystal microphone uses a number of these units connected in a series-parallel arrangement. This type of microphone gives excellent frequency response, is rugged and reliable, and requires no external power. The natural resonant frequency

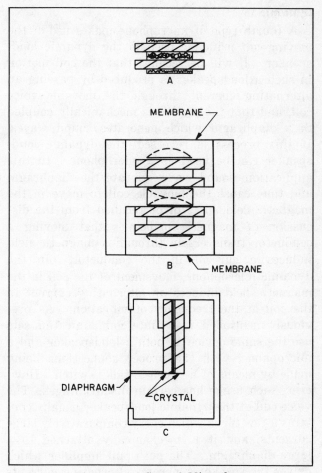

Figure 5-4. Crystal Microphone

of the crystals can be adjusted, by making the crystals sufficiently small, to be well above the audio-frequency range. The crystal microphone is therefore frequently found in sound studios, and is in many cases displacing the carbon microphone. Since it can be made extremely small, the crystal microphone is generally used for the "man in the audience" type of radio broadcasts. It is also desirable in this application because of its directivity characteristics. (A s m a l l crystal microphone is very nearly omnidirectional.)

The crystal microphone can also be constructed as shown in part C of figure 5-4. In this type of construction, the bimorph is clamped at three corners, and the fourth corner is attached to a pin. The pin is connected to a diaphragm, and mechanically couples the diaphragm vibration to the crystal. This type of crystal microphone has a higher output than the type previously discussed, because the diaphragm intercepts a larger area and applies the resultant motion at one point on the crystal. However, the frequency response is poorer and the unit is not as rugged.

Dynamic

A fourth type of microphone makes use of the moving-coil principle used in the dynamic loudspeaker. It will be recalled that the coil motion in such a loudspeaker is produced by passing an alternating current through the movable voice coil, and that the motion is mechanically coupled to a diaphragm which generates sound waves. If this process is reversed, the dynamic loudspeaker can be used as a microphone. In this application, sound waves vibrate the diaphragm and thus cause the movable coil to move in the magnetic field. It will be recalled from the discussion of magnetic principles that moving a conductor transversely through a magnetic field induces a current in the conductor. In the dynamic microphone, movement of the coil in the magnetic field induces an alternating current in the coil at the frequency of vibration. As previously mentioned, many intercommunication sets use the same device as both a loudspeaker and a microphone, with the proper connections being made by means of a "push-to-talk" switch. However, such usage has certain disadvantages. The voice coil of the dynamic loudspeaker usually contains a few turns which carry comparatively large currents, and it is mechanically attached to a large diaphragm. The push-pull amplifier which drives the speaker generates alternating currents of the amplitude necessary to produce the required volume of sound. In contrast, the sound waves appearing at the microphone are generally much lower in amplitude, and a coil with only a few turns would not generate sufficient current. Therefore, the voice coil of the dynamic microphone usually contains a comparatively large number of turns to provide a high reactance, so that a small current can generate a usable emf. A permanent magnet is generally used to provide the magnetic field, in order to eliminate the necessity of supplying power to the microphone.

The loudspeaker-microphone unit used in intercommunication systems is a compromise between conflicting requirements; however, it is satisfactory for voice-frequency communication. A well designed dynamic microphone (illustrated in figure 5-5) is not usable as a loudspeaker.

One other important use of the dynamic microphone is in the sound-powered telephones used extensively in military ground operations. Since no power is required to operate the microphone, its output may be coupled directly to a telephone

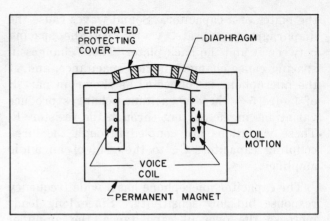

Figure 5-5. Dynamic Microphone

line and used to operate a small dynamic loudspeaker. Both the microphone and the loudspeaker must be especially designed for this application, and both units are built into a telephone handset. The connection of either microphone or loudspeaker to the telephone line is accomplished by use of a "push-to-talk" switch mounted on the handset. For military operations, such a system has the distinct advantage that no external power is needed.

Velocity

A fifth type of microphone is the velocity-ribbon microphone. This device makes use of the current produced when a corrugated aluminum ribbon suspended in a strong magnetic field is caused to vibrate. Figure 5-6 illustrates the construction of such a microphone.

The operation of the velocity-ribbon microphone is essentially the same as that of the dynamic microphone. Sound waves cause the aluminum ribbon to vibrate, and, since the ribbon is suspended in a strong magnetic field, the vibration induces an electric current in the ribbon. The amplitude of the current depends on the velocity with which the ribbon moves through the field, and thus on the volume of the sound (hence, the term *velocity ribbon*).

The velocity-ribbon microphone is a fairly rugged device which reproduces speech or music of good quality and needs no external power. It is highly directional — an important advantage in applications where the pick-up of surrounding noise would be undesirable.

5-3 PHONOGRAPH PICKUPS

If a small section of a disc recording (phonograph record) is enlarged, it will be seen that the single spiral groove is not a smooth spiral curve,

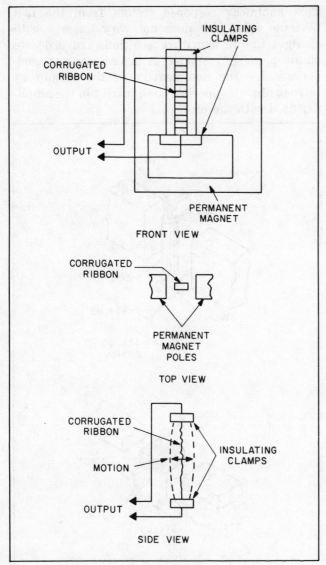

Figure 5-6. Construction of Velocity Ribbon Microphone

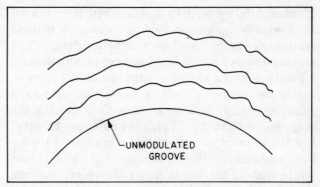

Figure 5-7. Groove Modulation

in order to minimize wear on the recording. Modern phonograph styli use a diamond or sapphire tip which is ground to the proper size and shape and mounted in a metal holder. The transducer converts the mechanical vibration of the stylus to an electrical signal of the same frequency, and is similar to a microphone. As in the case of microphones, several types of transducers are in general use. The tone arm is an arm which pivots freely about a point outside the record, allowing the stylus and transducer to follow the spiral groove of the record.

Many problems must be solved in producing a phonograph pickup which will give good reproduction with minimum wear on the recordings. For example, the type and shape of the stylus depend upon the type of recording (microgroove or standard); the amplifier must compensate for distortion introduced by the pickup; and the tone arm must be properly located and balanced. All three elements of the pickup must be carefully selected to form a complete pickup with the desired characteristics.

Types of Transducers

The transducers in general use in phonograph pickup systems can be divided into two major groups — velocity-responding and amplitude-responding. The output of the velocity-responding type is proportional to the velocity of the stylus as it follows the groove modulation, while the output of the amplitude-responding type is proportional to the distance through which the stylus moves from side to side in the groove.

Velocity

The velocity-responding pickups can be further subdivided into two groups, known as the *moving-iron*, or *variable-reluctance pickup*, and the *moving-coil*, or *dynamic pickup*. It will be recalled from the discussion of magnetic principles that

but varies from side to side as shown in figure 5-7. This variation contains the music or other sounds which are converted to audible sound waves by the phonograph. The phonograph pickup is an electromechanical transducer which converts the mechanical variation in the groove to an electrical signal. This signal is then amplified, and converted to audible sound waves by a loudspeaker.

Basic Elements

All phonograph pickups consist of three basic elements — a stylus (or needle), a transducer, and a tone arm. The stylus, or needle, converts the variation in the record groove to a mechanical vibration, and may be of a number of different types. Early phonograph needles were made of iron, and were discarded after being used once, a current is induced in a coil when it is moved in a steady magnetic field or when it is held stationary in a moving magnetic field. The moving-iron, or variable-reluctance pickup utilizes a fixed coil and a variable magnetic field. In most cases, the magnetic field is varied by moving a small piece of iron in an air gap, thus varying the magnetic reluctance. (This is analogous to varying the current in an electric circuit by varying the resistance.) The reluctance of the iron is low, while that of the air is high; therefore, varying the size of the effective air gap varies the total reluctance.

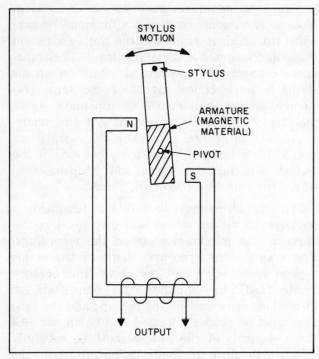

Figure 5-8. Variable-Reluctance Pickup

Figure 5-8 illustrates the principle of operation of the variable-reluctance pickup. As the stylus moves from side to side, following the groove modulation, the reluctance of the magnetic circuit changes, varying the flux. The change of flux induces a current in the coil, the direction of the current depending upon whether the total flux is increasing or decreasing.

There are many different patented types of variable-reluctance pickups, each having both advantages and disadvantages. However, the principle of operation is the same in all cases, and is illustrated by the simplified diagram shown in figure 5-8.

The greatest drawback of the variable-reluctance pickup is its inherent nonlinear response.

This nonlinear response results from the fact that the reluctance does not vary linearly with changes in the armature position. In order to obtain a linear response, it is necessary to compensate for the nonlinearity of the pickup by introducing an opposing nonlinearity in the amplifier used with the pickup.

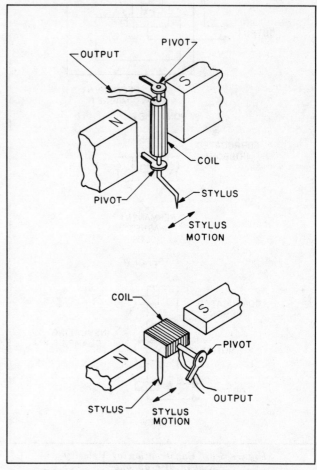

Figure 5-9. Two Types of Dynamic Pickup

A second type of velocity-responding pickup is the dynamic, or moving-coil pickup, illustrated in figure 5-9. The operation of this type of pickup is very similar to that of a D'Arsonval galvanometer. It will be recalled that rotation of the meter coil results from the interaction of magnetic fields when current flows through the coil. The dynamic pickup utilizes this same principle, except that the groove modulation is translated by the stylus into a mechanical rotation of the coil. Since the coil is in a steady magnetic field, the mechanical rotation induces a current in the coil which is proportional to the velocity of the coil rotation. If the total angle through which the coil rotates is small (this is the case with the dynamic pickup), the output will be very nearly a linear function of the angle of rotation, and thus no appreciable distortion will be introduced by the pickup.

Two other advantages of the dynamic pickup are its extended high-frequency response, resulting from the small mass of the coil (which contains no iron or other magnetic material), and the low hum pickup, resulting from the use of a low-impedance coil containing only a few turns of wire. The greatest drawbacks to the use of the dynamic pickup are its low output, requiring the use of a step-up transformer, its delicate and precise construction, and the fact that the stylus cannot be replaced by the user without special equipment.

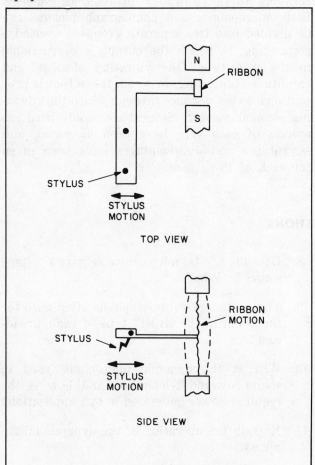

Figure 5-10. Velocity Ribbon Pickup

The final type of velocity-responding pickup to be discussed is the velocity-ribbon pickup. The operation of this type of pickup is identical to that of the velocity-ribbon microphone discussed previously, except that the ribbon motion is supplied by connection to the stylus, as illustrated in figure 5-10, rather than by sound waves. As the stylus moves from side to side, following the groove

modulation, the ribbon is vibrated in a magnetic field, setting up a current flow proportional to the ribbon velocity.

Amplitude

The amplitude-responding pickups produce an output which is proportional to t h e distance through which the stylus moves in following the groove modulation. Two types — the crystal pickup and the capacitance pickup — are in common use.

Figure 5-11 illustrates the construction of the crystal pickup. The side-to-side motion of the stylus causes mechanical flexing of the crystal, and thus produces an electrical potential across it. Older crystal pickups use Rochelle salt as the crystal element, and are extremely sensitive to changes in temperature and humidity. To avoid this condition, ceramic crystals are used in most of the newer models.

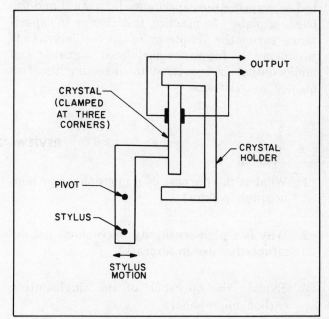

Figure 5-11. Crystal Pickup

The disadvantages of the crystal pickup are twofold: There is an excursion limit (or elastic limit) which if exceeded will change the physical characteristics of the crystal and result in permanent distortion; the output is highly nonlinear near this limit. The major advantage is that the crystal offers a high impedance, and therefore, may be coupled to the grid of an audio amplifier without the use of a transformer.

A second type of amplitude-responding pickup is the FM capacitance pickup, illustrated in figure 5-12. This device is almost identical to the capa-

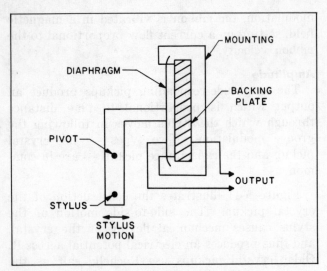

Figure 5-12.   FM Capacitance Pickup

citance microphone described previously. The motion of the stylus causes the thin diaphragm to flex, varying the capacitance between it and the backing plate. In practice, this change in capacitance varies the frequency of an oscillator, thus producing a frequency-modulated signal. The audio output is recovered by detecting the frequency modulation.

Although the FM capacitance pickup has excellent frequency response, its construction is delicate, and the FM oscillator and associated circuitry require careful maintenance.

5-4 SUMMARY

The microphone and the phonograph pickup are transducers which convert mechanical vibrations into electrical energy. The microphone picks up audible sound waves and converts them to mechanical vibrations, and in turn, converts these vibrations to electrical energy. Similarly, the stylus of the phonograph pickup converts the groove modulation to mechanical vibrations, and in turn, converts these vibrations to electrical energy. Both microphones and phonograph pickups can be divided into two separate groups — velocity-responding, in which the output is proportional to the velocity of the vibrating element, and amplitude-responding, in which the output is proportional to the distance through which the vibrating element moves. Several commonly used examples of each type have been discussed, and advantages and disadvantages have been given for each of these examples.

REVIEW QUESTIONS

1.   What is the purpose of a microphone or phonograph pickup?

2.   Why is a high-sensitivity microphone not desirable for use in aircraft?

3.   Explain the operation of the single-button carbon microphone.

4.   Why is it necessary to connect a d-c voltage source in series with the carbon microphone circuit?

5.   What are two disadvantages of the carbon microphone?

6.   How is the capacitance varied in the capacitor microphone?

7.   Why is the capacitance microphone often used in laboratory work?

8.   Does the crystal microphone require a voltage source?   Why?

9.   Why is the crystal microphone often used for the "man in the street" type of radio broadcast?

10.   Why is the dynamic microphone used in sound-powered telephones, and how is the required power generated in this application?

11.   Explain the operation of the dynamic microphone.

12.   What are the two major groups into which phonograph pickups are divided?

13.   How do these two groups differ?

14.   Explain the operation of the variable-reluctance pickup.

15.   Why is the response of the variable-reluctance pickup nonlinear?

CHAPTER SIX

Basic Oscillator Circuits

6-1 Introduction

An oscillator circuit is one which delivers an alternating current or voltage output, usually having a definite desired waveform and frequency, without the use of an external input signal. In almost all oscillators, the oscillations are started by slight variations in the plate current as the oscillator tube heats up. These variations build up because of the feedback path and the amplifying action of the circuit. Basically, an oscillator is an amplifier which derives its input signal from its own output.

6-2 REVIEW OF R-C AND L-C CIRCUIT ACTION

Ohm's law for both d-c and a-c circuits states that the voltage across a resistance is equal to the product of the current through the resistance and the value of resistance.

A capacitor is capable of storing a charge of electrons. Both plates of the capacitor contain the same number of electrons when uncharged; and when charged, one plate contains more free electrons than the other. The difference in the number of free electrons on the plates of a charged capacitor is a measure of the charge on the capacitor. The accumulation of this charge builds up a voltage across the terminals of the capacitor, and the charge continues to increase until this voltage is equal to the applied voltage. Thus, the greater the applied voltage, the greater the charge on the capacitor. A perfect capacitor will keep its charge indefinitely, unless a discharge path is provided, even if the applied voltage source has been removed. However, any practical capacitor has some leakage through the dielectric, so that the charge will gradually leak off.

If a steady voltage is applied to a circuit that contains a resistor and a capacitor, the capacitor charges through the resistor at an exponential rate. The rate of charge, called the *R-C time constant*, is determined by the values of resistance and capacitance in the circuit. After five R-C time intervals, the capacitor attains a charge very nearly equal to the applied voltage. Meanwhile, the voltage drop across the resistor decreases, at an exponential rate, from a value equal to the applied voltage to practically zero. This action is called R-C charging.

If the applied voltage is removed and the circuit closed, the charged capacitor discharges through the resistor, again at an exponential rate. At the end of five R-C time intervals, the voltages across both R and C will be approximately zero. This action is known as R-C discharging. The charging and discharging action of R-C circuits is widely used in electronic circuit applications.

If a steady voltage is connected across an inductance, the current builds up to full value (as determined by the source voltage, the internal resistance of the source, and the inductor resistance) at a gradually decreasing, or exponential, rate. The current buildup is gradual because of the counter emf generated by the self-inductance of the inductor. As the current just starts, the magnetic lines of force expand, cut the turns of

wire of the inductor and generate a counter emf which opposes the emf of the source. This opposition, which decreases as time passes, causes a delay in the current buildup to a steady value. When the voltage source is disconnected, the lines of force collapse, again cutting the turns of the inductor, but now inducing an emf which tends to prolong the current. Thus, the action of an inductor is to oppose a change in current.

Tuned L-C circuits consist of inductors and capacitors. As mentioned above, current passing through an inductor produces a magnetic field around the windings. When the current through the inductor begins to decrease, the field collapses into the windings and induces a voltage. If there is a capacitor connected across the inductor, the induced voltage causes a current and the capacitor becomes charged. In other words, electrostatic energy is stored in the capacitor. When the collapsing magnetic field has finally vanished, the capacitor discharges through the inductor. This discharge current once more sets up a magnetic field around the inductor, leading to a repetition of the entire cycle. The frequency at which these repetitions, or oscillations, occur is the resonant frequency of the tuned circuit. The oscillations of a tuned circuit tend to die out unless the energy losses caused by the inherent resistance of the circuit are replaced in some manner.

6-3 BASIC OSCILLATOR CIRCUIT PRINCIPLES

If an oscillator having an output of constant amplitude is required, some means must be provided to supply energy to the grid circuit to overcome its losses.

The use of tubes as oscillators is made possible by their ability to amplify. Part of the energy in the plate circuit can be applied to the input of the tube, which amplifies the signal. If the energy losses of the circuit are replenished sufficiently, sustained oscillations occur.

Figure 6-1 shows the basic oscillator circuit. The tube is shown with a feedback network connecting the plate and grid circuits. The signal applied to the grid tuned circuit must be of the correct polarity to aid the initial oscillations in the tuned circuit, or *tank*, as it is frequently called. As was learned in the study of amplifiers, the plate signal voltage is 180° out of phase with the grid signal voltage. If a small portion of the amplified output voltage were fed back directly to the grid, it would tend to cancel the oscillations rather than sustain them. Therefore, for the

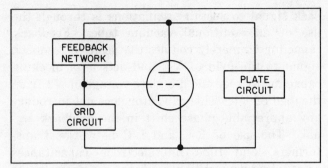

Figure 6-1. Basic Oscillator Circuit

voltage being fed back to the grid to be effective in sustaining oscillations, it must undergo an additional 180-degree phase shift.

The feedback circuit provides the necessary phase shift to sustain oscillations. Any small variation in the grid circuit is amplified by the tube and appears across the plate tank circuit. Part of this plate-circuit energy is fed back to the grid through the feedback network and used to supply the input power. In this way the tube supplies its own input and oscillates at a frequency determined by the constants of the circuit.

Feedback

The term *feedback* is applied to the process of transferring energy from the output circuit of a device to its input circuit. As applied to vacuum-tube circuits, the feeding of a signal from the plate circuit back to the grid circuit out of phase with the input voltage so as to hinder oscillations is called *negative feedback,* or *degeneration.* The feeding back of a signal in phase with the input signal so that it aids oscillations is called *positive feedback,* or *regeneration.*

The effect of negative feedback is to reduce the gain of the amplifier stage. Although this improves the appearance of the output waveform by reducing the distortion which is introduced within the amplifier tube itself, the amplitude of the output signal is reduced. On the other hand, the effect of positive feedback is to increase the gain of an amplifier. If the regeneration is made sufficiently large, the energy fed back to the input maintains the operation of the amplifier, and the amplifier becomes an oscillator. Thus, it is apparent that the feedback network in an oscillator circuit must provide a positive feedback voltage.

There are several methods of coupling part of the oscillatory energy back to the grid circuit. It may be coupled through the use of transformers, R-C networks, L-C networks, or other circuits

outside the tube which are connected directly to the elements, through the interelectrode capacitance of the tube, or through the use of additional vacuum tubes.

Oscillations Produced by Two-Stage Amplifier

The use of an additional vacuum tube to obtain regenerative feedback for sustaining oscillations is shown in figure 6-2. The circuit consists of two R-C coupled audio amplifiers in cascade, with the output of the second stage (V2) coupled back to the input of the first stage (V1). This output signal, which is in phase with the grid signal of V1, satisfies the positive feedback requirement necessary to sustain oscillations.

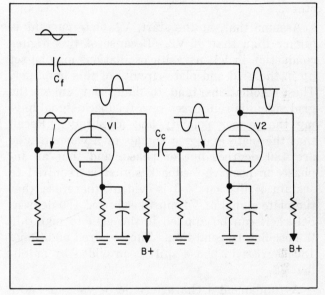

Figure 6-2. Two-Stage Amplifier with Regenerative Feedback

To understand why the two-stage amplifier can act as an oscillator, the characteristics of unwanted oscillations must be considered. Any unwanted oscillations in vacuum-tube circuits are termed *parasitic* oscillations. Parasitic oscillations occur in amplifiers, as well as oscillators, and may cause undesirable effects, such as distortion, loss of useful power, or erratic operation. Parasitic effects occur because there are numerous frequencies for which the conditions of oscillation are satisfied. Frequently, the presence of tube capacitances and stray inductances in the circuit establish oscillatory conditions at a high frequency. For example, the wiring in the grid and plate circuits of an amplifier may act as inductances, forming a resonant circuit with the tube capacitances. Thus, the amplifier functions as an oscillator at the particular parasitic frequency.

As shown in figure 6-2, the feedback signal from the plate of the second amplifier stage to the grid input of the first amplifier stage is coupled through feedback capacitor C_f. The value of this capacitor is such that it introduces negligible reactance or phase shift at the amplified frequencies. When power supply voltages are applied to the circuit, plate current starts off in both tubes. If both amplifiers are alike (balanced), the tube currents may at first be nearly equal. However, a perfect balance is impossible, since there is always some slight difference between the corresponding components (including the tubes) in the two circuits. Such an unbalance necessarily causes one of the tubes to conduct more than the other.

Assume that, at the start, V1 plate current is higher than that of V2. Because of this higher conduction in V1, parasitic oscillations may be set up in the grid and plate circuits of this amplifier. These oscillations tend to damp out unless the grid signal is reinforced by a feedback signal having the proper polarity and amplitude. Recall that the plate and grid signals of a vacuum tube are 180 degrees out of phase, and that an in-phase or positive-feedback signal is required to sustain oscillations. It is evident, therefore, that the plate signal of V1 must be shifted 180 degrees before it can be applied to the grid to maintain the oscillatory condition. The required additional 180 degrees in phase shift is provided by amplifier V2.

A fundamental characteristic of vacuum tubes is that an increase in current through the tube causes a decrease in plate voltage. Since V1, in this case, is assumed to be conducting more initially, the voltage at its plate decreases. This decrease in plate voltage is coupled through capacitor C_c to the grid of V2. Another fundamental characteristic of vacuum tubes is that a fall in grid voltage causes a drop in tube current. The result of decreased current through V2 is an increase in its plate voltage. This change in plate voltage, shifted 180 degrees from the plate voltage of V1, is then coupled to the control grid of V1 through feedback capacitor C_f. This feedback signal is then of the proper phase to reinforce the oscillations of V1.

From the above it is seen that the function of the second stage (V2) is to act as a feedback network in order to provide the necessary 180-degree phase shift for the plate signal of V1. Thus, one means of providing the required feedback signal to sustain oscillations is through the use of an additional vacuum tube. Feedback capacitor C_f merely couples the positive feedback signal to the grid of V1, and acts as a blocking capacitor to keep the d-c plate voltage of V2 from the grid of V1. This capacitor does not introduce any appreciable phase shift in the feedback signal. The use of R-C and L-C networks, transformers, and tube interelectrode capacitances as coupling devices to provide the necessary phase shift to maintain oscillation will be presented in subsequent discussions of the various types of oscillator circuits.

Oscillators as a Source of Energy

The frequency at which oscillations occur in a circuit is determined by the constants of the circuit. For example, the oscillatory action described above was produced by two audio-frequency amplifiers. Hence, an oscillator of this type is termed an *audio-frequency* or a-f oscillator. Such an oscillator possesses the ability to furnish other circuits with its audio-frequency output. Thus, the oscillator is considered to be a source of audio energy. Audio-frequency oscillators are used in electronic equipments where it is desired to produce an audible tone, or where low frequencies are used for control purposes. A few specific applications of a-f oscillators are in the tone circuits of communication equipments, electronic organs, and audio-frequency signal generators and in the antenna control circuits of an automatic radio compass.

By changing the circuit constants, or by using various circuit configurations, oscillators having the ability to produce oscillations at radio frequencies can be obtained. *Radio-frequency*, or *r-f*, oscillators are a necessary part of every radio transmitter and every superheterodyne radio receiver. The "master" oscillator in the radio transmitter generates the r-f carrier upon which is impressed the intelligence or message to be transmitted. In the receiver, the "local" oscillator serves to decrease the high r-f carrier to a lower radio frequency (called the *intermediate frequency*) from which the transmitted message can be detected or removed. Other applications of r-f oscillators are as sources of radio-frequency energy in instruments used for testing and adjusting equipment operating in the radio-frequency portion of the spectrum.

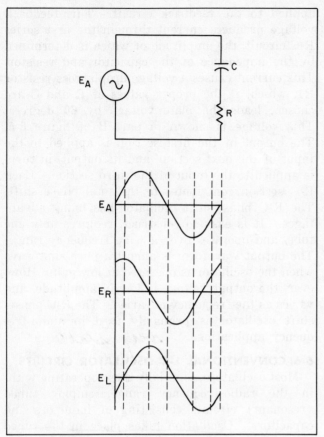

Figure 6-3. Phase Shift in R-C Circuit

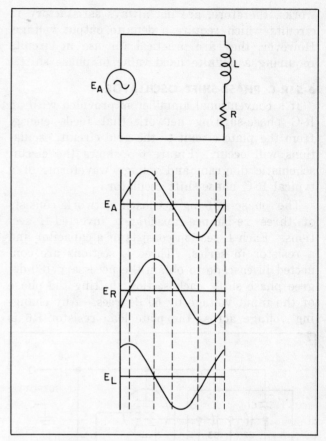

Figure 6-4. Phase Shift in R-L Circuit

6-4 R-C AND R-L PHASE SHIFTING

One property of a capacitor is its opposition to any change in applied d-c voltage. If a sine wave of voltage is applied to a resistor and capacitor in series, the voltage across each component is out of phase with the applied voltage. The actual phase difference is dependent upon the frequency of the applied signal, the value of capacitance, and the amount of resistance.

Figure 6-3 shows the resultant waveforms when an a-c voltage is applied to a series R-C circuit. The current through the circuit has a magnitude determined by the total impedance of the circuit. Because of the capacitor, the impedance appears capacitive and the current leads the applied voltage. In this case, the circuit constants are chosen to produce a phase shift of 60 degrees. The voltage drop across the resistor is in phase with the current through it; hence, this voltage drop leads the applied voltage by 60 degrees. If the frequency is decreased, the resistor voltage will come closer to being 90 degrees out of phase with the applied voltage, but because there is resistance in the circuit, the phase shift will never quite arrive at that value.

R-C circuits are used in certain types of oscillators to provide the feedback required for oscillation. A simple R-C combination can provide any desired phase shift between zero degrees and almost 90 degrees by merely varying the relative values of resistance and capacitance. By cascading several R-C circuits, practically any degree of phase shift can be obtained.

Substitution of an inductor for the capacitor in the circuit, as shown in figure 6-4, yields an R-L phase-shifting circuit. Since the current always lags the voltage across inductance, the voltage across the resistor also always lags. The output voltage normally is taken from across the inductor. An increase in the resistance of the circuit will cause an increase in the phase difference between the input and output voltages. By decreasing the circuit resistance, the input and output voltages are brought more nearly in phase with each other.

A disadvantage of both R-C and R-L phase-shifting networks is that the voltage across either the capacitor or the inductor becomes smaller as the resistance is increased. Such networks, therefore, are not always satisfactory in circuits which require a definite output voltage. However, they are practical for use in circuits requiring a definite fixed value of phase shift.

6-5 R-C PHASE-SHIFT OSCILLATOR

If a conventional amplifier is provided with an R-C phase-shifting network that feeds energy from the plate circuit to the grid circuit, oscillations will occur. Figure 6-5 shows the circuit schematic diagram and voltage waveforms of a typical R-C phase-shift oscillator.

The phase-shifting feedback network consists of three resistance-capacitance inverted-L sections. Each L section consists of a capacitor and a resistor in series. Three L sections are connected in cascade to obtain the necessary 180-degree phase shift, each section shifting the phase of the input voltage by 60 degrees. Any changing voltage across the plate load resistor R6 is

applied to the feedback circuit. This feedback voltage produces current through the first series R-C circuit, the amplitude of which is determined by the impedance of the capacitor and resistor. This current causes a voltage drop across resistor R1, which, if the proper values of R and C are chosen, leads the plate voltage by 60 degrees. This voltage is shown in part B of figure 6-5. The output of the first section is applied to the input of the next section, and its output, in turn, is applied to the input of the third section. Each R-C section contributes to the total phase shift. The R-C phase-shift oscillator has many advantages. It is easy to construct, requires only one tube, and operates over a wide frequency range. The output waveform is almost a pure sine wave when the oscillator is operated at low gain. However, the output voltage is low in amplitude, and varies as the frequency is varied. The R-C phase-shift oscillator is primarily used in audio-frequency applications. *very stable.*

6-6 CONVENTIONAL L-C OSCILLATOR CIRCUITS

Most oscillators, especially those operating within the radio-frequency range, employ tuned (resonant) circuits consisting of inductors and capacitors. Oscillation takes place in the tuned circuits rather than in the tube used in the oscillator circuit. Since the operation of such oscillator circuits is started by their own unbalance, they are called *self-excited* oscillators.

Tuned-Plate Tuned-Grid Oscillator

An oscillator which employs a tuned L-C tank circuit in both the grid and plate circuits is called a *tuned-plate tuned-grid* oscillator. The circuit schematic diagram of a typical tuned-plate tuned-grid oscillator is shown in figure 6-6. There is no magnetic coupling between the two tuned circuits. Feedback is provided by capacitive

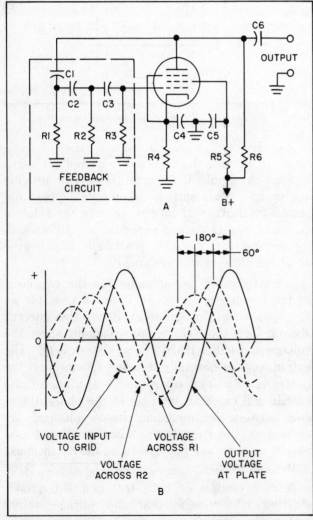

Figure 6-5. Phase-Shift Oscillator and Associated Waveforms

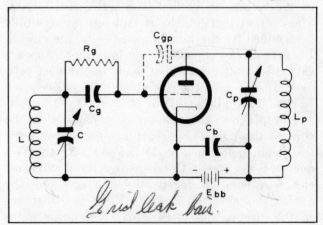

Figure 6-6. Tuned-Plate Tuned-Grid Oscillator

Grid leak bais.

*if oscillation drop down in tank
Tube conduct more.*

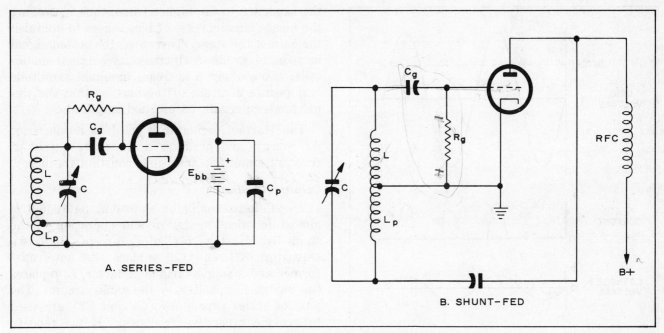

Figure 6-7. Hartley Oscillator Circuits

coupling through the grid-to-plate capacitance of the tube. Sometimes it is helpful to increase this coupling by means of an externally connected capacitor. At the frequency of oscillation, both the plate and grid circuits are slightly inductive, and the phase relationship between plate and grid is nearly 180 degrees. Therefore, the frequency at which this oscillator operates is slightly lower than the natural frequency of both the plate tank and the grid tank.

Hartley Oscillator

Two forms of the Hartley oscillator are shown in figure 6-7. The Hartley oscillator employs a simple L-C circuit in which a 180-degree phase relationship between plate voltage and grid voltage results from connecting these electrodes to opposite ends of the inductor. This is the phase relationship necessary for positive feedback. The coupling is inductive, since the plate current passing through L_p produces a magnetic field that induces a voltage in L by autotransformer action.

When the part of the tuned circuit between the cathode and the plate of the tube is in series with the power supply voltage, so that there is direct current through a portion of the tuned circuit, the stage is *series-fed*. An example of the series-fed Hartley is shown in part A of figure 6-7. In the series-fed Hartley oscillator the d-c plate current and the alternating component of the plate current have a common path. This series path is through L_p in the plate-cathode circuit. Only one

coil is used, part of which is in the plate circuit and part in the grid circuit. The lower part of the coil, L_p, is inductively coupled to the upper part, the combination forming an autotransformer. Since the variable capacitor C is connected across both coil sections, together they form with it a resonant tank circuit.

Capacitor C_p in the series-fed Hartley oscillator is a feedback capacitor which allows the a-c component of the plate current to bypass the battery. This bypassing action effectively places the plate at the bottom of coil L_p for the a-c plate current, and therefore L_p acts as the a-c plate load. With the grid and plate at opposite ends of the autotransformer, the a-c grid voltage is of opposite polarity to that of the plate, and thus the requirement for positive feedback is satisfied. The waveforms of the series-fed Hartley oscillator are shown in figure 6-8. Since the output may be taken from more than one place, no d-c reference level is specified.

An objection to series feed is the detuning effect of the plate-supply capacitance to ground. The solution to this problem is a *shunt-fed* circuit, as shown in part B of the figure. Here the tuned circuit is shunted across the plate supply, and direct current is excluded by means of a blocking capacitor. An r-f choke (RFC) prevents the low impedance of the power supply from shorting out the tuned circuit. At the same time the choke, in conjunction with the filtering capacitors of the

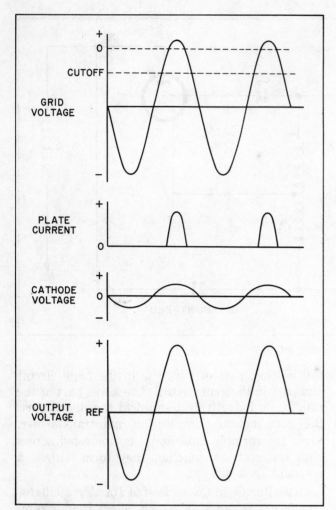

Figure 6-8. Series-Fed Hartley Oscillator Waveforms

power supply, keeps the r-f voltage across the power supply at a minimum.

Note that a grid-leak combination is used to produce bias. This biasing method is almost always used in oscillators, since it tends to stabilize circuit operation. As oscillations build up, the maximum signal across the grid circuit becomes increasingly positive. Eventually, the peaks become positive enough to cause the grid to draw current, charging the capacitor, C_g. Shortly afterward, as the signal goes less positive, grid current stops and capacitor C_g discharges through the grid resistor, R_g. Because of the large value of R_g only a small amount of charge is lost by the time the signal again is positive enough to draw a new surge of grid current into the capacitor. This action produces an average negative grid-to-cathode voltage, or bias, whose value is fairly near the maximum voltage to which the capacitor is charged. Whenever the signal amplitude increases, the resulting higher grid current charges

the capacitor to the higher value, thus increasing the bias. This increase of bias serves to diminish the gain of the stage. Therefore, the output signal is reduced to approximately its original amplitude. Conversely, a decrease in signal amplitude results in a decrease of the bias, so that the signal tends to regain its original amplitude.

The Hartley oscillator is used as a source of r-f energy, and produces a sine-wave output of constant amplitude and fairly constant frequency.

Colpitts Oscillator

The Colpitts oscillator shown in figure 6-9 is almost identical in design and operation to the shunt-fed Hartley oscillator, except that two capacitors, C1 and C2, replace the autotransformer and a single variable inductor, L, replaces the variable capacitor in the tank circuit. The pair of series capacitors (C1 and C2) are used to provide capacitive feedback. If the relative values of C1 and C2 are changed, the feedback voltage amplitude will change. The inductor L resonates with these capacitors at the frequency of oscillation.

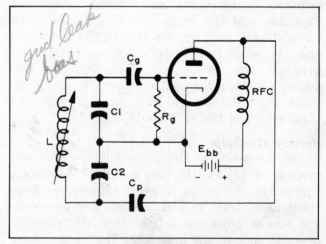

Figure 6-9. Colpitts Oscillator Circuit

A low-high impedance path, provided for harmonic currents by C1 and C2, improves the shape of the sine-wave output. Offsetting this advantage, however, is the fact that the circuit is more critical and difficult to adjust than the Hartley. For a constant frequency of oscillation the total capacitance across L must be kept constant. Therefore, if the capacitance of C1 is increased to lower the excitation voltage, C2 must be decreased and vice versa. Since any adjustment will affect frequency, fixed values of capacitance are preferred. Tuning is then accomplished by means of a variable inductor.

Armstrong Oscillator

In the Armstrong oscillator circuit shown in figure 6-10, energy of the proper phase and amplitude is fed from the plate circuit to the grid circuit by mutual induction between the coil in the plate circuit and the coil in the grid tank circuit. The coil in the plate circuit is commonly called the *tickler* coil. The feedback voltage receives a phase shift from plate to grid circuit of 180 degrees. Therefore, the proper relationship exists to replenish the energy lost in the tuned circuit, and thus to sustain the oscillations set up in the circuit.

tuned grid & tickler coil osc.

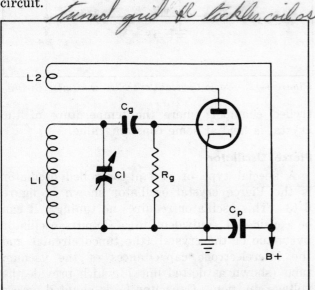

Figure 6-10. Armstrong Oscillator Circuit

Note that a grid-leak capacitor-resistor combination is used to produce the operating bias. The value of bias operates the tube class C. Grid-leak bias allows the circuit to be self-starting, since a zero-bias condition exists before the circuit begins oscillating. A quick check to ascertain if any oscillator circuit that uses grid-leak bias is operating is to measure the voltage drop (Bias) across R_g. A negative d-c voltage of several volts indicates the presence of oscillations.

The output frequency of the Armstrong oscillator is determined by the resonant frequency of the tank circuit. In most circuits a variable tuning capacitor is used to change the frequency; however, a variable inductor in the tank circuit can be used for the same purpose.

Electron-Coupled Oscillator

The oscillator circuits just discussed have a tendency to shift in frequency when changes in their load occur. This effect can be eliminated by

isolating the load from the oscillator circuit, thus enabling it to deliver moderate power without serious impairment of stability.

The circuit shown in figure 6-11 is essentially a series-fed Hartley oscillator in which the screen grid acts as the plate. Feedback voltage to the control-grid circuit is inductively coupled from the cathode. The screen, which is bypassed for r-f energy by C_s, serves as a shield that isolates the plate output circuit from the oscillator circuit. Loading is provided by the tuned plate circuit, which may be adjusted to either the fundamental or a harmonic frequency.

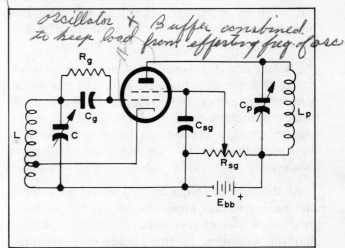

oscillator & Buffer combined to keep load from effecting freq. of osc.

Figure 6-11. Electron-Coupled Oscillator Circuit

Variations in supply voltage have a particularly fortunate effect in electron-coupled oscillators. An increase of screen voltage will decrease the frequency of oscillation, but an increase of plate voltage will increase the frequency. Since plate and screen voltage are supplied from the same source, this double effect enables the frequency to be held fairly constant regardless of supply-voltage variations, provided that the tap on resistor R_{sg} is adjusted properly. When stability requirements are more rigid, crystal-controlled oscillators are employed.

6-7 CRYSTAL-CONTROLLED OSCILLATORS

In many oscillator applications it is necessary for the frequency to remain constant over both short and long periods of operation, or it is important for the oscillator to resume oscillations at the same constant frequency after each interruption. The ordinary L-C oscillator is unsuitable for such applications because many factors introduce slight variations in its output frequency. For example, humidity and temperature affect circuit parameters, tube properties, and, to a lesser extent, the influence of shielding, or the effective values of inductance and capacitance in the tuned circuit. Other factors are changes in load impedance and variation of supply voltages. A crystal-controlled oscillator, on the other hand, is almost completely insensitive to these influences, and its frequency stability is therefore exceptionally good.

The substance most suitable for oscillator crystals is quartz because of its availability, performance, low-temperature coefficient, and high mechanical Q. Tourmaline has similar properties, but is more expensive. Rochelle salt also has piezoelectric properties, but is more satisfactory for microphones and phonograph pickups.

The natural frequency at which a crystal vibrates is dependent upon its size. To vibrate at a higher frequency, the crystal must be ground to smaller dimensions. Since there is a limit to the size to which a crystal can be ground, there is an upper limit to the frequency of oscillations produced.

At the natural frequency of the crystal, a small alternating voltage applied to the crystal produces mechanical vibration of relatively large amplitude, and the vibration in turn produces a terminal voltage. If the voltage generated by the vibration is applied to a vacuum tube, a small amount of energy from the output circuit of the tube can then be used to sustain the vibration of the crystal.

Basic Crystal Oscillator Circuit

The crystal is usually connected in the grid circuit of the tube, as shown in figure 6-12. The resulting circuit is equivalent to the tuned-plate tuned-grid oscillator circuit. Grid-leak bias is retained, but the equivalent capacitance of the crystal acts in place of the usual grid-leak capacitor.

The frequency of oscillation of a crystal oscillator is substantially constant, because the natural frequency of the crystal is critical. To prevent slight departures from this frequency caused by fluctuations in plate-supply voltage, regulated power supplies are used to hold voltage variations within a prescribed range, usually 2 volts. Another cause of frequency drift in a crystal-controlled oscillator is a change in the temperature of the crystal. To overcome this, the crystal, in many cases, is mounted in a temperature-con-

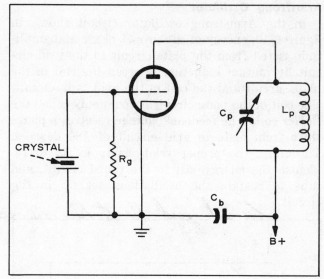

Figure 6-12. Basic Crystal-Controlled Oscillator Circuit

trolled chamber where the temperature of the crystal is held at some constant value.

Pierce Oscillator

A special type of crystal-controlled oscillator is the Pierce crystal oscillator shown in figure 6-13. This oscillator requires no tuning. It can be considered equivalent to a Colpitts oscillator by virtue of the crystal (the tuned circuit) and the interelectrode capacitances of the vacuum tube (shown as dotted lines), which provide the voltage division. Capacitor C_g is shunted across the grid-to-cathode tube capacitance, to supply the desired amount of feedback, and R_g is the grid-leak resistor. Capacitor C1 prevents injury to any personnel who might touch the crystal. This circuit is used in applications where only a low output is required.

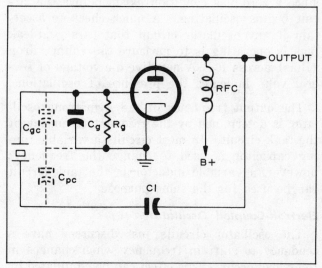

Figure 6-13. Pierce Crystal Oscillator Circuit

Crystal Overtone Oscillator

As was previously discussed, the high-frequency limit of a conventional crystal oscillator is restricted by the dimensions to which a crystal can be ground, and still be sufficiently rugged to be useful. For this reason, considerable attention has been given to the development of circuits in which a crystal will vibrate at a multiple of the fundamental frequency for which it is ground. In such circuits, a crystal of practical size can be used to produce oscillations at a rather high frequency, and thus reduce the number of frequency-multiplier circuits that would otherwise be required.

The crystal is energized so that a ripple-type of displacement occurs in it, producing what is known as overtone oscillation. A crystal overtone differs from a harmonic in that the overtone is never an integral multiple of the crystal frequency. Almost any crystal can be made to oscillate at the odd overtone frequencies, and the use of special care during manufacture increases the probability of oscillation at the higher overtones. Crystals intended for use in overtone oscillators are marked with the overtone frequency to which they have been ground, rather than the fundamental.

Figure 6-14 shows a cathode-coupled oscillator circuit, consisting of a grounded-grid amplifier and a tuned amplifier which operates as a cathode follower. This has proven to be one of the better circuits designed for overtone operation. Sus-

tained oscillations are produced in a manner similar to that employed in conventional oscillators, in that an output signal of sufficient amplitude is fed back to the input circuit in phase with the input signal to overcome the circuit losses.

Briefly, the operation of the circuit is as follows: If a positive-going signal is applied to the cathode of V1, plate current in this tube decreases and produces a positive-going signal in the plate circuit. A positive pulse is thus coupled through C1 to the grid of V2. This pulse increases the plate current of V2, and produces a positive signal at the cathode of this stage. Since there is no phase shift through the crystal at resonance, the signal is coupled to the cathode of V1 in phase with the original signal. The signal is amplified sufficiently so that the feedback signal overcomes the losses in the circuit and maintains oscillations.

The plate tank circuit, consisting of C2 and L1, is tuned to the desired overtone frequency and prevents oscillation from occurring at some undesired overtone frequency. An advantage of this circuit is that the plate circuit can be heavily loaded without affecting the condition of oscillation.

6-8 SUMMARY

An oscillator circuit is one which converts a direct current into an alternating current having a frequency that is determined by the constants of the circuit. In almost all oscillators, the oscillations are started by a slight variation in the plate current when power supply voltages are applied to the tube. To maintain the oscillatory action, a portion of the output signal must be fed back in phase to the tube input circuit to overcome the losses in the circuit. This type of feedback is known as positive feedback, or regeneration. The necessary phase shift to sustain oscillations is obtained through the use of R-C or R-L networks, transformers, or additional tubes, or through the interelectrode capacitance of the oscillator tube. Because oscillators are used for many purposes and many frequency ranges, a number of different oscillator circuits have been derived. However, the operation of all vacuum-tube oscillators is fundamentally the same.

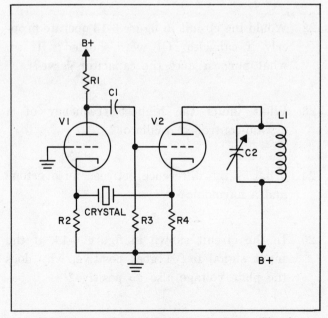

Figure 6-14. Crystal Overtone Oscillator Circuit

REVIEW QUESTIONS

1. What is an oscillator? *Page 69*

2. What is the function of the feedback circuit in an oscillator? *Provides the phase shift to maintain oscillations*

3. Explain the difference between positive feedback and negative feedback. What type of feedback is required in oscillator circuits? *Positive* *Negative reduce the gain of amp. Positive increases the gain*

4. List the various methods used to obtain the proper feedback signal in oscillators. *Page 71*

5. Define *parasitic oscillations*. *any unwanted oscillation*

6. List some applications of oscillators as a source of a-f energy, and as a source of r-f energy. *Page 72*

7. Briefly describe the operation of an R-C phase-shifting circuit.

8. The phase-shift oscillator utilizes what type of circuit for feedback and frequency selection?

9. Explain why at least three R-C circuits are required in the phase-shifting network of the phase-shift oscillator. *because each circuits shift around 60 degrees*

10. Does the phase-shift oscillator require an external pulse to trigger it into oscillation?

11. How is feedback coupling accomplished in the tuned-plate tuned-grid oscillator?

12. Name the two types of Hartley oscillators and describe their differences.

13. How is feedback accomplished in the Hartley oscillator?

14. Describe the action of grid-leak bias.

15. What type of oscillator does the Colpitts oscillator resemble? How?

16. What type of oscillator uses a tickler coil?

17. What advantage does the electron-coupled oscillator offer over the other tunable r-f oscillators?

18. What effect does variation in the supply voltage have upon the electron-coupled oscillator?

19. Name three factors which might cause variations in the output frequencies of a tunable r-f oscillator.

20. Upon what is the natural frequency of vibration of a crystal dependent?

21. Why are some crystals in crystal oscillators kept in an oven?

22. Would the circuit in figure 6-13 operate properly if capacitor C1 were shorted? If so, what purpose does the capacitor serve?

23. What limits the highest frequency of a crystal-controlled oscillator?

24. What is the difference between an overtone and a harmonic?

25. In the circuit shown in figure 6-14, if the input signal to V1 goes positive, why does the plate voltage also go positive?

CHAPTER SEVEN

Radio-Frequency Amplifiers

7-1 Introduction

Radio-frequency amplifiers differ in component appearance and values, as well as circuitry, from audio-frequency amplifiers. These differences are due primarily to the higher frequencies involved in radio-frequency amplification, and to the greater selectivity requirements. The radio-frequency spectrum extends from 20,000 cycles to over 300,000,000 cycles, whereas the audio-frequency spectrum extends from about 20 to 20,000 cycles. For efficient use of the radio-frequency spectrum, radio-frequency amplifiers are designed to amplify single frequencies or very limited portions of the radio-frequency spectrum. In contrast, audio-frequency amplifiers are designed to amplify a relatively large portion of the audio-frequency spectrum. Radio-frequency amplifiers, therefore, are distinguished by the use of tuned (resonant) circuits to provide the necessary frequency selectivity.

Radio-frequency amplifiers, like audio amplifiers, can be classed as voltage or power amplifiers. Radio receivers use r-f voltage amplifiers to increase the amplitude of the received signal, while radio transmitters use r-f power amplifiers to deliver the necessary voltages and currents to the antenna system for transmission.

7-2 RADIO-FREQUENCY VOLTAGE AMPLIFIERS

R-F voltage amplifiers, as mentioned above, are used to increase the amplitude of very small signals in radio receivers, test equipment, etc. These amplifiers may be termed either *r-f* or *i-f amplifiers*, depending on the application. An i-f (intermediate-frequency) amplifier is the stage, or group of stages, in a receiver which is used to amplify a narrow band of frequencies lower than the original rf, but still in the region above 20,000 cycles.

Part A of figure 7-1 shows a typical r-f voltage amplifier. Notice that the circuit is quite different from that of the audio voltage amplifier studied previously. The circuit employs a pentode vacuum tube to provide relatively high voltage gain. The distinguishing feature of this amplifier is that the input and output circuits, consisting of T1C1 and T2C2, are tunable networks mechanically connected to provide simultaneous adjustment. The secondaries of the transformers form parallel tuned circuits with the variable capacitors connected across them. Considering the tuned

circuit T1 and C1, when the r-f input signal is at the resonant frequency of the circuit, this parallel network offers maximum impedance at that frequency. This maximum impedance, in series with the grid circuit to ground, allows the maximum voltage to be developed across the network, thus providing a large input signal to the grid of the vacuum tube. The plate circuit of the vacuum tube uses the primary of the transformer as an inductive load, which is broadly tuned over the desired frequency range by the distributed capacitance of the plate circuit and the primary winding. The secondary winding is tuned exactly to the resonant frequency of the primary, to provide maximum signal input to the following stage. Since interstage r-f transformers usually have a turns ratio of 1:1, the overall stage gain depends upon the amplification of the tube and the degree of coupling of transformer T2.

The bias of most r-f voltage amplifiers is adjusted so the tube will operate class A. The amplifier in part A of figure 7-1 uses cathode bias. In some r-f voltage amplifiers the grid cir-

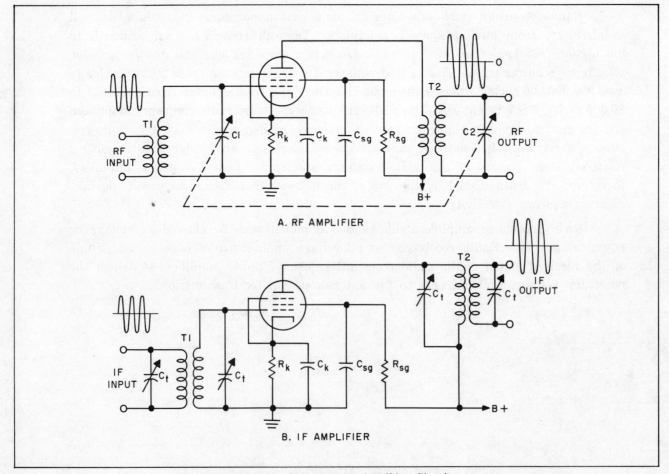

Figure 7-1. R-F Voltage Amplifier Circuits

cuit is returned to ground through either a manually or automatically variable bias supply so the gain of the circuit can be varied within the limits of class A amplification.

Part B of figure 7-1 illustrates the circuit of an i-f amplifier. This circuit is identical to the r-f voltage amplifier, except that it ordinarily uses double-tuned transformers, which under normal operating conditions, are pre-tuned to a specific frequency. Adjustment of capacitors C_t allows a small change in the resonant frequency of the tank circuits. The bandpass of these transformers is relatively narrow as applied to standard communications receivers. Like the r-f amplifier interstage transformer, the maximum transfer of energy at the desired frequency depends upon the degree of coupling between the primary and secondary transformer windings. Figure 7-2 illustrates the effects of coupling on the transfer of energy.

The gain of any r-f or i-f amplifier is dependent upon many variable factors, such as the type of tube, circuit component values, and the operating frequency. Since an r-f or i-f amplifier is designed to operate at a specific point in the frequency spectrum, the tuned circuits will be resonant at that point. At resonance the gain can be expressed in terms of the tube transconductance and the total circuit output impedance — two factors which combine all the pertinent variables. The expression for gain is:

$$A_{res} = -g_m Z_o \qquad (7-1)$$

where:

A_{res} = circuit gain
g_m = tube transconductance
Z_o = total output impedance

(The negative sign indicates the phase reversal in a grounded-cathode circuit.)

The value of Z_o is very difficult to calculate, requiring different formulas for each circuit configuration. At frequencies off resonance, calculation is even more complicated, and is of primary interest to circuit designers. Because of the complex mathematics involved, this method of determining gain will not be discussed further.

At frequencies off resonance, the gain is reduced, because the tuned circuit makes Z_o quite reactive and thus reduces the circuit efficiency. The amount of reduction depends on how far off resonance the particular signal is, and on the tuned-circuit characteristics (namely, the value of Q and, in a double-tuned circuit, the degree of coupling).

Regardless of the formulas used in the initial design of an amplifier circuit, the gain of the amplifier can be determined by measurement of the input and output signal amplitudes at various frequencies and using the relationship $A = e_o/e_{in}$ to calculate the gain at each frequency. This method of determining amplifier gain is commonly used to check the operational characteristics of equipments in order to detect any decrease in circuit performance. Should a decrease be observed, corrective action can be taken to return the circuit to peak operating condition. As in the case of audio amplifiers, changes in tube characteristics and in values of circuit components which affect tube element voltages are usually the cause of decreased gain.

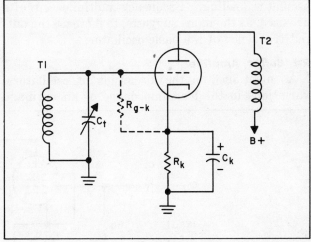

Figure 7-3. Effective Grid-Cathode Resistance of R-F Voltage Amplifier

Radio-frequency voltage amplifiers used in receiver applications are usually biased to provide class A amplification. As discussed previously, a class A biased circuit allows the complete input

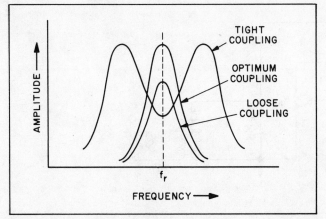

Figure 7-2. Effect of Coupling on the Transfer of Energy

signal to appear at the output, and no current is drawn by the control grid. This last factor is of the greatest importance. Refer to figure 7-3, which illustrates a typical r-f amplifier. In this circuit, the grid-to-cathode resistance (shown by the dashed lines) is effectively in parallel with the tuned input circuit. Since the grid draws no current, this resistance is high; however, if the grid were to draw current, the grid-to-cathode resistance would be reduced. Placing a high resistance in parallel with a tank circuit has little effect on the Q of the circuit; but placing a low resistance in parallel lowers the Q, and thus results in an increased bandpass and a reduction in the signal amplitude developed across the resonant networks. Since the main purpose of a radio-frequency voltage amplifier is to amplify a very small input signal, the amplifier must be biased class A to reduce the possibility of input-circuit loading due to grid current.

7-3 RADIO-FREQUENCY BUFFER AND FREQUENCY-MULTIPLYING AMPLIFIER CIRCUITS

R-F buffer and frequency-multiplier circuits are special types of r-f amplifiers which provide a specific function other than purely voltage or power amplification. These circuits are usually found in a radio transmitter or other similar type device. The r-f buffer is commonly used to provide isolation and voltage amplification between the basic oscillator and the following stages, to prevent frequency changes caused by changes in oscillator loading. Frequency-multiplier circuits are used, as the name suggests, to increase the output frequency of the basic oscillator.

R-F Buffer Amplifier

As mentioned in the discussion of oscillators, variations in the load impedance of an ordinary L-C oscillator cause the frequency of oscillation to fluctuate. This problem can be avoided of course, by the use of an electron-coupled oscillator or a crystal oscillator, which inherently have great frequency stability. In those cases where an L-C oscillator is used, the possibility of frequency variation can be prevented and some amplification achieved by the use of an r-f buffer circuit similar to the one illustrated in figure 7-4. The pentode r-f buffer amplifier is capable of providing the necessary isolation and amplification. Pentodes are commonly used because they require only a small amount of driving power to deliver considerable amplification. A triode buffer amplifier, illustrated in figure 7-5, can also be used to provide the required isolation and amplification. Triodes, of course, are not capable of providing as much amplification as pentodes; however, they are used in some transmitter applications. The amount of bias used for the buffer stage, regardless of the tube used, depends on the required degree of isolation. Normally the buffer amplifier is designed to operate either class A or B. As may be seen in figures 7-4 and 7-5, its operating bias consists of a combination of cathode and grid-leak bias. A buffer amplifier is seldom operated class C because of the loading effect it would have on the oscillator stage.

Since the circuit contains a tuned tank circuit, the plate current, which is present for less than a complete input cycle, produces a sine-wave output because of the "flywheel" effect of the tank circuit. The term *flywheel* is used to express the fact that the resonant circuit, when excited momentarily, is capable of providing an oscillatory current between the tuned elements. Therefore. it is not mandatory that power be supplied continually to produce a complete cycle of the output waveform. If the buffer amplifier were biased

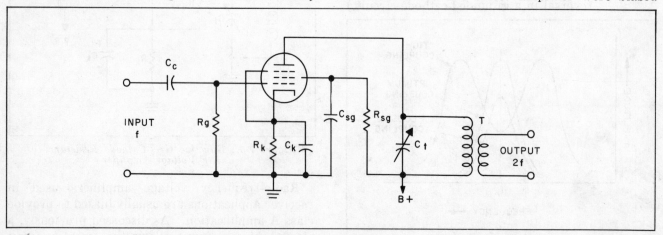

Figure 7-4. Pentode R-F Buffer Amplifier with Transformer-Coupled Output

for class B operation, the pulses of plate current would provide the necessary replenishment of energy to produce a complete voltage waveform in the output of the buffer amplifier.

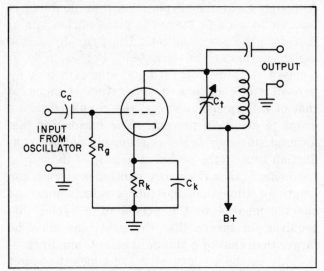

Figure 7-5. Triode R-F Buffer Amplifier with Capacitor-Coupled Output

Frequency-Multiplier Amplifier

Frequency multiplication is used in many radio transmitting applications to achieve a desired output frequency. As mentioned previously, the crystal oscillator circuit is used as the frequency source in various r-f devices, because the crystal-controlled oscillator is almost insensitive to circuit changes. The output frequency of a crystal oscillator depends upon the mechanical vibrations of the piezoelectric crystal. The maximum frequency obtainable from this type of oscillator is limited by the physical characteristics of the crystal itself. By placing frequency-multiplier circuits, similar to the one shown in figure 7-6, after the buffer amplifier, an increase in the resultant output frequency can be obtained. For all practical purposes the circuit illustrated in figure 7-6 is identical to the buffer amplifier illustrated in figure 7-4; however, the frequency-multiplier circuit is operated differently.

Frequency multipliers are always operated class C. The principal advantage of a class C amplifier is its ability to deliver large amounts of power and the pulses of current have a high harmonic content. When the tube of a class C amplifier is biased well below cutoff, plate current is restricted to only a small part of the input signal cycle. During the brief conduction period, the plate voltage is minimum, and therefore the power consumed by the tube is minimum also. Although

the amount of plate current is small, there is enough to reinforce the large current within the tuned circuit. In this manner, large signal voltages and currents are developed by the tuned circuit, enabling it to deliver considerable power.

Since the frequency multiplier is biased class C, it will always draw grid current. As a result, grid-leak bias can be utilized, as shown in figure 7-6. When capacitor C_g discharges, a negative voltage with respect to ground is developed across resistor R_g. As will be recalled, the advantages of grid-leak bias are its simplicity of circuit arrangement and its automatic adjustment feature, with respect to grid voltage, which provides good tube efficiency. One disadvantage of grid-leak bias is that removal of the input signal causes loss of the bias voltage and thus results in a large plate current. To avoid this possibility, the circuit of figure 7-6 also employs cathode bias, developed by the action of R_k, to maintain a safe level of static bias on the vacuum tube.

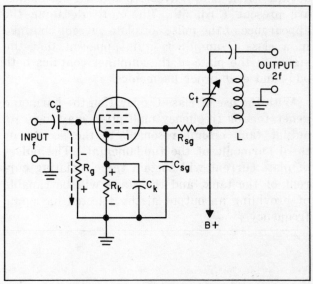

Figure 7-6. Frequency-Multiplier Circuit

The presence of grid current indicates that a relatively large input signal is required to drive the circuit. The power supplied by the input (exciting) signal is consumed in the grid structure of the tube and in the bias arrangement used. An excessive amount of grid current results in lower output power and requires greater driving power to maintain circuit efficiency. The amount of grid bias generally used varies from approximately one and one-half to four times the cutoff potential of the tube. More bias is required as the desired efficiency of operation becomes greater.

A frequency-multiplier amplifier is simply a class C amplifier with the plate tank resonant to a harmonic of the applied signal. As mentioned previously, the pulses of plate current produced by a vacuum tube operated class C are extremely rich in harmonic content. Any vacuum tube, through its ability to amplify and the nonlinearity of the transfer curve (E_g-I_p), is capable of producing in its output the fundamental input signal plus reduced-amplitude harmonics. This action is commonly referred to as *amplitude distortion*. Examination of a pure sine-wave voltage reveals that it contains only its fundamental frequency. Also, it is symmetrical above and below the zero reference line, and the rise and fall of each alternation are identical. When a voltage waveform is asymmetrical (not symmetrical above and below the zero reference line), even-order harmonics are present (2nd, 4th, 6th, etc). When a voltage waveform is symmetrical but does not follow a true sine curve (alternations equal but deviate from sine waves), odd-order harmonics are present (3rd, 5th, 7th, etc). Recalling the appearance of the pulses of plate current obtained in a class C amplifier, it is apparent that the signal at the plate of the amplifier contains both odd- and even-order harmonics.

With the use of class C operation the harmonic generator, or frequency multiplier, may have its output tank circuit resonant to the second or third harmonic of the fundamental. The pulses of plate current will sustain the circulating current of the tank, and the stage will be capable of providing an output at the selected harmonic frequency.

Often, frequency multipliers are cascaded, so that the final frequency is a rather large multiple of the basic oscillator frequency. A common practice is to double the frequency in each stage. Although greater multiplication than doubling is possible in a single stage the plate efficiency, and therefore the power output, drops rapidly as the higher harmonics are selected. For example, if a class C amplifier operating at approximately 80 percent efficiency has its operation changed to that of a frequency doubler, the circuit efficiency drops to about 70 percent. The reason for this lowered efficiency is the relationship of tube conduction time to the period of a cycle of the output frequency. In a frequency-multiplier circuit, the length of time that the tube conducts must be short compared to the period of a cycle; this requirement means that the grid bias must be larger than that of a standard class C amplifier — roughly in the vicinity of 2 1/2 times the cutoff value. Short conduction intervals, however, result in decreased output power, as previously discussed. This interdependence of efficiency and power results in decreased power, compared to the power of a standard amplifier, to achieve the desired result of frequency multiplication.

An increase over the power provided by a single-tube frequency-multiplier stage can be obtained by using a push-pull type circuit similar to that illustrated in figure 7-7. This circuit has a split-tuned input consisting of L, C1, and C2; one half of L is resonated by C1, the other half by C2. The split-tuned circuits are adjusted to be resonant to the incoming frequency. The

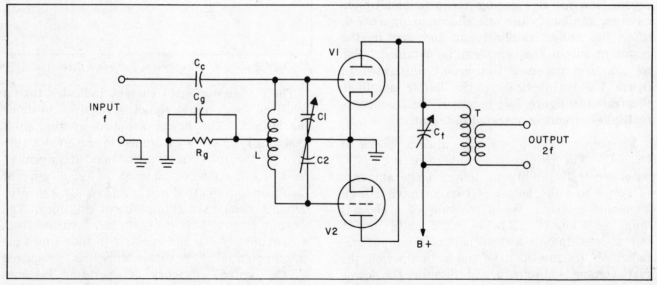

Figure 7-7. Push-Pull Frequency Doubler

autotransformer action of inductor L provides the required 180-degree phase difference between the input signals for proper push-pull operation. Stage bias is obtained by the action of a common grid-leak network, R_g and C_g. This push-pull circuit differs from standard push-pull circuits in that the plates of V1 and V2 are connected in parallel and supply the current variations through a single-primary plate-load t r a n s f o r m e r. Doubling is accomplished because each tube conducts on the positive peak of the input to that tube, and the output is tuned to twice the input. As a result, two pulses of plate current occur during each complete input cycle; therefore, the plate tank is pulsed once every cycle at the doubled frequency, causing the power and efficiency to be greater than that of a single-ended circuit.

The push-pull circuit is also suitable for the production of odd-order harmonics if a push-pull output transformer is used. As will be recalled from the study of the push-pull audio power amplifier, the use of such a transformer results in cancellation of the even harmonics by the opposing magnetic fields. The push-pull doubler circuit relies less on the distortion characteristics of vacuum tubes to produce harmonics and therefore it has a relatively high efficiency of operation. The push-pull tripler is efficient because of the rich odd-harmonic content of the plate-current pulses.

7-4 RADIO-FREQUENCY POWER AMPLIFIERS

The radio-frequency power amplifier, like the audio-frequency power amplifier, is designed to deliver rather large values of current to a load, rather than large voltage variations. R-F power amplifiers are used to increase the r-f power output of a radio-frequency generator to supply energy to another power amplifier, to a transmitting antenna, to an electromechanical transducer, to an induction heating device, or to any other special device that requires radio-frequency power. Amplification, either voltage or power, occurs because the relatively small variations of the applied signal can be utilized to produce large variations in cathode-to-plate current. The power to sustain the flow of vacuum-tube current is obtained from the d-c supply source. Vacuum tubes used as power amplifiers must be capable of dissipating considerable heat produced by the large currents that are present during conduction

time. To insure adequate heat dissipation, r-f power tubes are frequently forced-air or water cooled.

Similar to the audio power amplifier, the r-f power amplifier circuit may use a single-ended or push-pull output arrangement. The single-ended r-f power amplifier shown in part A of figure 7-8 is typical of the output stage used in low-power r-f devices. This circuit uses a combination of cathode and grid-leak bias, the value of which determines the operating point of the vacuum tube. Usually power amplifiers are biased to operate either class B or C. Since a large driving signal from a preceding stage is required to overcome this bias, plate current is produced during only a small portion of each input cycle. These pulses provide the required energy to replace that taken from the plate tank by the following stage or unit. As mentioned before, the flywheel action of the tank circuit permits its output to be sinusoidal even though the tube current is in the form of pulsations. Power amplifiers are tuned to the same frequency as the input in most applications to assure that maximum power and efficiency are obtained. Inductors L1 and L2 are radio-frequency-chokes; their purpose is to filter out the radio-frequency signal. In the case of L1, its filtering action maintains the grid-leak bias at a constant value because the inductor is in series with R_g. The filtering action of L2 isolates the B+ supply from the r-f signal present in the plate tank. Notice that an adjustable capacitor, C_n, is placed between the plate tank and the grid circuit. This capacitor is called the *neutralizing* capacitor; its purpose and function will be explained in the discussion of r-f amplifier neutralization.

For greater r-f power output capability the final output stage is operated as a push-pull power amplifier. An example of such a stage is illustrated in part B of figure 7-8. Referring to the figure, observe that both fixed and grid-leak bias are used to establish the required operating point. The necessary 180-degree phase difference between input signals is provided by the center-tapped input transformer, T1. Simultaneous tuning of the input circuits is provided by ganged capacitors C_{t1}. This circuit also employs neutralizing capacitors. The plate circuits of V1 and V2 use a push-pull transformer to permit the application of B+ potential upon the plates, and ganged

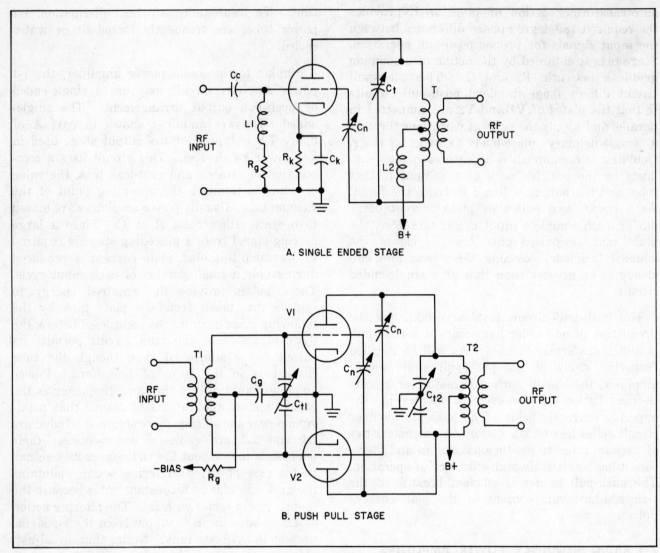

Figure 7-8. R-F Power Amplifiers

tuning capacitors C_{t2} adjust the frequency of these circuits to the input frequency. Transformer T2 provides the proper impedance match between the output circuit and the power amplifier for maximum transfer of r-f energy.

7-5 NEUTRALIZATION OF R-F AMPLIFIERS

Radio-frequency voltage and power amplifiers use both triodes and pentodes. As is well known, a pentode will provide much greater gain than a triode for a specific input signal amplitude. In radio-frequency circuits, other factors, besides gain, enter into the choice of whether a triode or pentode should be used. Triodes may be used at the lower radio frequencies; however, at the higher radio frequencies the use of triodes is limited, because of their relatively large inter-electrode capacitances. Consequently, pentodes

are nearly always employed in high-frequency, high-power r-f generating devices.

When the operating frequency of a triode r-f amplifier is raised, the output energy coupled back to the input circuit by the grid-plate interlectrode capacitance eventually becomes large enough to cause sustained oscillation of the type which occurs in a tuned-plate, tuned-grid oscillator. The amplifier then oscillates at the resonant frequency of the tank circuits, thereby reducing the stage efficiency and producing unwanted oscillations. Oscillation can be prevented by use of a process, called *neutralization*, in which a portion of the output signal voltage is fed back to the input. The polarity and amplitude of the neutralizing voltage is adjusted so that the effect of the regeneration caused by the grid-to-plate interelectrode capacitance is completely cancelled out.

The methods of providing neutralization for triode r-f amplifiers can be classed into two general categories: One of these utilizes some form of bridge circuit to provide the neutralizing signal, while the other makes use of a suitable inductor shunted across the feedback capacitance to develop a high series impedance at the oscillating frequency.

The bridge method is illustrated in figure 7-9. In this method of neutralization, the vacuum tube is effectively placed in the center of a bridge network. In part A of the figure, a tapped inductor is utilized in the plate tank circuit of a single-ended triode r-f amplifier. Since r-f voltages at the ends of the tank are 180 degrees out of phase, proper adjustment of the neutralizing capacitor will result in a null across the grid circuit at the operating frequency. This method is successful at frequencies below 7 mc.

The split-stator method shown in part B of the figure is more widely used. This arrangement makes the electrical balance almost independent of the mutual coupling within the coil, and also of the point where the coil is tapped. If adjustment is made at relatively high frequencies, such as 15 mc, the stage usually can be operated at lower frequencies without requiring further adjustment.

In part C of figure 7-9 there is shown another plate neutralizing circuit similar to the one in part A, but lacking its limitations. A separate neutralizing coil is inductively coupled to the plate tank inductor. Note that there is no circulating tank current in the neutralizing coil. The size of the neutralizing capacitor depends on the amount of coupling between the tank and the coil, and on the relative values of the inductances. By proper proportioning of the neutralizing coil used, it is possible for one value of capacitance to be used over several frequency ranges.

Grid-circuit neutralization is illustrated in part D of the figure. As may be seen, this circuit is similar to that in part C of the figure, except that the coil is inductively coupled to the grid circuit instead of the plate circuit.

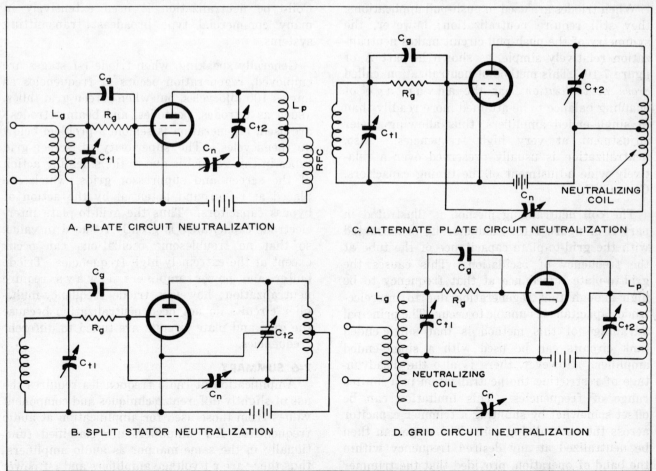

Figure 7-9. Bridge Neutralization Circuits

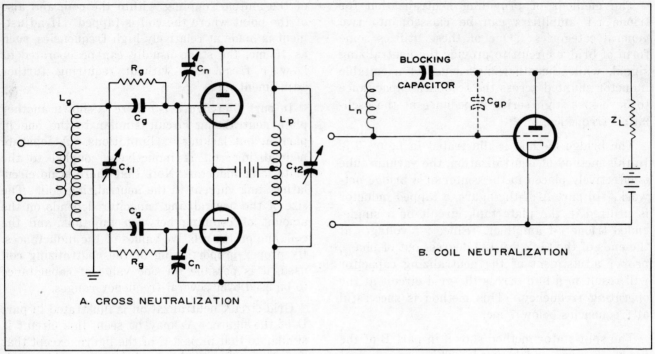

Figure 7-10. Cross and Coil Neutralization

When triodes are used in push-pull applications, they still require neutralization; however, the symmetry of the push-pull circuit makes neutralization relatively simple, as shown in part A of figure 7-10. This method of neutralization, called *cross neutralization*, has the a d v a n t a g e of enabling balance to be attained more readily than in single-ended amplifiers, thus allowing easier adjustment at very high frequencies. Also, neutralization is usually preserved over a relatively wide adjustment of the tuning capacitors, C_{t1} and C_{t2}.

The coil neutralizing method is illustrated in part B of figure 7-10. Inductor L_N is resonated with the grid-to-plate capacitance of the tube at the frequency of oscillation. This causes the grid-to-plate impedance at that frequency to be high enough that regeneration due to interelectrode capacitance is unable to occur. The principal advantage of this method is that single-ended tank circuits can be used with a single-ended amplifier. However, there is also the disadvantage of restricting the neutralization to a limited range of frequencies. This limitation can be offset somewhat by shunting a trimmer capacitor across the neutralizing coil. The stage can then be neutralized at any desired frequency within the band of operation, provided that the trimmer is tuned along with the main tuning capacitors.

Coil-type neutralization is used extensively in many commercial type broadcast transmitting systems.

Generally speaking, when triode r-f stages are employed, regeneration occurs at frequencies as low as 100 kilocycles, but when screen-grid tubes, (such as tetrodes, pentodes, and beam tetrodes) are used, regeneration is seldom a problem below 30 megacycles. The superiority of screen-grid tubes in this regard is due to the shielding action of the screen and suppressor grids, which are placed at r-f ground potential by the action of bypass capacitors. Thus the grid-to-plate interelectrode capacitance is greatly reduced in value, so that no troublesome oscillations can occur except at the extremely high frequencies. Triode buffer and power amplifiers a l w a y s require neutralization; however, triode frequency-multiplier circuits do not need neutralization because the grid and plate circuits are tuned to different frequencies.

7-6 SUMMARY

Amplification at radio frequencies requires the use of slightly different techniques and component values from those used for amplification at audio frequencies. R-F amplifiers are classified functionally in the same manner as audio amplifiers; thus there are r-f voltage amplifiers and r-f power amplifiers. R-F voltage amplifiers usually employ pentodes biased to produce class A amplification. Triodes may be used, but they require neutralization to prevent the stage from breaking into self-oscillation at the applied frequency. Radio-frequency power amplifiers are found in transmitting and frequency-generating devices. The power amplifier is biased to produce class B or C operation to provide good circuit efficiency and deliver the required energy to the component to which it is providing power. Either triodes, pentodes, or tetrode beam-power tubes may be used, depending upon the resultant frequency of operation. Again, if triodes are employed, neutralization is required.

Another classification of r-f amplifiers is the buffer and the frequency multiplier. The buffer amplifier is used to isolate the source (oscillator) of r-f energy in order to prevent loading, which could result in a change in operating frequency. Frequency-multiplication circuits rely on the fact that energy applied to a tuned circuit will cause the circuit to oscillate at its resonant frequency. If a radio-frequency amplifier has its plate circuit tuned to twice the frequency of the applied signal, radio-frequency energy at the new frequency can be taken from the circuit. By cascading several multiplier stages, a basic frequency can be efficiently increased to a much higher frequency.

REVIEW QUESTIONS

1. State typical examples of the application of r-f voltage amplifiers.

2. What class of operation is used in r-f voltage amplifiers? *A*

3. Determine the mid-frequency gain of an r-f voltage amplifier with a μ of 36 and a 1:1 interstage transformer.

4. State the circuit characteristic which limits the low-frequency gain of an r-f amplifier.

5. State the circuit characteristic which limits the high-frequency gain of an r-f amplifier.

6. What factor determines the amount of signal transfer from one r-f stage to another?

7. The purpose of an r-f buffer amplifier is to ....

8. To what class of operation is the bias of a buffer amplifier usually adjusted?

9. Describe the flywheel effect of a tuned circuit. *oscillation between tuned elements*

10. Why is the efficiency of a class A amplifier low in comparison with that of a class C amplifier?

11. Describe the difference in circuit component arrangement between an r-f voltage amplifier and a frequency multiplier.

12. Explain the reason for the use of class C operation of a frequency-multiplier circuit. *because more power due to harmonics Page 86*

13. If a voltage waveform is symmetrical but is not a true sine curve, what is its harmonic content?

14. To what harmonic is the plate circuit of a frequency multiplier tuned to provide relatively good plate efficiency and power output? *2nd harmonic*

15. What advantage does a push-pull frequency doubler have over a single multiplier stage? *Power and efficiency. and does away with even harmonics*

16. Explain the characteristic which requires the use of neutralization in a triode radio-frequency voltage or power amplifier.

17. State the requirements of the feedback signal used for neutralization purposes. *Page 88-90*

18. Describe several neutralizing arrangements for an r-f power amplifier. *Page 89*

19. What neutralization circuit arrangement provides the advantage of good balance and sufficient feedback to operate over a relatively wide band of frequencies? *88-90*

20. Explain why pentodes require no neutralization. *88*

CHAPTER EIGHT

The Radio Transmitter

8-1 Introduction

The function of a radio transmitter is to supply power to an antenna at a definite radio frequency, and to convey intelligence by means of the signal radiated. Radio transmitters radiate waves which may be either of two types — continuous wave (cw) or modulated wave.

The continuous wave is used only for radiotelegraphy, or the transmission of short or long pulses of radio frequency to form the dots and dashes of Morse code. In this type, the peaks of all cycles of the waveform of the radiated signal are equal and even, and resemble the output of the basic oscillator.

The modulated wave is used primarily for radiotelephony, and consists of voice or other intelligence-bearing signals superimposed on a radio-frequency carrier. Several methods of modulation are in use, depending primarily on whether the amplitude (AM), frequency (FM), or phase (PM) of the r-f carrier is modulated. Of these, perhaps the oldest and most commonly used is amplitude modulation.

8-2 BASIC TRANSMITTERS

The simplest radio transmitter must consist of a means of generating the desired radio-frequency signal and a means of radiation or propagation of the r-f wave. An r-f oscillator provides the desired r-f signal and an antenna serves as the radiator. However, such a simple transmitter can be used only for very limited applications for two reasons: first, an oscillator alone can supply only a very small amount of power and, second, an oscillator may shift in frequency when connected to a load such as the antenna.

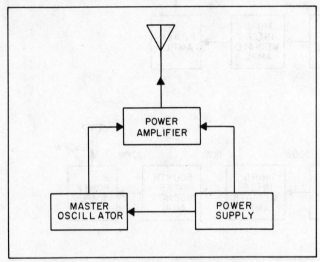

Figure 8-1. Block Diagram of a Simple M-O-P-A Transmitter

In order to overcome these objectionable qualities, a power amplifier stage is usually added between the oscillator output and the antenna. Such a transmitter, shown in block form in figure 8-1, is classed as a *master-oscillator power-amplifier*, or *m-o-p-a* transmitter.

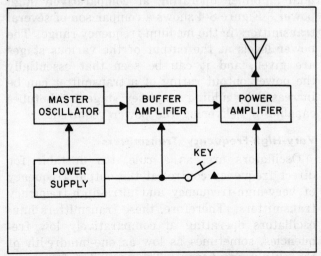

Figure 8-2. Block Diagram of Complete C-W Transmitter with Buffer Amplifier Stage

Large power amplifiers require considerable excitation, or drive. In order to prevent loading of the master oscillator, in such applications, a buffer amplifier is connected between the oscillator output and the input to the final, or power amplifier, as shown in figure 8-2. In either case, the output is a continuous wave.

C-W Transmitters

Essentially, the c-w transmitter is one which transmits a pure r-f signal. In order that intelligence can be transmitted in the form of Morse code, a telegraph key such as shown in figure 8-3 is usually used to control the output of the transmitter. By means of the key, one or more circuits in the transmitter are interrupted, so that the output of the transmitter is turned on and off when the key is depressed and released.

Despite the inconvenience of using code, c-w transmission has four important advantages:

1. The transmission range of a c-w transmitter is greater than that of a radiotelephone transmitter of the same power, because at a distant point speech may be audible but not intelligible.

2. For the same power, the c-w transmitter is smaller, simpler to operate, and easier to maintain.

3. Code receivers can eliminate much of the interference typical of radio transmission,

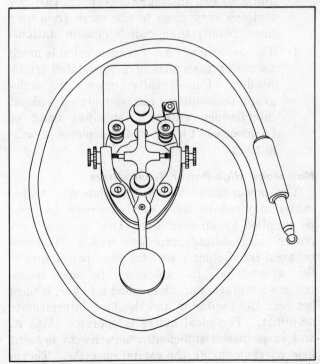

Figure 8-3. Radiotelegraph Transmitting Key

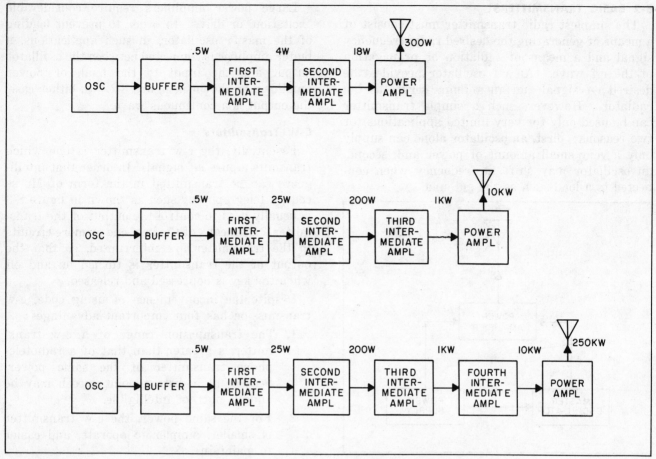

Figure 8-4. Block Diagram of Several Medium-Frequency Transmitters

and also can distinguish between two c-w stations very close to the same frequency more readily than radiotelephone stations.

4. The spectrum of a c-w transmission is much narrower than that of a modulated transmission. Consequently, m o r e radiotelegraph transmitters can be operated without interference within a specified band of frequencies t h a n radiotelephone transmitters.

Multistage High-Power Transmitters

The power amplifier of a high-power transmitter may require more driving power than can be supplied by an oscillator. One or more low-power intermediate amplifiers may be inserted between the oscillator and the final power amplifier which feeds the antenna. In most transmitters a voltage amplifier, called a *buffer*, is used between the oscillator and the first intermediate amplifier. The ideal buffer is operated class A, and so is biased sufficiently negative to prevent grid current during the excitation cycle. Therefore, it does not require driving power from the

oscillator and consequently does not load down the oscillator. Its purpose is to isolate the oscillator from the following stages and to minimize changes in oscillator frequency that occur with changes in loading. A buffer is essential when keying takes place in an intermediate amplifier or final amplifier operating at comparatively high power. Figure 8-4 shows a comparison of several transmitters in the medium-frequency range. The power levels at the output of the various stages are given, and it can be seen that essentially the power output rating of a transmitter can be increased by adding amplifier stages with tubes capable of delivering the power required.

Very-High-Frequency Transmitters

Oscillators are, as a rule, too unstable for direct frequency control at the output frequency of very-high-frequency and ultra-high-frequency transmitters. Therefore, these transmitters have oscillators operating at comparatively low frequencies, sometimes as low as one-hundredth of the output frequency. The oscillator frequency is raised to the required output frequency by

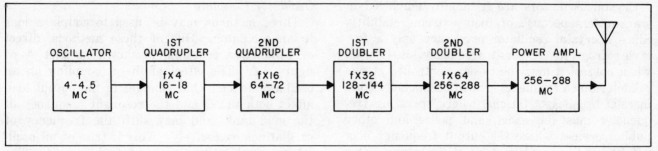

Figure 8-5. Block Diagram of Typical VHF Transmitter

passing its signal through one or more frequency multipliers. Frequency multipliers are simply r-f amplifiers designed so that the output, or plate circuit, operates at some multiple of the input, or grid circuits. In practice, the multiplication factor is seldom larger than four in any one stage.

The block diagram of a typical vhf transmitter designed for continuous tuning between 256 and 288 mc is shown in figure 8-5. The stages which multiply the frequency by two are doublers; those which multiply by four are quadruplers. The oscillator is tunable from 4 to 4.5 mc. The multiplier stages increase the frequency by a factor of 64 by multiplying successively by four, four, two, and two. In high-power high-frequency transmitters, one or more intermediate amplifiers may be used between the last frequency multiplier and the power amplifier.

8-3 TRANSMITTER CONSIDERATIONS

Radio transmitters differ in physical size, design, and output power and frequency, depending upon their use. Obviously, all transmitters can not be operated on or near the same frequency without serious interference.

The useful radio-frequency spectrum consists of frequencies from 0.03 mc to above 30,000 mc. Specific channels or bands of frequencies within this range are provided for marine and aeronautical navigational aids, standard broadcast, amateur radio, military services, international broadcast, and miscellaneous services. These bands are assigned by international agreement.

Each transmitter must be operated on an assigned frequency, or within the band to which assigned, to prevent the transmitter from interfering with others. Rules and regulations governing the operation of transmitters and the assignment of operating frequencies are controlled by the Federal Communications Commission (FCC), Washington, D.C.

Classification of Emissions

The radio waves emitted from a transmitter system may consist of a pure rf, as from a c-w transmitter, or they may be modulated waves such as are used in radiotelephony, broadcast, or television. All of the various possible forms of emission fall into certain groups. By international agreement, radio-wave emissions have been classified according to the type of modulation used. The letter and number designation and the corresponding type of emission is given in the following tabular form.

Designator	Type of Emission
A0	Continuous wave, no modulation.
A1	C-W telegraphy, on-off keying.
A2	MCW telegraphy, on-off keying of a single-tone audio modulating signal or a tone-modulated wave.
A3	Telephony. Amplitude-modulated waves carrying voice or music. Type of emission used by broadcast stations and for all voice communication.
A4	Facsimile. Type of modulated emission used for transmitting photographs and printed matter, such as by the domestic press and overseas news bureaus.
A5	Television.

8-4 R-F CIRCUIT CONSIDERATIONS
Oscillators

An oscillator capable of producing the desired radio-frequency currents may be used in a transmitter. Factors governing the choice of an oscillator circuit for frequency generation and control in a transmitter are the degree of stability necessary, the frequency or range of frequencies to be generated, and the power required from the oscillator. Operating voltages and emission requirements are also factors, along with physical factors of space, weight, and temperature range, which must be considered.

Crystal oscillators are frequently employed in transmitters because of their extreme stability. Since a crystal oscillator may vary only a few cycles from its resonant frequency, it is used when operation must be closely controlled at one predetermined frequency. Such use includes commercial broadcast stations, where operating frequencies must be exact, and police and other public services where the output frequency may not be readily monitored by other means. One disadvantage of crystal-controlled operation is that the crystal must be changed whenever the operating frequency is to be changed.

In many applications, it is required to change the frequency of the transmitter rapidly and continuously. For these applications a variable-frequency oscillator, or vfo, is preferred, since it may be operated at any frequency within a band at the turn of a dial. Any of the oscillator circuits employing inductance and capacitance, either of which may be variable, can be used as the vfo of a transmitter. Thus, the oscillator may be a Hartley, Colpitts, tuned-grid tuned-plate (tptg), tickler-coil, or electron-coupled oscillator, or any of the possible variations of each.

Frequency stability is of paramount importance in oscillator design because of the required close frequency tolerances of transmitters. The most important causes of frequency instability are changes in tube characteristics, in temperature, in load or coupling, and in supply voltages, and vibration.

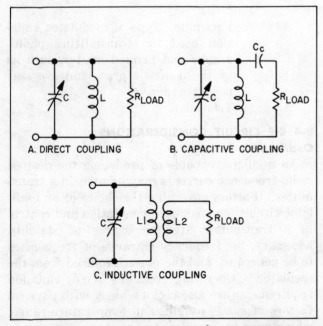

Figure 8-6. Oscillator Coupling Methods

Oscillator Coupling

Three methods may be used to couple a load to an oscillator. One of these methods, direct or conductive coupling, is shown in part A of figure 8-6. The effect of direct coupling on an oscillator is such that changes in the output load affect both the Q and the resonant frequency of the grid tank, and may shift the frequency of oscillations excessively. This is true of all oscillators which utilize a tuned tank circuit. The effective Q of the tank circuit can be increased somewhat at the expense of power output by tapping the load across a part of the inductor, L. Direct coupling, therefore, is the least favored of all coupling methods. Another disadvantage is that it provides no d-c isolation between the tank circuit and the load.

Capacitive coupling, shown in part B of figure 8-6, is used commonly in oscillators employed in transmitters. The coupling to the load increases as the coupling capacitance, C_c, is made larger. The capacitance required for maximum energy transfer between the oscillator tank and load is generally quite small.

When the load is inductively coupled to the oscillator, as shown in part C of figure 8-6, the two coils (L1 and L2) constitute the primary and secondary of an air-core transformer. As with all forms of coupling, the greater the coupling and consequent power output, the lower is the effective Q of the tank circuit, and the frequency stability is consequently reduced.

R-F Amplifiers

The relatively weak signal coupled from the oscillator must be amplified to provide a signal of usable proportions for radio transmission purposes. Since r-f energy is taken from the transmitter output terminals, power must also be provided by the transmitter. This power is predetermined and proportional to the physical size of the transmitter and the power-handling capabilities of its individual circuits. This power is dissipated in the antenna system, which forms the transmitter load.

All of the power delivered by a transmitter into the antenna is provided by the final power amplifier stage. Large power amplifier tubes require proportionally high grid voltages and currents, or drive. Sufficient power for such purposes must be provided by the intermediate r-f amplifiers.

For these reasons, the r-f amplifiers used in transmitters are power amplifiers.

The r-f amplifiers used in c-w transmitters are usually operated class B or class C, because of the efficiency of these classes of operation. Likewise, class B or class C amplifiers may be used in amplitude-modulated transmitters when the modulation takes place in the final r-f amplifier stage.

Linear Amplifier

A linear amplifier is one in which the output waveform closely follows the input waveform. A linear amplifier is operated class A, class AB, or class B. Linear amplifiers must be used in all r-f stages subsequent to the modulated stage in an amplitude-modulated transmitter; otherwise, distortion of the modulated-wave envelope, or signal, would occur. The use of linear amplifiers, however, is not restricted to such applications; they may be used in the r-f stages of any transmitter, with some reduction in efficiency. Commercial broadcast stations favor the use of linear r-f amplifiers in their transmitters, since signal quality (reduction of distortion) is of primary concern.

Heat Dissipation

Since relatively high plate currents must be handled by power amplifiers, the tubes used must be capable of dissipating a considerable amount of heat. Power tubes used in transmitters are usually forced-air cooled, or in larger installations, water-cooled to insure adequate heat dissipation.

Filaments of larger tubes require considerable power for heating, because of the larger area of the tube elements. Usually the filaments are directly heated with ac for simplicity. In such cases the plate return is normally connected to a center-tap in the filament circuit.

Grid Drive and Bias

Most r-f amplifiers in transmitter circuits employ grid-leak bias. This type of bias depends on the applied signal, or drive, from the preceding stage. It is possible that this drive may be removed, as, for example, when the transmitter is detuned, or in the event of failure of the oscillator or some subsequent stage. High values of plate (and screen) currents result when the bias is removed. In transmitting-type tubes, such currents can quickly damage the tubes. Some form of protective bias, such as fixed or self bias, is therefore usually incorporated. In this manner, plate current can be limited to a safe value.

Neutralization

Triodes are frequently employed in the r-f stages of a transmitter. To eliminate self-oscillation in r-f stages, these circuits must be neutralized. Tetrodes and pentodes usually require little or no neutralization because of the isolation of the grid and plate circuits afforded by the screen grid. Several methods of neutralization to prevent self-oscillation are possible. Proper neutralization, regardless of the method employed, occurs when the only output of the stage is the applied r-f being amplified.

Interstage Coupling Methods

Interstage coupling circuits are necessary to insure that the required amount of r-f energy is transferred from one electron-tube stage to another. For maximum efficiency, the energy must be transferred with a minimum amount of power loss and a minimum amount of loading on the oscillator or driver stage. Also, the interstage coupling system should introduce a minimum of stray coupling between stages. In a transmitter, the commonly used types of interstage coupling circuits are capacitive, impedance, and inductive (transformer).

Capacitive coupling is sometimes used in low-level (intermediate amplifier) stages of transmitters. An advantage of this type of coupling is that it makes it possible to provide a continuous variation in the load. Further, it makes possible variation of the grid-excitation voltage over a wide range. A disadvantage is that the tuning range is limited, because of the physical size of the components.

Impedance coupling is very similar to capacitive coupling. The advantages are low cost and minimum space requirements. A disadvantage is that the absence of a tuned circuit between stages makes it possible for the driver to feed unwanted harmonic frequencies into the amplifier, where they are amplified along with the fundamental. Although the harmonic may be considerably weaker than the desired signal, it may be strong enough to cause serious interference to other stations. Besides, the indiscriminate use of r-f chokes or tapped coils in coupling circuits can cause low-frequency parasitic oscillations at a frequency different from the frequency the stage is designed to pass.

Inductive, or tranformer, coupling consists of two tuned circuits. Both the primary and the secondary are tuned to resonate at the desired

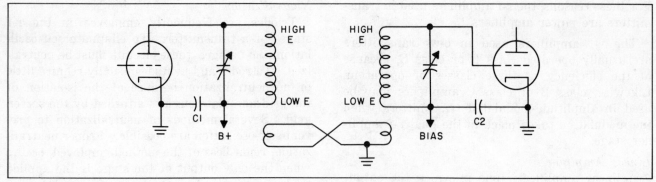

Figure 8-7. Unbalanced Link Coupling

frequency, and the coupling may be varied by changing the spacing between the coils, or the angle of one coil with respect to the other. The advantage of this method of coupling is that only the desired frequency is coupled by the tuned circuits. A disadvantage is that some mechanical difficulty may be encountered in adjusting the coupling to provide the proper excitation for the driven amplifier.

Link coupling is a special form of inductive coupling. It requires the use of two tuned circuits, one in the plate circuit of the driver tube and the other in the grid circuit of the amplifier. A low-impedance r-f transmission line having a coil with one or two turns at each end is used to couple the plate and grid tank circuits. One method of link coupling is shown in figure 8-7. The coupling links, or loops, are coupled to each tuned circuit at its cold end (point of zero r-f potential). Circuits which are cold near one end are called *unbalanced* circuits. Link coupling

systems normally are used where the two stages to be coupled are separated by a considerable distance. One side of the link is grounded in cases where harmonic elimination is important or where stray capacitive coupling between stages must be eliminated.

Some types of transmitter circuits require the use of a balanced circuit. This is one in which the d-c voltage is fed to the center of the tuned coil and equal r-f voltages are developed at the ends. In this case, neither end of the circuit is at r-f ground potential. Figure 8-8 shows how an unbalanced circuit is link-coupled to a balanced circuit.

Link coupling is a very versatile interstage coupling method. It is used extensively in transmitters when the equipment is sufficiently large to permit the coupled coils to be so positioned that there is no stray capacitive coupling between them. Link circuits are designed to have low impedance so that r-f power losses are low. Coup-

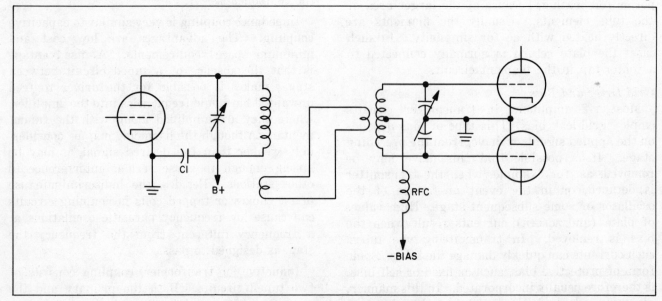

Figure 8-8. Balanced Link Coupling

ling between the links and their associated tuned circuits can be varied without complex mechanical problems. These adjustments provide a means of obtaining very low coupling between stages. The elimination of stray capacitive coupling makes neutralization easier and provides for reduction of harmonic transfer between stages.

Parasitics and Harmonics

Suppression of Parasitics

Parasitic oscillations are oscillations at some frequency usually far removed from the frequency to which the transmitter is tuned. Any inductor is resonant at some frequency when associated with a capacitance. Occasionally, various transmitter components which possess both inductive and capacitive properties may cause the circuit to oscillate at their resonant frequency. The inductance may be that of the wiring, the leads of capacitors, a section of a coil or r-f choke, or the element leads within a tube. The capacitance may be that of the normal circuit capacitors, the capacitance between the turns of a coil or choke, or the interelectrode capacitances of the tube. Parasitics usually are eliminated in the design of the transmitter, but they sometimes appear after the set has been modified or some parts have been replaced. Defective tubes are another cause of parasitics.

Parasitics reduce the useful power output of the transmitter by absorbing some of the power which should be useful output. They may cause excessive currents that blow fuses, trip overload relays, ruin capacitors and inductors in the oscillating circuit, and damage the tubes.

High-frequency parasitics usually can be removed by inserting small r-f chokes or resistors in series with each grid and plate connection. These should be placed as close as possible to the tube terminals. Chokes for parasitic suppression have very low inductance and negligible distributed capacitance. The resistor can be approximately 50 ohms. An efficient parasitic suppressor consists of a coil of wire wound on the body of a small carbon resistor. The coil and resistor are connected in parallel. This combination usually is most effective in grid circuits, but its use may be necessary in some plate circuits. The presence of the parasitic suppressor in grid circuits makes the amplifier more difficult to drive at high frequencies, but the decrease in the power sensitivity is compensated for by the lack of spurious oscillations.

Low-frequency parasitics occur most often in amplifiers having r-f chokes in both grid and plate circuits. Sometimes a portion of a circuit may be tuned to a lower frequency when the tube or tuning capacitor is tapped down on a tank coil to provide proper impedance matching and to insure maximum energy transfer at the desired frequency. These methods should be avoided if possible.

Suppression of Harmonics

Harmonic radiation is particularly undesirable in a transmitter. It can cause severe interference to other stations authorized to operate on the harmonic frequencies. Furthermore, the generation of harmonics produces a definite power loss at the assigned frequency.

Suppression or elimination of harmonic radiation can be accomplished in a number of ways. Some devices for the purpose are built into the transmitter and are beyond the control of the operator. He can do much to suppress harmonics, however, merely by tuning the transmitter properly and adjusting the operating voltages to the correct values. The harmonic content of an amplifier output increases as the bias and excitation voltages are increased. Therefore, by keeping the bias and excitation within specified limits, harmonic radiation is minimized. When r-f energy is transferred from one circuit to another by an inductive arrangement such as an r-f transformer or link coupling, the inductors have a certain amount of stray capacitance. The capacitance between the coils is small, but far from negligible. Energy at the resonant frequency is transferred through magnetic coupling alone. However, harmonics are transferred between the inductors by electrostatic coupling through the capacitance. Therefore, if harmonics are to be eliminated, the coupling must be purely magnetic, and the capacitive effects must be excluded by inserting a *Faraday shield* between the two inductors (figure 8-9). The Faraday shield (sometimes called an *electrostatic shield*) consists of a group of parallel conductors, connected at one end only. This forms an effective shield against electrostatic coupling without affecting the transfer of energy by magnetic coupling.

An imporant factor in reducing harmonic radiation from high-frequency transmitters is the use of low-power frequency multipliers. When multiplication is at low-power levels, direct radiation

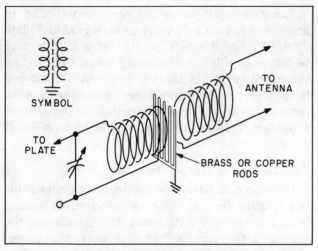

Figure 8-9. Faraday Shield

from the circuits involved is minimized, and there is less danger of the multiplier signals and their harmonics leaking through to the antenna where they may be radiated. For this reason high-frequency transmitters often use receiving tubes as frequency multipliers. After the oscillator frequency is multiplied to the required output frequency, it is amplified to the required power levels by class C amplifiers that are biased only slightly beyond cutoff and supplied with the minimum excitation required to produce sufficient driving power for the following stage. By operating the class C amplifiers with a large angle of plate current, harmonic generation is minimized. Some transmitters have small, auxiliary, parallel tuned circuits in series with the plate lead and in series with each power line to the power transformer. These circuits are tuned to the transmitter harmonics. They offer a high impedance to the harmonic currents. The tuned circuits in series with the power lines prevent harmonics from being radiated from the power lines. Radiation of harmonics can be reduced also by using an antenna which does not respond to the harmonic frequencies. Special antenna coupling networks may also be used to eliminate harmonics.

8-5 C-W TRANSMITTER KEYING

The c-w transmitter is one in which the r-f signal is interrupted, or turned on and off, for periods of time corresponding to the dots and dashes of Morse code. Any modulated transmitter may be operated as a c-w transmitter, and often provisions for this type of operation are included in the transmitter. A telegraph key is used for smooth and efficient interruption of the transmitter output, and the operation is called *keying*.

In general, the keying of a transmitter is considered satisfactory if the r-f output is zero when the key is open and maximum when the key is closed. If the output does not drop to zero under key-up conditions, the signal is said to have a *backwave*. A strong backwave may reach a distant receiver and make the keying difficult to read. The effect is as though the dots and dashes were simply louder portions of a continuous carrier. In code transmissions, there are intervals between dots and dashes and between letters and words. No r-f wave should be radiated during these brief intervals.

To avoid backwaves, the oscillator stage may be keyed directly. When keying takes place in a stage other than the oscillator, the oscillator is on all the time. It must operate at very low power and must be well shielded and isolated to prevent radiation of a backwave. If the oscillator does not meet these conditions, the backwave may be radiated even though the stages between the oscillator and the antenna are cut off. Energy from the oscillator may leak to the antenna through improperly neutralized amplifiers or capacitive or inductive coupling between the oscillator and antenna circuits.

In the absence of a backwave at the transmitting station, the receiver may be operated simultaneously while transmitting, thus making it possible for the receiving operator to signal the transmitting operator immediately when he has not been able to copy a part of the message because of fading, static, or interference. The ability of an operator to hear the other operator's signals during key-up intervals permits break-in operation. The oscillator may run continuously to permit break-in if the backwave is inaudible in the receiver at the transmitting station.

Another requirement of satisfactory keying is that it should take place smoothly without key clicks, which cause interference to stations receiving on other frequencies. Key clicks are caused when the output of the transmitter is changed too abruptly, and under these conditions noise, or clicks, are produced. The oscillator should be absolutely stable while it is being keyed. If it is not, the frequency shifts and causes a varying note (chirp) which makes the signal difficult to copy.

It is easier to avoid chirps by keying the transmitter in a stage between the oscillator and the antenna. Since any chirp resulting from frequency shift is multiplied in each frequency multiplier in very-high-frequency transmitters it is difficult to produce chirpless keying in a keyed oscillator circuit operated at a frequency several times lower than the output frequency. The effects of oscillator chirp and backwave should be taken into account when the keying circuit or keyed stage is considered.

Keying of a transmitter may be accomplished in either the oscillator or amplifier stages or both. One of several methods of keying vacuum-tube circuits may be used; among these are plate-, grid-, screen-, and cathode-circuit keying. Effectively, all result in the interruption of the plate current of one or more of the tubes in the transmitter. Each has certain advantages or disadvantages.

Plate-Circuit Keying

A transmitter can be keyed by simultaneously opening and closing the plate circuits of all the stages. In small, battery-operated portable transmitters this is both practical and economical, since all plate current ceases when the key is open. In larger transmitters, the plate voltage and current applied to the final amplifier and even the preceding stages may be very high. Interruption of circuits operating under these conditions by the use of a telegraph key would be both impractical and hazardous to the operator of the key. In larger transmitters, it is sufficient to key only the oscillator or one of the low-level amplifier stages or both. This is called *excitation keying* because excitation is applied to and removed from the input to the final amplifier while its plate voltage remains applied.

One method of plate keying of an oscillator or amplifier stage is shown in figure 8-10. The key is usually placed in the negative lead of the plate supply. In this manner, one terminal of the key is always grounded, although it must be remembered that full plate voltage can appear at the other terminal. When higher voltages or currents are involved, a keying relay should be used.

Cathode Keying

By placing the key in the cathode circuit of an oscillator or an amplifier, both the grid and plate (and screen, if any) circuits are opened by the key. Such a circuit is shown in figure 8-11. Although similar in appearance to negative-lead plate keying, the connection of the grid resistor or grid tank circuit is such that the grid-cathode circuit is opened by the key. Cathode keying is often used with amplifiers, because the proper shaping of the keyed signal can be accomplished readily. It is also widely used with oscillators, but the shaping is often complicated by the grid-circuit time constant. As with plate-circuit keying, a keying relay or keyer tube should be used when higher voltages or currents are encountered.

Simple Blocked-Grid Keying

Blocked-grid, or *grid-block keying*, as it is often called, is a form of grid-circuit keying which uses a blocking bias applied to the grid of an oscillator or amplifier when the key is up or open. This negative bias must be considerably higher than the normal cutoff grid bias because it must overcome the excitation voltage. It is removed by closing the key.

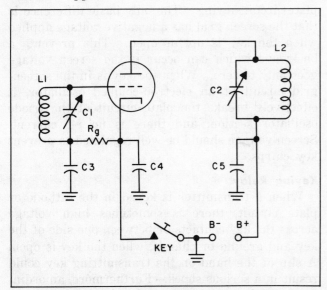

Figure 8-10. Negative-Lead Plate Keying

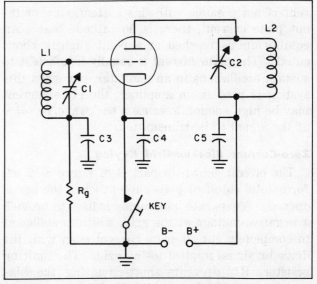

Figure 8-11. Cathode Keying

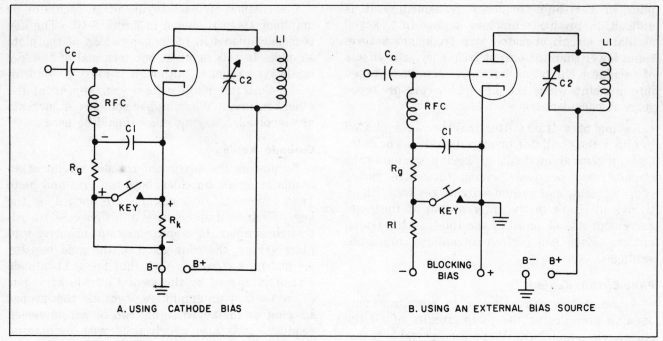

Figure 8-12. Two Methods of Grid-Block Keying

A simple method of obtaining the negative bias voltage is by the use of a combination of cathode and grid-leak bias as shown in part A of figure 8-12. When the key is open, plate current through the cathode resistor, R_k, causes a voltage drop which makes the cathode positive with respect to the ground or grid end of R_k. If R_k is large enough, the voltage drop is sufficient to reduce the plate current to almost zero, or cutoff. Closing the key short-circuits R_k, removing the cathode bias and permitting normal plate current. Resistor R_g is the usual grid-leak resistor which produces the normal operating bias. Total cutoff of plate current is not possible with this system, since without plate current, there is no cathode bias. An equilibrium is reached at a point slightly above cutoff. The plate current is usually insufficient to sustain oscillations in an oscillator, but when this system is used in an amplifier, the plate current may be high enough to cause a backwave, or some of the signal to be transmitted.

Zero-Current Blocked-Grid Keying

The circuit shown in part B of figure 8-12 affords total cutoff of plate current when the key is opened. A separate bias supply is used to provide a negative voltage at the grid, which is sufficient to completely cut off plate current even with the drive or signal applied to the grid. The limiting resistor, R1, prevents short-circuiting the bias supply when the key is closed. In some cases, a

single supply is used for both plate and bias voltage. The cathode may be connected to a voltage-divider circuit across the power supply, with the grid resistor connected at its negative end. A disadvantage of this method is that the plate voltage is reduced by the amount of bias voltage applied to the blocked-grid circuit. An advantage is that plate voltage does not appear at the key.

Screen-Grid Keying

Another form of keying, which is suitable for oscillators or amplifiers using screen-grid tubes, is screen-grid keying, which is closely related to plate-circuit keying. The only basic difference is that the screen grid has a negative voltage applied when the key is up, or open. This prevents a backwave which can occur if the screen voltage goes only to zero. When the key is in the screen-grid circuit of an electron-coupled oscillator, it effectively breaks the plate circuit of the triode oscillator section, and there is no r-f current. Screen voltage should be well regulated to prevent key chirps.

Keying Relay

When a transmitter is keyed in the cathode or plate circuit, there is sometimes high voltage across the key contacts or between one side of the key and ground or chassis, when the key is open. A slip of the hand on the transmitting key could result in a serious shock. Furthermore, an ordinary hand key cannot carry heavy currents without arcing. For these reasons, a keying relay is sometimes used in conjunction with a low-voltage source to open and close the keyed circuits. The relay may be mounted near the circuit to be keyed, and the key then located at a remote point, if desired. A relatively low voltage is used to operate the relay, and only the low voltage is present at the key. A fast-responding relay must be used for normally fast keying speeds.

Electron-Tube Keying

Large fixed-station transmitters often h a v e their output keyed at very high speeds. Mechanical relays may lag in operation or not respond at all to the high keying speeds. In such cases, a keyer tube circuit is used. A typical elecron-tube keying circuit consists of a triode tube connected between the cathode and ground of the r-f amplifier or oscillator to be keyed. This tube, called a *keyer tube*, operates with its grid bias at cutoff when the key is open. Since this tube is cut off, it acts as an infinitely high resistance, or an open circuit, between cathode and ground of the amplifier stage. Closing the key removes the bias, so that the keyer tube becomes highly conductive. This allows normal plate current in the amplifier stage. Generally, zero-current blocked-grid keying is used on the keyer tube to insure that it and the keyed stage are cut off completely. As with the use of keying relays, the keyer-tube type of keying makes remote operation easy to accomplish.

Key-Click Filters

Transmitter keying should produce clean-cut dots and dashes which cause a minimum of interference in nearby receivers. However, keying does not instantaneously start and stop radiation of the carrier, or r-f energy. The sudden application and removal of power causes high current surges which produce unwanted oscillations and interference in the form of clicks that can be heard over a wide frequency range. To prevent such interference, key-click filters are used in the keying systems of most c-w transmitters.

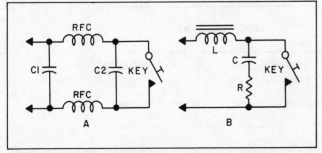

Figure 8-13. Two Types of Key-Click Filters

Two types of filters are shown in figure 8-13. The r-f chokes and bypass capacitors, in part A of the figure, isolate the key from the rest of the circuit, and bypass and prevent r-f surges caused by arcing of the key contacts. A lag-circuit keying filter is shown in part B of the figure. The inductor, L, causes a slight delay in the current as the key is closed. The current then builds up gradually instead of rapidly. Capacitor C releases its energy slowly when the key is opened. Resistor R controls the rate of charge and discharge of the capacitor when the key is opened and closed.

8-6 AMPLITUDE-MODULATION PRINCIPLES

Another method of radio transmission, in contrast to c-w transmission, is accomplished by varying the carrier, or r-f waveform, in accordance with the variations in the intelligence to be transmitted. Using this method, speech, music, or any other form of intelligence is first converted into alternating voltages, and these voltages in turn are superimposed on a carrier waveform and then transmitted. This varying process is called *modulation*. In practice, the frequency of the carrier wave is much higher than the highest modulating frequency. In this type of transmission, the carrier remains uninterrupted during the entire transmission period.

Several forms of modulation of a carrier wave are possible. *Amplitude modulation,* or AM, is the result of varying the amplitude of the carrier at the modulating (audio) rate. *Frequency modulation* (FM) occurs when the frequency of the carrier is varied and the amplitude remains constant. *Phase modulation* (PM) is similar to FM except that the phase of the carrier is varied. Of these perhaps the oldest and most commonly used method is amplitude modulation.

Analysis of Amplitude Modulation

The process by which an audio signal or other modulating frequencies are impressed on an r-f carrier wave to vary its amplitude is called *amplitude modulation*. Actually, the amplitude of the carrier remains constant and a varying *wave envelope* is produced. To better understand this phenomenon, an analysis of the frequency spectrum in the vicinity of the carrier frequency must be made.

Sidebands

When a carrier is modulated by a single audio frequency, or note, two additional frequencies are produced, as shown in figure 8-14. One is the

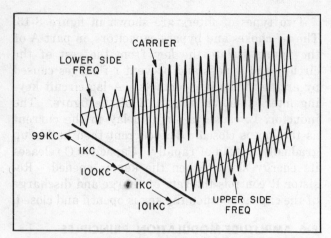

Figure 8-14. Side Frequencies Produced When a 100-KC Carrier Is Modulated by a 1000-Cycle Tone

upper side frequency, which is the sum of the frequency of the r-f carrier and the frequency of the audio note. The other is the lower side frequency, which is the difference between the carrier and the audio frequency.

When the modulating signal is made up of complex tones, as in music, each individual tone, or frequency component, of the modulating signal produces its own upper and lower side frequencies. These side frequencies occupy a band of frequencies lying between the carrier frequency plus and minus the lowest modulating frequency, and the carrier frequency plus and minus the highest modulating frequency. The bands of frequencies which contain the side frequencies are called *sidebands*. The sideband which contains the sum of the carrier and the modulating frequencies is called the *upper sideband,* and the band which contains the difference of the carrier and the modulating frequencies is called the *lower sideband.*

The space which a carrier and its associated sidebands occupy in a frequency spectrum is called

a *channel.* The width of the channel, or *bandwidth,* is equal to twice the highest modulating frequency. For example, if a 5000-kc carrier is modulated by a band of frequencies ranging from 200 to 5000 cycles (.2 to 5 kc), the upper sideband will extend from 5000.2 to 5005 kc, and the lower sideband will extend from 4999.8 to 4995 kc. The bandwidth is then 4995 to 5005 kc, or 10 kc (twice the value of the highest modulating frequency of 5 kc). This is illustrated in figure 8-15.

The carrier wave itself contains none of the intelligence of the modulating signal, all such intelligence being in the sidebands. If the modulating signal is removed, the sidebands will no longer be present and only the carrier will remain. Therefore, it can be stated that the sidebands are directly related to both the modulating signal and the carrier, the carrier remaining constant in frequency and amplitude, and the sidebands varying in frequency and amplitude as the modulating signal is varied.

Modulated-Wave Envelope

The carrier wave together with the upper and lower sidebands forms the complete modulated carrier, called the *modulated-wave envelope,* or simply the *modulation envelope.* The waveforms of an r-f carrier, audio modulating signal, and the amplitude-modulated wave are represented in figure 8-16. Although the modulating signal is very seldom a pure sine wave in actual practice, such a waveform is usually used to illlustrate the concepts of amplitude modulation.

Further analysis of the modulation process can be realized by the development of a modulated wave using a single tone or sine wave. In figure 8-17, a 100-kc carrier is modulated by a 3000-cycle tone. The lower side frequency of 97 kc and the upper side frequency of 103 kc remain constant in

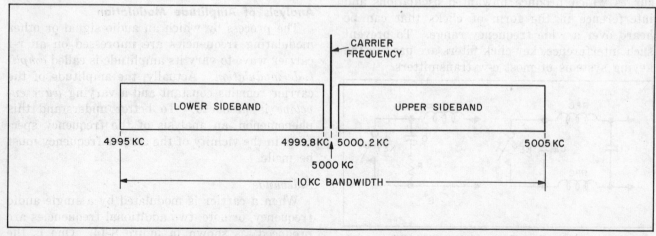

Figure 8-15. Sidebands Produced by Amplitude Modulation

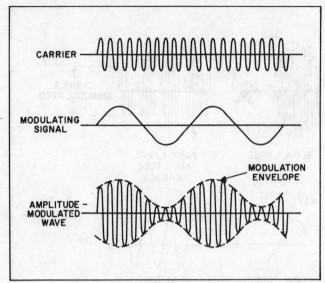

Figure 8-16. Illustration of Carrier, Modulating Signal, and Amplitude-Modulated Wave

amplitude and frequency so long as the carrier and the modulating signal remain constant. Variations in amplitude occur in the resultant wave envelope at the rate of the 3-kc modulating signal. This is true because the amplitude of the wave envelope is the *vector addition* of the amplitudes of the carrier and the sidebands at any given instant. Thus the wave envelope actually consists of three (or more) different frequencies whose phase relationships are continuously changing.

A complete vector analysis is not necessary to determine the resultant waveform, since regardless of the number of side frequencies contained in the wave envelope, the amplitude of the wave envelope will always be an exact replica of the modulating signal when the modulating process is properly accomplished.

The amplitude-modulated wave, then, is actually the wave envelope, and not simply a carrier varying in amplitude. Whether the waveforms are those of voltage, current, or power, the amplitude relationships among the carrier, modulating signal, sidebands, and the modulated-wave envelope are the same. If the modulating signal frequency is high, the amplitude variations of the carrier will be more rapid than if the modulating signal frequency were low. Similarly, if the volume of the modulating signal is loud, the carrier amplitude variations will be larger than those for low-volume modulating signals. Examples of both these facts are illustrated in figure 8-18.

Percentage of Modulation

There are certain limitations as to the strength (volume) of the modulating signal. For example, in order to produce an amplitude-modulated wave having maximum modulation and no distortion, the modulating signal should decrease the amplitude of the wave envelope to zero and raise the wave amplitude to twice the carrier value at the

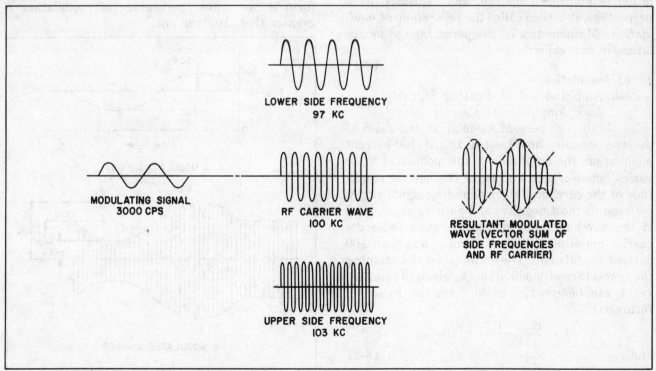

Figure 8-17. Sideband Frequencies and Resultant Waveform Generated During Amplitude-Modulating Process

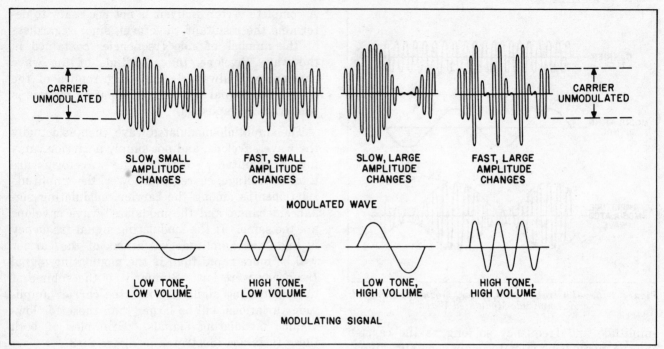

Figure 8-18. Waveforms of an Amplitude-Modulated Carrier Signal for Varying Types of Modulating Signals

peaks of the modulating signal. The extent to which the modulating signal modulates the carrier is called the *degree of modulation*. This degree of modulation is the ratio of the peak amplitude of the modulating signal to the peak amplitude of the carrier wave. When the degree of modulation is multiplied by 100, and expressed as a percentage, it is then called the *percentage of modulation*. Mathematically, the percentage of modulation is expressed:

$$(8-1)$$

% of Modulation =

$$\frac{\text{Peak Amplitude of Modulating Signal}}{\text{Peak Amplitude of Carrier}} \times 100$$

To obtain 100 percent modulation, the ratio of the two signals should equal 1. At 100-percent modulation, the amplitude of the modulated wave varies between zero and twice the normal amplitude of the carrier as the modulating signal varies between its most negative and positive excursions. If the envelope amplitude is less than twice the carrier amplitude, the waveform is less than 100 percent modulated. The formula for determining the percentage of modulation, M, given in equation (8-1) can be rearranged to form the following formulas:

$$M = \frac{E_{max} - E_{car}}{E_{car}} \times 100\%$$

and

$$(8-2)$$

$$M = \frac{E_{car} - E_{min}}{E_{car}} \times 100\%$$

where:

E_{max} = maximum amplitude of envelope

E_{min} = minimum amplitude of envelope

E_{car} = amplitude of carrier.

This formula is valid only for waveforms which are not overmodulated. An overmodulated waveform is one whose percentage of modulation is greater than 100 percent.

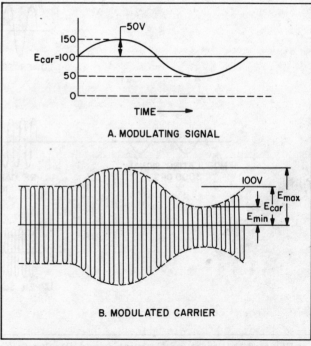

A. MODULATING SIGNAL

B. MODULATED CARRIER

Figure 8-19. Illustration of 50-Percent Modulation

Part A of figure 8-19 shows a modulating signal, and part B shows the modulated carrier. By substituting in equations (8-2) the voltage values given in the figure, the percentage of modulation (M) equals:

$$M = \frac{E_{max} - E_{car}}{E_{car}} \times 100\%$$

$$= \frac{150 - 100}{100} \times 100\% = 50\%$$

and

$$M = \frac{E_{car} - E_{min}}{E_{car}} \times 100\%$$

$$= \frac{100 - 50}{100} \times 100\% = 50\%$$

Consequently, the percentage of modulation is 50 percent.

If the peak of the modulating signal equals the carrier voltage (100 volts), the modulated carrier varies from 0 volt to 200 volts. This is shown in figure 8-20. Again applying the modulation percentage formulas:

$$M = \frac{E_{max} - E_{car}}{E_{car}} \times 100\%$$

$$= \frac{200 - 100}{100} \times 100\% = 100\%$$

$$M = \frac{E_{car} - E_{min}}{E_{car}} \times 100\%$$

$$= \frac{100 - 0}{100} \times 100\% = 100\%$$

The percentage of modulation is 100 percent. Whenever the modulating signal varies between zero and twice the unmodulated carrier voltage, there is a 100-percent modulation.

A transmitter usually is operated so that the average percentage of modulation approaches, but does not exceed, 100-percent modulation, since the signal-to-noise ratio of the received signal is higher as the modulation percentage approaches 100 percent. Strong sidebands make the received signal less susceptible to interference from stations operating on the same channel. Also, because of the increased power in the sidebands, a fully modulated transmitter transmits a greater distance for a given carrier power.

Overmodulation

When the percentage of modulation exceeds 100%, distortion occurs in the modulated wave. This distortion, called *overmodulation*, will cause a loss of fidelity in the signal by changing the

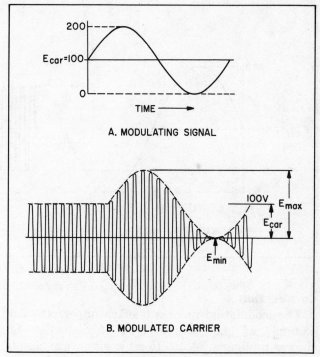

Figure 8-20. Illustration of 100-Percent Modulation

modulation envelope waveshape. Overmodulation also causes a loss in transmitter output power, since maximum undistorted power output of a transmitter is obtained at 100-percent modulation.

Consider the case where a 100-volt carrier is modulated by a 150-volt audio signal. The two voltages add to produce an instantaneous peak of 250 volts on the positive excursion of the modulation cycle; on the negative excursion the audio voltage swings to 50 volts below the zero line, as in part A of figure 8-21. This condition produces an overmodulated carrier, as in part B, where area A represents the period during which the modulated-wave envelope is cut off. This break in the r-f output of the transmitter produces distortion at the receiver. This condition exists whenever the peak a-f signal voltage exceeds the carrier voltage.

Whenever a transmitter is modulated in excess of 100 percent, the momentary interruption of the carrier in the modulated-wave envelope produces serious changes in the wavelength of the original wave envelope. New frequencis and harmonics are generated. Their number and intensity vary with the degree of overmodulation. These spurious modulating frequencies produce additional sidebands which extend far beyond the normal bandwidth and cause interference to stations on adjacent channels.

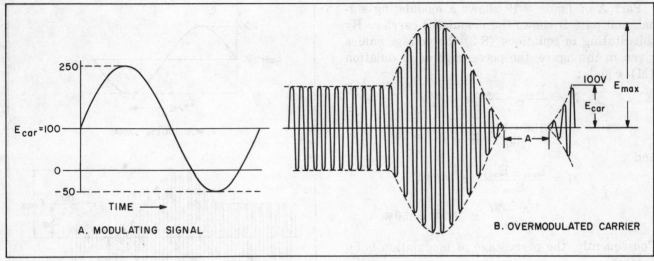

Figure 8-21. Overmodulation

Carrier Shift

The modulation process is often imperfect. An example of one possible type of distortion is shown in figure 8-22. Here a sine-wave audio note has modulated a carrier in an unequal manner, so that the positive excursions of the upper envelope pattern exceed the negative excursions. This condition results in an increase of the average value of the modulated carrier component. In other words, the power associated with the carrier has increased, and the carrier power is said to have shifted upward. This condition is known as positive-carrier shift. If the distortion had been such to make the negative excursions larger than the positive swings, the carrier power would then have shifted downward, resulting in negative-carrier shift. Expressed more exactly, the shift is upward when the time average of the positive half cycles of the modulation signal is greater than the time average of the negative half cycles, and vice versa. The term *carrier shift* must not be interpreted to mean a shift in frequency.

For purposes of voice communication, positive-carrier shift occasionally has an advantage over conventional modulation. Although the distortion is higher, experience has shown that the intelligibility is actually improved. In some applications, positive-carrier shift is e m p l o y e d deliberately.

Distribution of Power in an Amplitude-Modulated Wave

The power in an amplitude-modulated wave is divided between the carrier and the sidebands. Since the carrier power is constant (except in cases of overmodulation), the sideband power is the difference between the carrier power and the total power in the modulated wave. When a carrier is modulated by a single sinusoidal tone, the total power output is found by using the formula

$$P_{mod} = (1 + \frac{M^2}{2}) \times P_{car} \qquad (8\text{-}3)$$

where:

P_{mod} = total power in the modulated wave

M = degree of modulation

P_{car} = power in carrier

Assuming that a 500-watt carrier is modulated 100 percent, the power in the signal is:

$$P_{mod} = (1 + \frac{(1)^2}{2}) \times 500 = 750 \text{ watts}$$

Of this total, 500 watts are in the carrier and 250 watts are in the sidebands. The percentage of

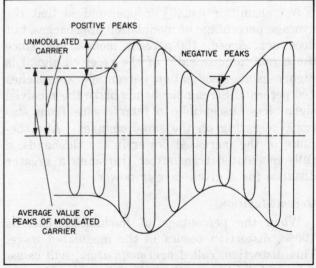

Figure 8-22. Positive Carrier Shift

sideband power is 250/750 times 100 percent, or 33.3 percent. Of the 250 watts of sideband power, there are 125 watts in each sideband and the power content of each sideband, therefore, is 16.6 percent of the total power output with 100-percent modulation.

The available sideband power takes a marked drop when the average percentage of modulation is well below 100 percent. This is shown by modulating the carrier only 50 percent when the power in the carrier is 500 watts.

$$P_{mod} = (1 + \frac{(.5)^2}{2}) \times 500 = 562.5 \text{ watts}$$

The total modulated power is now 562.5 watts. Since there are 500 watts in the carrier, only 62.5 watts of power remain in the sidebands. Since 62.5 watts are one-fourth the value obtainable with 100-percent modulation, it can be seen that lowering the modulation to 50 percent causes a 75-percent reduction in the available sideband power. Since all of the intelligence being tranmitted is contained in the sidebands, the desirability of a high percentage of modulation is evident.

8-7 AMPLITUDE-MODULATION CIRCUITS

The highest values of r-f voltages occur in the final power-amplifier plate circuit of a transmitter. Consequently, high power levels, voltages, and currents are present at the tube elements. In order to modulate 100 percent the r-f carrier in this stage, the modulating signal amplitude must equal the amplitude of the r-f carrier.

Speech Amplifier

The a-f voltages generated by a microphone or other signal source are comparatively low, usually less than 1 volt, whereas the d-c potentials applied to the r-f amplifier tube electrodes are high. The addition of the low a-c voltage to the high d-c potentials on the tube electrodes results in a very small variation in the power output. Therefore, it is necessary to amplify the alternating signal voltage, or audio frequencies, to a level high enough to cause the proper amount of variation in the r-f envelope.

The speech amplifier is simply an audio amplifier designed primarily for the amplification of the speech signals, in contrast to one designed for high fidelity, or music. Radiotelephone transmitters for communication purposes usually employ simple speech amplifiers, whereas broadcast

stations employ high-fidelity audio circuits. Either may be considered in the audio circuit of any transmitter.

The audio amplification usually takes place in at least two stages. The a-f speech amplifier is a class A voltage amplifier. The output of this stage drives a second stage, which may be a voltage amplifier or a power amplifier, depending on the required input power to the modulator.

Modulator

A modulator is essentially an audio output stage. The only difference is the modulation transformer, which has a different turns ratio and higher current capacity than the conventional output transformer. In a small transmitter, the speech amplifier and modulator may be combined into one stage.

Since the modulator is an audio power amplifier, it may be operated class A, class AB, or class B. If it is operated other than class A, it must, of course, be a push-pull stage.

Modulated Stage

The audio-modulating signal from the modulator stage is applied to one of the r-f amplifiers in the transmitter. The r-f stage to which the modulating signal is applied is called the *modulated stage*. Frequently the modulation process is effected in the last stage, where the power of the system is highest. In some cases, the modulated stage is one of the intermediate r-f amplifiers.

High-Level and Low-Level Modulation

In the transmitter shown in figure 8-23, the modulating signal is applied to the final power amplifier. This type of transmitter is generally referred to as a *high-level* modulated transmitter,

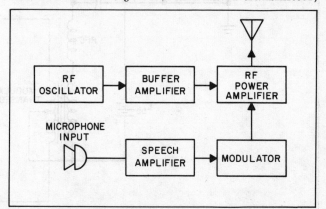

Figure 8-23. Basic AM Transmitter (High-Level Modulation)

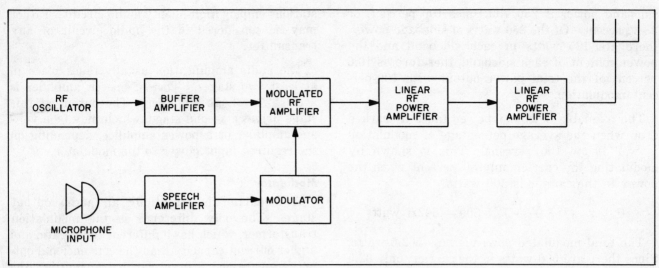

Figure 8-24. Low-Level Modulation

since the modulation process is effected at a relatively high power in the final (power amplifier) stage.

A *low-level* modulated AM transmitter, shown in figure 8-24, is one in which the modulation process is performed in one of the low-power intermediate r-f amplifiers. To obtain the desired transmitter output-power level, the modulated r-f carrier is then amplified in linear amplifiers to preserve the relationships of the modulating components (wave envelope). Because linear amplifiers are used in this system, the efficiency of the low-level modulated transmitter is much lower than that of a high-level system. However, an advantage of the low-level system (over a high-level system) is that lower a-f power is required to drive the r-f amplifier being modulated.

8-8 AMPLITUDE-MODULATION METHODS

The modulating voltage may be applied in series with any of the modulated tube's elements. The

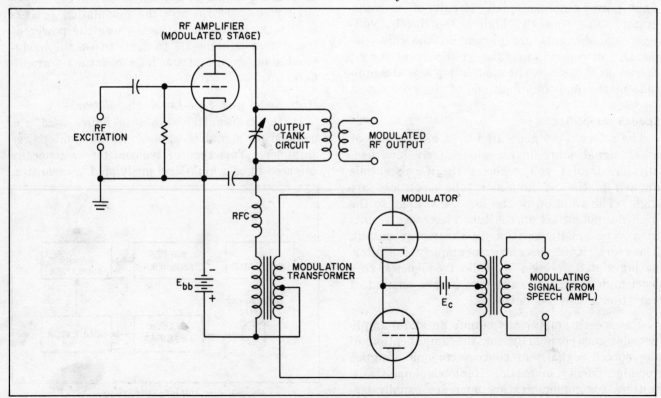

Figure 8-25. Transformer-Coupled Plate Modulation (Neutralization Omitted)

name of the type of modulation used derives from the tube element to which the secondary winding of the modulation transformer is connected. Plate modulation is achieved by connecting the output of the modulator in series with the plate circuit of the modulated stage. Other types of modulation used with triode tubes are grid modulation and cathode modulation. In tetrode or pentode tubes, screen-grid modulation or suppressor-grid modulation may be used in place of the other methods.

Plate Modulation

In the simplified circuit of the modulator and modulated r-f stage shown in figure 8-25, the modulation is applied to the plate circuit of the r-f amplifier. The audio voltage, being in series with the d-c plate-supply voltage, E_{bb}, causes the total plate voltage applied to the r-f amplifier to vary above and below its normal value by an amount equal to the peak audio voltage, and at a rate equal to the frequency of the audio modulating signal. While the applied plate voltage is varying, a constant amplitude of r-f voltage (excitation) is applied to the grid of the r-f amplifier tube from the output of the buffer or an intermediate power amplifier. During the positive half-cycles of the audio modulation, a greater r-f voltage is produced across the tuned circuit, since the higher value of plate voltage causes increased plate current. During the negative half-cycles of the audio modulation voltage, the plate voltage is lower than B plus, resulting in less current and consequently less r-f voltage across the tank circuit. As a result, the amplitude of the r-f output varies at the audio rate.

Figure 8-26 illustrates the development of the modulated wave by the plate-modulation method. Part A shows the r-f excitation applied to the grid circuit, in relationship to the cutoff bias of class C operation. The modulation voltage of 300 volts, in part B, is applied in series with the 500-volt plate supply, as in part C of the figure. Thus, in this case, the plate voltage is made to vary from 200 volts to 800 volts. For 100-percent modulation, the modulating voltage would be equal to the plate supply voltage, or 500 volts in this case. The resultant plate-current pulses are shown in part D of the figure, with the r-f output voltage formed in the tank circuit shown in part E.

When complete modulation occurs, the power supplied by the modulator is one-half that supplied by the plate supply of the r-f amplifier. In general, the power associated with the carrier is furnished by the plate supply of the amplifier, while the power associated with the sideband components is contributed by the modulator.

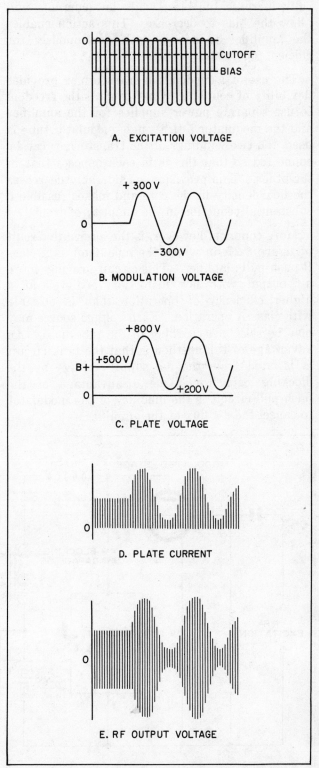

Figure 8-26. Development of Modulated Wave by Plate Modulation

During the negative-going portion of a modulation cycle, the plate voltage of the amplifier is low, and tends to cause a high d-c grid current. To combat this tendency, grid-leak bias should be used. High grid currents will then automatically increase the bias, while low currents will allow the bias to decrease. This action enables the amplifier to adjust itself continuously for efficient operation.

The use of a modulation transformer provides flexibility of coupling. One benefit is the freedom to use separate power supplies for the amplifier and the modulator. If a single modulator tube is used, the two windings of the transformer can be connected so that the dc in each opposes that in the other. This provision considerably decreases the flux density in the core and makes feasible a substantial reduction in the quantity of iron.

More common, however, is the alternate circuit of figure 8-27, in which the modulator is a class B push-pull amplifier. This circuit provides more a-f output with low distortion, achieved at a higher efficiency of operation than is possible with class A operation. Each voltage source may now be selected according to the tube used. An advantage of this method is that the tank circuit is isolated from the d-c supply voltage by the blocking capacitor. One disadvantage of the push-pull circuit is the inability of the modulator to cancel the d-c flux of the amplifier.

Another circuit for plate modulation is shown in figure 8-28. In this circuit the modulator produces an output across a load impedance consisting of a choke instead of a transformer. This method of plate modulation is also called *Heising modulation* after its inventor. The choke is in series with the plate supply voltage, E_{bb}, used by both the modulator and the class C amplifier. If the voltage-dropping resistor, R, is temporarily ignored, it is evident that the effective plate voltage on the r-f amplifier is the sum of E_{bb} and the instantaneous voltage across the choke. The r-f amplifier must be adjusted so that its condition is proportional to the plate voltage. As the modulating signal varies from small to large values the voltage across the tank is then varied proportionately. An amplitude-modulated wave is thus produced in the tank circuit.

The meter shown in figure 8-28 will indicate a constant current, because the current drawn by the class C amplifier decreases when the current through the modulator becomes greater. Therefore, the circuit is sometimes called a *constant-current* system.

To attain 100-percent modulation, the plate voltage of the amplifier must vary from zero to twice the value of E_{bb}. However, the requirement of distortion-free audio amplification means that the modulator must be operated as a class A amplifier when a choke is used. Since the tube characteristics become nonlinear when the plate

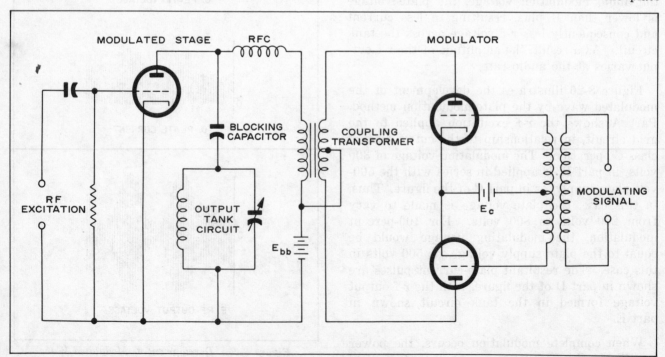

Figure 8-27.   Alternate Circuit for Transformer-Coupled Plate Modulation (Neutralization Omitted)

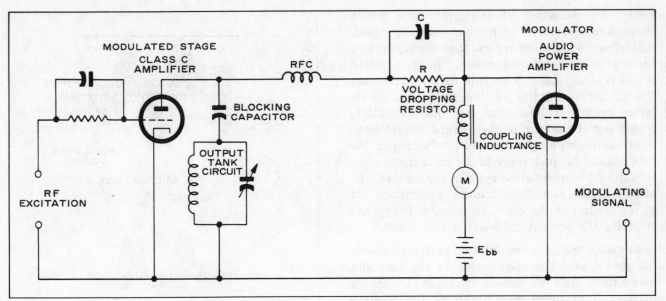

Figure 8-28.   Circuit for Choke-Coupled Plate Modulation (Neutralization Omitted)

voltage is very low, it is not possible to allow a voltage drop equal to E_{bb} across the choke. This restriction would prevent 100-percent modulation but for the inclusion of voltage-dropping resistor R in the circuit. Its value is such that, when the maximum allowable drop is produced across the choke, the additional drop across R leaves the potential of the amplifier plate at zero. Although the amplifier cannot take advantage of the full plate-supply voltage, it is now possible to accomplish 100-percent modulation. The capacitor serves as an r-f bypass.

An alternative method for securing complete (100-percent) modulation is the use of an auto-transformer as the coupling impedance. Dropping resistor R is omitted, and the amplifier utilizes the full plate supply. The transformer steps up the a-f voltage, self-induced across relatively few turns, to a value just equal to E_{bb} on modulation peaks. To obtain the optimum load impedance for the modulator, the autotransformer also steps down the plate impedance of the amplifier. For proper conditions, the plate impedance of the amplifier is equal to E_{bb} divided by the unmodulated average plate current.

Grid Modulation

Another method of modulating the r-f amplifier is shown in figure 8-29. This particular circuit is essentially a push-pull class C amplifier con-

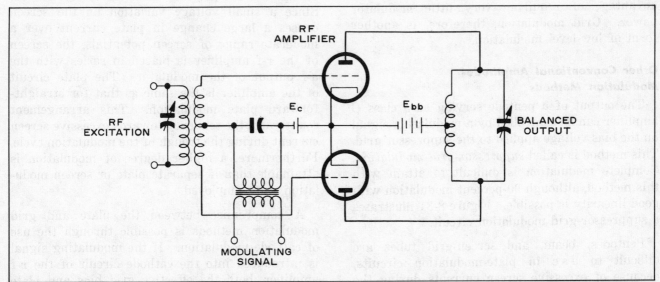

Figure 8-29.   Push-Pull Grid-Modulated Amplifier Circuit

trolled by variation of the grid bias, which changes in accordance with the modulating signal. Adjustments are more critical than those required for a plate-modulated amplifier. When adjusted properly, the tube will operate as a typical class C amplifier during the positive crest of the modulation cycle. At this time the total excitation, consisting of the sum of the a-f and r-f voltages, is at maximum amplitude, and conduction in the tube should be just short of saturation. As the trough of the modulation cycle is approached, the output of the amplifier declines appreciably. If at the trough of the cycle, the output disappears entirely, 100-percent modulation will result.

Actually, the audio modulation is in series with the grid bias. The relationship of the bias and modulation and excitation voltages is shown in part A of figure 8-30. During the positive half-cycles of the modulating voltage, the effect is that of less bias, and a greater amplification of the r-f excitation occurs. The opposite is true when the negative half-cycles of the modulation voltage occur. If sufficient audio and fixed bias voltages are applied, the plate current is reduced to zero, for 100-percent modulation. The resultant plate-current pulses are shown in part B, and the r-f output, or modulation envelope, is shown in part C of the figure.

The primary disadvantages of grid modulation are the comparatively low-power output and the low efficiency of operation. To increase the power somewhat, push-pull circuits such as the one in figure 8-29 are frequently employed. On the other hand, grid modulation systems have the advantage of requiring very little modulator power. Grid modulation, therefore, is another form of low-level modulation.

Other Conventional Amplitude-Modulation Methods

The output of a pentode serving as a class C amplifier can be controlled by a modulating signal on the bias voltage applied to the suppressor grid. This method is called *suppressor-grid modulation.* Complete modulation is difficult to attain with this method, although 90-percent modulation with good linearity is possible. Figure 8-31 illustrates a suppressor-grid modulation circuit.

Pentodes, beam, and screen-grid tubes are difficult to use in plate-modulation circuits, because of excessive screen currents during the trough of the modulation cycle. A possible

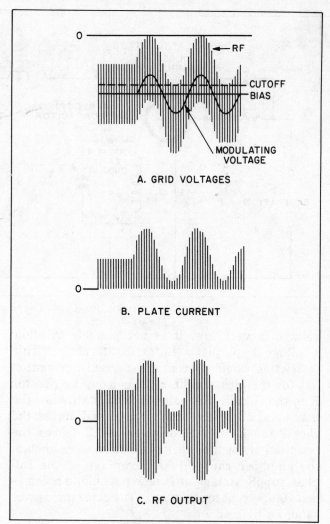

Figure 8-30. Development of Modulated Wave by Grid Modulation

solution to the problem is shown in figure 8-32. Since a small voltage variation on the screen causes a large change in plate current over a moderate range of screen potentials, the screen of the r-f amplifier is placed in series with the a-f output of the modulator. The plate circuit of the amplifier is the same as that for straightforward plate modulation. This arrangement counteracts the tendency towards excessive screen current during the trough of the modulation cycle. Furthermore, a higher degree of modulation is attainable than if separate plate or screen modulation were employed.

A compromise between the plate and grid modulation methods is possible through the use of cathode modulation. If the modulating signal is introduced into the cathode circuit of the r-f amplifier, both the effective grid bias and plate supply voltage will be altered during modulation.

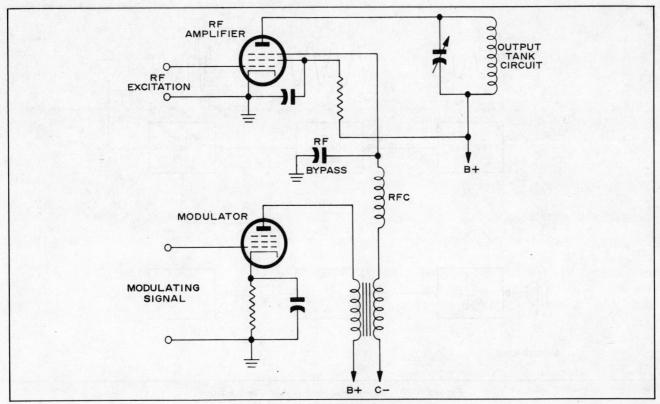

Figure 8-31. Circuit for Suppressor-Grid Modulation

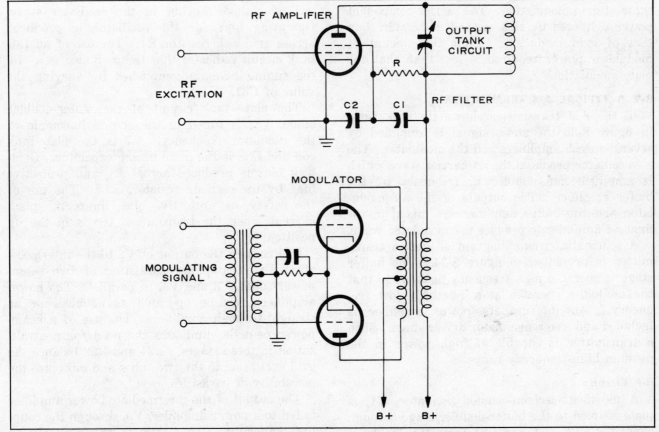

Figure 8-32. Circuit for Combined Plate- and Screen-Grid Modulation

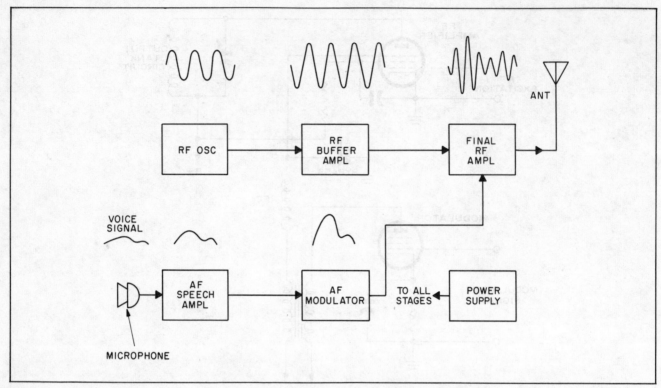

Figure 8-33. Block Diagram of AM Transmitter

The necessary adjustments rather closely resemble those of grid modulation. The carrier-component power delivered by this method is greater than that of grid modulation, while the amount of modulator power required is less than that for plate modulation.

8-9 A TYPICAL AM TRANSMITTER

In the AM transmitter shown in block form in figure 8-33 the audio signal is amplified by several speech amplifiers and the modulator. The r-f oscillator produces the r-f carrier wave which is amplified and doubled in frequency by the buffer amplifier. The outputs of the a-f modulator and the buffer amplifier are mixed in the final r-f amplifier to produce the modulated wave.

A schematic circuit diagram of such a transmitter is presented in figure 8-34. The buffer stage is operated as a frequency doubler, so that the oscillator operates at a relatively low frequency. An intermediate power amplifier is included and also a modulator driver stage. Such a transmitter is capable of high power in the medium high-frequency range.

R-F Circuits

A modified electron-coupled oscillator, V1, is plate-coupled to the buffer-doubler stage through capacitor C13. L1 and C31 form the oscillator tank circuit, and the transmitter is keyed by the use of cathode keying in the oscillator stage. Operating bias for the oscillator is produced across grid-leak resistor R1. The use of an L-C tank circuit indicates that the oscillator is a vfo, the tuning being accomplished by varying the value of C31.

The plate tank circuit of the buffer-doubler stage, V2, is tuned to the second harmonic of the oscillator frequency. L7 is the plate-tank coil and C32 is the plate tuning capacitor. Grid-leak bias is produced across R_{23} and protective bias by the cathode resistor, R24. The use of the safety, or protective bias, limits the plate current when the transmitter key is in the up position.

C14 couples the output of V2 to the intermediate power amplifier consisting of two beam-power tubes, V3 and V4, in parallel. The power amplifiers can be operated as doublers or as straight-through amplifiers. The use of a beam-power pentode eliminates the need for neutralization in these stages. R21 and R22 balance the grid excitation to the two tubes and minimize the possibility of parasitics.

The output of the intermediate power amplifier is fed to a power amplifier, V5, through the coupling capacitor, C15. C18 is the neutralizing

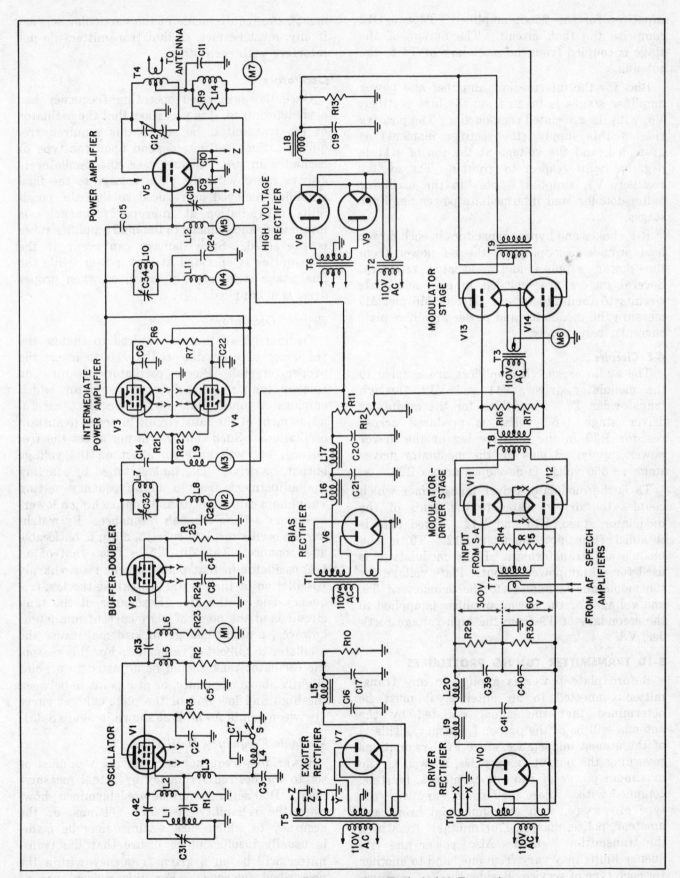

Figure 8-34. Schematic Diagram of a Typical AM Transmitter

capacitor for the triode amplifier. T4 and C12 comprise the tank circuit. The output of the stage is coupled from the secondary of T4 to the antenna.

Bias for the intermediate amplifier and power amplifier stages is taken from the bias rectifier, V6, with its associated components. The positive side of this supply (the rectifier filament) is grounded, and the voltage at the top of R11 is negative with respect to ground. The exciter rectifier, V7, supplies B plus to the oscillator buffer-doubler, and intermediate power amplifier stages.

R-F chokes and bypass capacitors in each power lead provide decoupling of the r-f power from the power supplies and associated circuitry. Several meters are included in grid and plate circuits to facilitate tuning. Meters M6 and M7 measure the modulator and power amplifier plate currents, respectively.

A-F Circuits

The audio or speech amplifiers are coupled to the modulator driver, V11 and V12, through transformer T7. Fixed bias for the modulator driver stage (–60 volts) is produced across resistor R30 in the negative leg of the driver power supply. B plus for the modulator driver stage (+300 volts) is developed across R29.

T8 is the modulator-driver transformer which couples the driver plates to the grids of the modulator stage, V13 and V14. Fixed bias is obtained from potentiometer R12. T9 is the modulation transformer. Plate modulation is used for a high-power output. Plate voltage for the modulator is applied to the primary of T9, and voltage for the power amplifier is applied to the secondary of T9 from the high-voltage rectifier, V8.

8-10 TRANSMITTER TUNING PROCEDURES

Before plate power is applied to any transmitter connected to an antenna, it must be determined that the signal radiated by the antenna will be of the proper frequency. This is of the utmost importance, since FCC regulations governing the output frequencies, as well as the maximum power of radio transmitters, must be complied with. These regulations vary with the type of service, such as commercial broadcast, amateur, police, maritime, or military, for which the transmitter is used. Also, power and frequency limits may vary from one band to another for each type of service. Besides the FCC require-

ments, the requirements of the particular service, if any, must be met, so that transmitters do not interfere with each other.

Oscillators

Once the authorized operating frequency has been determined, it is necessary that the oscillator of the transmitter be set to this required frequency. Such settings depend upon the type of oscillator in use. In any case, the oscillator is always tuned with the plate voltage to the final amplifier removed or reduced so that the possibility of radiation at improper frequencies is minimized, and damage to the final amplifier tubes is prevented. Such damage can occur if the transmitter is operated at high power while the final stage is improperly tuned, or when proper drive is not applied.

Crystal Oscillators

Ordinarily, all that is required to change the frequency of a crystal oscillator is to insert the proper crystal. Pierce oscillators require no further tuning. A crystal oscillator which employs a tuned plate circuit requires careful adjustment of the tank circuit in order to sustain oscillations. Such tuning will not affect the frequency, but will have an effect on the voltage output, or drive. The tank is tuned by starting the adjustment from a high-frequency setting (minimum capacitance) and approaching a lower-frequency setting through resonance. By watching the oscillator plate current, a dip is noticeable at resonance. This dip differs from that of an L-C oscillator in that plate current rises sharply (oscillation of the crystal ceases) at the low-frequency end of the dip. Resonance of the tank circuit is at the point of plate current minimum; however, a slight change in load may cause the oscillator to fall out of resonance. For this reason, the oscillator tank should be adjusted to a point slightly above resonance, or at a point in-between the high and low end of the plate-current curve (between points A and B as shown in figure 8-35).

Variable-Frequency Oscillators

A variable-frequency oscillator, or vfo, must be set to the desired frequency by actual measurement. Dial settings may be predetermined; however, the reliability of such settings, or the accuracy to which such settings may be made, is usually insufficient to insure that the transmitter will be on a given frequency within the prescribed tolerance. For this reason, use of

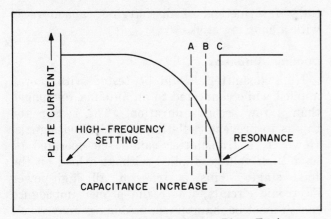

Figure 8-35. Crystal Oscillator Plate Tuning

a vfo is usually restricted to operators who are qualified to make such measurements, and who have such measuring equipment available. A calibrated receiver may be used in most cases. More accurate results can be obtained by the use of wavemeters or heterodyne frequency meters. Where frequencies must be more exact, methods based on the use of an oscilloscope or interpolation oscillator may be employed.

Regardless of the oscillator used, proper oscillation and drive is indicated at the grid of the next stage. This may be a buffer stage or, in the case of an m-o-p-a, the final amplifier. A metering circuit is usually included in the grid circuit of each amplifier stage to measure the grid drive, or excitation. When variable coupling or tuned circuits are used, the drive from the oscillator should be adjusted for the proper amount as determined by the particular tube in use. This is usually the maximum drive available. Absence of drive usually indicates that the oscillator is not oscillating. Measuring oscillator grid voltage will provide an additional check here.

The plate-tank c i r c u i t s of electron-coupled oscillators are tuned for a minimum plate current. Some interaction between plate and grid circuits may occur, so that the frequency of the oscillator should be rechecked whenever either adjustment is disturbed.

Buffer Amplifiers

Buffers and intermediate amplifiers are tuned when the plate current of each stage is minimized and proper drive is applied to the succeeding stage. If a stage is not tuned to resonance, the plate current will be high, and high plate dissipation, high power loss, and low output will result. When a stage is loaded by another stage or an antenna, the plate current of the stage in

question must be rechecked for circuit resonance (minimum plate current) after loading.

If grid-current meters are available in the transmitter, the grid-drive or grid-input circuit must be tuned so that maximum grid current is drawn. If no grid-current meter is available, grid-circuit resonance can be shown by a sharp increase in plate current of the previous stage.

Final Amplifier

The same considerations pertaining to intermediate amplifiers apply to the final amplifier. Methods of tuning and neutralization are the same. Final adjustment of plate current and drive should be made with full power applied. Plate tuning is accomplished by tuning for the dip in plate current. Antenna loading should be kept to a minimum while the plate tank is being adjusted. The antenna coupling and antenna tuning should then be accomplished. Antenna tuning, when provided, should produce maximum antenna current at resonance with a slight rise in the power-amplifier plate current. The antenna coupling is then adjusted for a rise in plate current, not exceeding the recommended plate current for the tube used. The grid and plate tuning adjustments should be retouched after the antenna load is applied, since some interaction is likely to occur.

Neutralization

The process of neutralization can be accomplished in a number of ways. Where it is possible to remove the plate voltage from the amplifier stage, neutralization can be accomplished in the following manner. With excitation present at the grid of the amplifier, the plate voltage is removed from the stage. If there is a meter in the amplifier grid circuit, the neutralizing capacitor is adjusted until there is no change of grid current when the amplifier plate circuit is tuned through resonance. If there is no meter in the grid circuit, a test for neutralization can be made by determining whether or not any r-f voltage is present in the amplifier plate circuit. A neon glow bulb, a loop of wire attached to a small flashlight bulb, or a sensitive r-f galvanometer loosely coupled to the tank should show no r-f voltage when the stage is properly neutralized. Also, if there is no reaction on the plate and grid currents of the exciting stage as the amplifier is tuned through resonance, the stage is properly neutralized.

In some transmitters, it is more convenient to turn off the filament voltage on the amplifier stage instead of removing the plate voltage. If this is done, the process of neutralization is carried out in the same manner as above.

Once a transmitter is neutralized, it is usually unnecessary to repeat t h i s operation unless changes have been made which might affect neutralization. It should not be necessary to re-neutralize a transmitter whenever the operating frequency is changed.

Safety Precautions

Normally a transmitter can be tuned and operated without opening the transmitter housing or case. However, in large transmitters and even in many small transmitters, it is necessary to remove the cover or open an access door to change crystal, coils, tuning units, or make adjustments when changing frequency, or when neutralizing the transmitter.

Most transmitters operate with plate voltages of 250 volts or higher. Contact with these voltages can cause a serious shock or even death. It is, therefore, necessary to be especially careful when making transmitter adjustments.

When the power is turned off in most transmitters, the bleeder and voltage-divider resistors discharge the filter capacitors. Occasionally, one or more of these resistors may open and prevent the filter capacitors from discharging properly. If body contact is made with a charged capacitor, the capacitor can discharge through the body and cause shock, severe burns, or even death.

Most transmitters with an output of a hundred watts or more are equipped w i t h interlock switches, relays, or timing devices, which open the primary circuits to certain high-voltage circuits whenever the doors to a transmitter are opened. Since such safety devices are not foolproof, do not rely on them for protection. Sometimes an interlock switch, for example, may become defective, so that a high-voltage circuit may continue to receive power even with a transmitter door open. At such times, the transmitter is even more dangerous than a charged capacitor for the maintenance man who may come in contact with it. As a precaution against accidental shocks, make sure that no high voltages are present, and discharge all capacitors before performing preventive maintenance or trouble shooting on a transmitter. The most convenient and the safest method of discharging capacitors is with a shorting stick.

Dummy Antennas

No transmitter should be tested with power applied while connected to an antenna for longer than a few seconds duration. The reason for this is to prevent radiation of undesired signals. However, a transmitter cannot be operated or have high voltage applied without a load on the final stage. This is true of all high-power electronic circuits, where the proper impedance match must be maintained, or damage may result from the reflected high impedance of an open circuit. Whenever such tests are to be made, the transmitter should be connected to a dummy antenna.

A dummy antenna, or dummy load, is a device designed to replace the normal antenna load of a transmitter. Just as the impedance of an antenna must match the output of a transmitter, so also the impedance of the dummy load must provide this match. Also, its wattage, or power dissipation capacity, should equal or exceed that of the transmitter output. It should be a purely resistive device, so that all of the energy from the transmitter is dissipated in the form of heat, and the r-f radiation minimized.

A resistor is often used as a dummy load. In the case of large transmitters, a resistive load, such as a bank of large resistors, a water rheostat, or a bank of lamps can be arranged to dissipate the required power. By series-parallel arrangements, the impedance of the transmitter output can be closely matched.

One advantage of using a lamp load is that a rough comparison of output power can be visually observed. Lamps of different wattage can be readily substituted until the desired combination is obtained. Actual power may be readily computed by the use of Ohm's law.

Unless they are well shielded, some radiation can be expected from even the best constructed dummy loads when high power is applied. It is therefore advisable to operate the transmitter at reduced output (reduced plate voltage to the final) when using a dummy antenna. The power should not be applied for longer periods than are actually required to perform the tests, and in all cases the transmitter should not be left unattended with plate power applied.

8-11 TRANSMITTER MEASUREMENTS

Measurements in the field of radio communications serve a variety of purposes. For example, measurements are indispensable for trouble shooting and adjustments, tests and alignments and laboratory experimentation. In addition, measurements made periodically can disclose a gradual decline in the quality of performance of equipment, enabling the prevention of many failures. Also, reliable measurements are the only means of establishing compliance with standards of broadcasting operation set by law. Measurements applicable to radio transmitters will be discussed at this time.

Frequency Measurement

There are two classes of frequency-measuring equipment. One class compares the unknown frequency against a standard of known accuracy. The other class consists of direct-reading instruments, called frequency meters, which are calibrated prior to use.

The comparison-type of instrument may use either of two kinds of standards, primary or secondary. A primary frequency standard is checked against the rotation of the earth by astronomical observations. This is done because frequency is a time-rate of recurrence. For most purposes, however, it is sufficiently accurate to use secondary standards, so called because they are compared, or c h e c k e d, against primary standards.

Calibrated Receiver

If n o specific instrument i s available for measuring radio frequency, a calibrated receiver may be used. Well designed receivers are accurate to better than 0.04 percent. Receivers designed for this purpose have calibrating crystals incorporated within the receiver. These usually provide crystal check points every 100 kc or 1000 kc. To calibrate a transmitter by this method, it is only necessary to correct the receiver dial at the nearest crystal check point, then set the dial to the desired frequency. The transmitter is then tuned until the signal is present at the receiver output. If an "S" (signal strength) meter is employed in the receiver, the transmitter is tuned to maximum deviation of the meter. Greater accuracy will be achieved if the transmission is unmodulated. When a nearby transmitter is being checked, the antenna

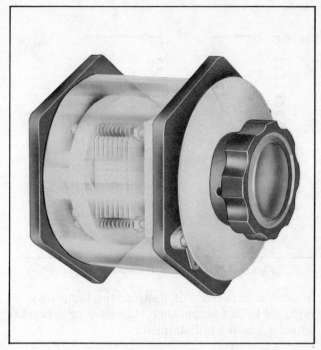

Figure 8-36. Absorption-Type Wavemeter

of the receiver should be disconnected. If the signal still blocks the receiver, the power amplifier of the transmitter should be turned off.

Absorption Frequency Meter

The absorption frequency meter, or wavemeter, consists of an indicating device and an inductance and capacitance, either or both of which may be variable. A capacitive-type wavemeter is shown in figure 8-36. Associated with the drive shaft of the variable member is a pointer and scale, either of which moves with the shaft. The scale may be calibrated directly in frequency or may be used with a calibration chart or table. Because of changes in capacitance or inductance due to vibration or to temperature and humidity changes, it is often necessary to recheck the calibration. When tuned to the frequency of the transmitter and loosely coupled to the tank coil, a device of this type will absorb a small amount of energy. The presence of this energy may be indicated in several ways. When a flashlight lamp or a sensitive meter is used, resonance is indicated by maximum brilliance of the lamp or maximum deflection of the meter. As a rule, the capacitor is the variable element, and the band of frequencies covered by the instrument is determined by the coil in use. Typical circuits of absorption meters are shown in figure 8-37. Above 200 mc special low-capacitance circuits, such as butterfly resonators or transmission lines, are used. If

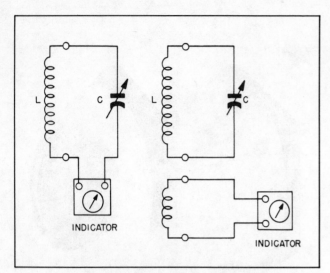

Figure 8-37. Typical Wavemeter Circuits

improved sensitivity is desired, the lamp may be replaced by a vacuum-tube voltmeter or a crystal detector and d-c milliammeter.

A well-made instrument will provide an accuracy of 0.25 to 2.0 percent. Although not suitable for precise measurement, the absorption wavemeter is nevertheless an extremely useful general purpose instrument. It is valuable whenever the detection of r-f energy in unwanted places is required, for instance, the presence of parasitic oscillations during the neutralization of an amplifier, or whenever only an approximate measurement of frequency is desired. Other specific uses include checking the fundamental frequency of an oscillating circuit, determining the amplitude and order of magnitude of harmonic frequencies, and providing a relative measure of field strength.

Occasionally, a measurement is possible even when the power available from the circuit being tested is not sufficient to actuate the indicator of the wavemeter. In the case of circuits that incorporate a grid-current or plate-current meter, the indications of these meters will change when the wavemeter is tuned through resonance. The coupling should be loose, so that the mutual inductance between the tank and the wavemeter does not appreciably change the frequency of oscillation.

Heterodyne Frequency Meter

More accurate frequency measurements are possible with heterodyne frequency meters. To be most effective, such a meter must incorporate a small, fully shielded oscillator that covers the

entire frequency range to be measured. The use of plug-in coils or switches is generally unsatisfactory since they introduce frequency instability. If the construction throughout is sturdy, and if high-grade ceramics are used as insulators in the oscillator circuit, a precise frequency calibration will hold over a long period of time. The tuning element of the oscillator is usually equipped with a vernier-type dial to permit an accurate setting. In some cases the divisions of the dial may be engraved directly in terms of frequency, but more often a calibration chart is used with the instrument.

Figure 8-38. Heterodyne Frequency Meter

An electron-coupled oscillator is well suited for heterodyne meters. By using a voltage-stabilized power supply and correctly proportioning the plate and screen voltages of the oscillator, it is possible to obtain extremely stable oscillations. Adequate power can be obtained from the plate circuit without impairing this stability. Another desirable property of the plate-circuit output is the presence of strong harmonics.

More elaborate heterodyne meters also include a quartz crystal-controlled oscillator, which is used to check the accuracy of multiple points on the calibrated dial. One such instrument is shown in figure 8-38. Calibration checks insure accurate measurements.

Power Measurement

There are two types of r-f output-power measurements which apply to all transmitters. One is the measurement of the actual radiated power. The other is the power input to the final stage. Commercial broadcast stations and many of the services are limited by the FCC to a specific maximum radiated power. Amateur and other radio services are limited to a specific maximum input power.

Input Power

The input power to the final stage of any transmitter may be constantly monitored by metering the plate current when the plate voltage is known. Power is determined by the formula:

$$P_{in} = E_{bb} \ I_p \qquad (8\text{-}4)$$

where:

P_{in} = power input to final amplifier, in watts
E_{bb} = applied plate voltage, in volts
I_p = plate current, in amperes

As an example, assume a transmitter with 1000 volts applied to the final power-amplifier plate. The plate current meter indicates 560 ma. The power input is determined as follows:

$$\begin{aligned} P_{in} &= E_{bb} \ I_p \\ &= 1000 \text{ x } 0.560 \\ &= 560 \text{ watts} \end{aligned}$$

Therefore, the power input to the final power amplifier is 560 watts.

Radiated Power

The actual radiated power at the antenna will be less than the input power to the final r-f amplifier because of circuit losses. Some of these losses are in the plate-tank circuit and in the antenna-coupling circuit. The major loss, however, occurs in the tube itself, and is dissipated in the form of heat. This loss is called *plate dissipation*. The plate dissipation factor can be determined from the tube manufacturer's specifications, and is usually expressed as a percentage of plate efficiency. Since this represents the greatest loss in the circuit, tuned circuit and coupling losses may be disregarded. Thus, the formula for determining the effective, or actual radiated power from a transmitter may be stated as follows:

$$P_{out} = P_{in} \text{ x plate efficiency in percent}$$

Assuming the same figures given previously, and a plate efficiency of 80 percent, the radiated power would be:

$$\begin{aligned} P_{out} &= 560 \text{ x } .80 \\ &= 448 \text{ watts} \end{aligned}$$

Therefore, the radiated power of a transmitter with an input of 560 watts to the final with a tube efficiency of 80 percent is 448 watts.

The maximum power obtainable from a given transmitter is determined largely by the final-amplifier tube. The power rating given by the manufacturer to a particular tube type is that at which the tube may be operated without causing distortion exceeding a given percentage. Tubes are often operated at reduced power in order to improve the distortion factor, or to conserve the tube or the power, or both.

Modulation Measurement

If a transmitter is not fully modulated, the power in the sidebands is low and the effective transmitting range is reduced. On the other hand, if the transmitter is overmodulated, the signal is distorted and may be broad enough to blanket stations operating on channels far from the offending transmitter.

A number of instruments have been designed or adapted for checking the modulation percentage of amplitude-modulated transmitters. The oscilloscope is the most useful of these. It is the most accurate and provides a picture of the modulation percentage. Two types of patterns can be observed on the oscilloscope. One is known as the *wave envelope* and the other the *trapezoid*.

Connections for wave envelope measurement are easier to make. The oscilloscope is connected as in part A of figure 8-39. A testing coil, consisting of a few turns of wire, is connected to the vertical deflection plates of the oscilloscope, D_3 and and D_4, through a length of twisted wire. When this coil is placed near the tank coil of the final r-f power amplifier, the sweep produces a modulation envelope of the transmitter output. The sweep generator in the oscilloscope is adjusted to a frequency lower than the lowest modulation frequency. The modulation factor or percentage of modulation can be found by making the necessary calculations, using the modulation formula that was discussed previously.

A complex speech wave is similar to that shown in part B of the figure. It is more difficult to

continue to next experiment # 8

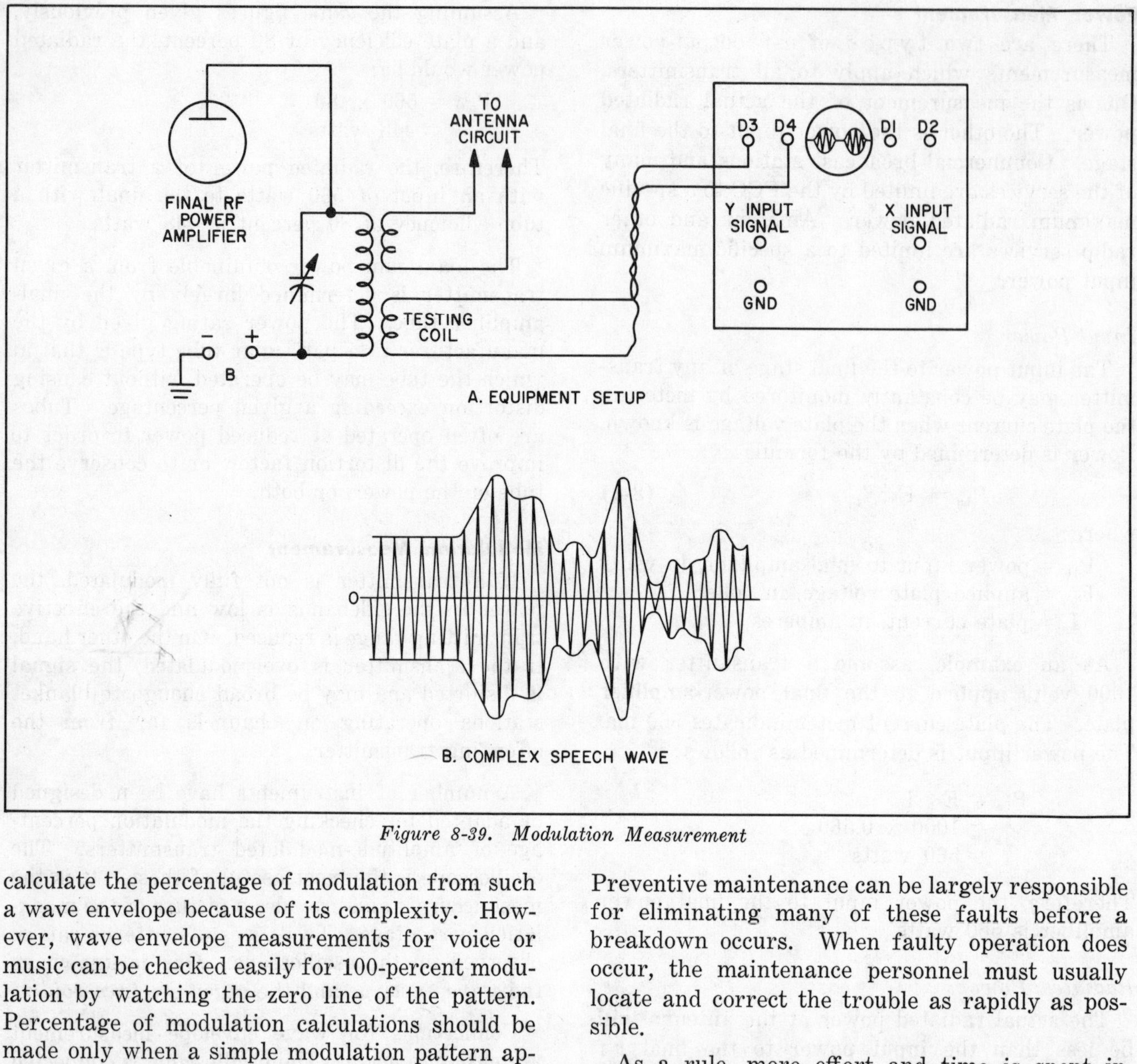

Figure 8-39. Modulation Measurement

calculate the percentage of modulation from such a wave envelope because of its complexity. However, wave envelope measurements for voice or music can be checked easily for 100-percent modulation by watching the zero line of the pattern. Percentage of modulation calculations should be made only when a simple modulation pattern appears on the face of the scope. A bright spot will appear in the trough at the instant that the transmitter is overmodulated.

The trapezoidal pattern is obtained when the oscilloscope is connected in the same manner, except that a portion of the audio voltage, which may be taken from the speech amplifier or the modulator stage, is applied to the horizontal plates, in place of the internal sweep of the oscilloscope. Patterns obtained and their interpretation are shown in figure 8-40.

8-12 TRANSMITTER TROUBLE-SHOOTING PROCEDURES

No matter how well equipment is designed and manufactured, faulty operation occurs in service.

Preventive maintenance can be largely responsible for eliminating many of these faults before a breakdown occurs. When faulty operation does occur, the maintenance personnel must usually locate and correct the trouble as rapidly as possible.

As a rule, more effort and time is spent in finding the trouble than in making the actual repair or correction.

Common Troubles

Many common troubles can occur in the operation of a transmitter, as in any electronic equipment, which render the equipment either entirely or partially inoperative, or which cause decreased performance or efficiency. These troubles may be of a permanent nature (until corrected) or intermittent, either periodic or momentary. Often the trouble is not a fault of the equipment itself, but rather that of operation.

Operational (or operator) troubles include power cords or cables unplugged, switches in an

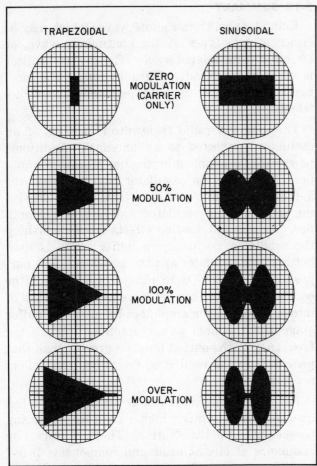

TRAPEZOIDAL   SINUSOIDAL

ZERO
MODULATION
(CARRIER
ONLY)

50%
MODULATION

100%
MODULATION

OVER-
MODULATION

*Figure 8-40. Trapezoidal and Sinusoidal Waveforms
Associated with Percent of Modulation*

improper position, overloading, and improper operating methods. These possibilities should not be overlooked when investigating a trouble. Other faults, not so obvious, are: broken cords, cables, or plugs; defective fuses; burned relay contacts; wires broken from vibration; defective tubes or crystals; and, in the case of battery-powered equipment, weak batteries. When failure is encountered and the cause is not immediately apparent, the above items should be checked before starting a detailed examination of the component parts of the transmitter. Fuses should be checked at an early stage in trouble shooting. The repairman should not continue to burn out fuses before looking elsewhere to determine the basic source of the trouble, if fuses continue to burn out.

The use of the manufacturer's data, including schematic diagrams and trouble-shooting charts, and a logical approach will almost always isolate the fault. The use of a step-by-step procedure for finding the more difficult troubles is helpful in quickly locating the trouble.

Step-by-Step Procedure

Four easy-to-follow steps, which can be applied to trouble shooting any electronic equipment, are presented here. They are:

1. Determine the *symptoms.*
2. *Localize* trouble to a major function.
3. *Isolate* trouble to a unit or circuit.
4. *Locate* specific trouble within unit.

The first step in finding a fault in any electronic equipment is to determine the *symptoms* of the trouble. Once these are known, an analysis of the trouble or fault may be made. Often this takes but a few moments, but occasionally it may take considerable time. The time spent on a proper analysis is usually repaid in the saving of time and material in the steps that follow.

By proper analysis, the fault may be *localized* to a major function, such as r-f generation, audio amplification, keying, or power amplification.

The next step is to *isolate* the trouble or fault to a unit, sub-unit, or circuit responsible for the fault. Careful observation of the performance of a transmitter and its associated equipment when the equipment is turned on often helps to localize the fault. Also observation of the meters on the transmitter front panel often helps to determine the stage or circuit at fault.

Location of the specific trouble within a circuit or unit may be made in a number of different ways. Tube faults can be eliminated by tube testing or tube substitution. Burned or charred resistors or coils can often be spotted by visual observation or by smell. The same holds true for oil or wax-filled capacitors, chokes, and transformers. When overheated, the oil or wax in these components expands and usually leaks out, or causes the case to buckle, or, if excessively overheated, the case may explode. Overheated components can be located quickly by touching with the fingers. When power is applied, high-voltage arcing can often be heard, which can assist in location of defective high-voltage components. Thus the senses of sight, smell, touch, and hearing can be used to locate many faulty components.

General Method of Locating a Trouble in a Circuit or Small Group of Circuits

To begin location of a trouble, a close visual inspection should be made by gaining access to the wiring and component circuitry of the faulty section, if this can be easily done, and an inspection for overheated parts or apparent damage made. This inspection may lead to the faulty component; however, replacement of parts that appear to be damaged should not be made until the cause of the trouble is determined.

Next, perform operation checks on the circuit that is known to be defective by checking controls, switches, etc, for their effects on the circuit. If built-in checking facilities are available, utilize them and compare the results with checks made previously, while the equipment was operating normally.

If the checks made up to this point do not indicate the cause of the trouble, it is generally advisable to make any circuit changes that can be easily accomplished, such as exchange of replaceable sub-units or chassis and exchange of replaceable tubes and components. Frequently, the repair time is reduced by such replacement, but the defective unit must be serviced further to determine the trouble and the cause of the defect.

To repair the defective unit, or to repair a circuit that is not removable from the equipment, proceed as follows:

1. Locate the cause of trouble by making waveform, voltage, and resistance checks.

2. Refer to previously compiled tables of normal waveforms, voltages, and resistance readings, and to the schematic diagram.

3. Perform these checks at the essential points, by reference to the schematic diagram.

4. Compare these readings with normal readings, and recall the principles of circuit operation; then analyze the results to determine which component is defective. In many cases the oscilloscope will provide the only means for determining abnormal operation, especially in circuits where the amplitude, the frequency, or the voltage waveshapes are critical.

After the trouble has been located, a follow-up for the purpose of locating the cause is essential. The cause of trouble should be found before a new component is inserted. If the cause was present only momentarily and cannot be located, the equipment should be given extra attention, watching for recurrence of the same trouble. It is usually necessary, and certainly advisable, to keep a record of the details of all troubles encountered.

8-13 SUMMARY

Radio transmitters radiate waves which may be either of two types — the continuous wave, or cw, and the modulated wave. The c-w transmitter is used only for radiotelegraphy, while the modulated transmitter is used primarily for radiotelephony.

The simplest radio transmitter consists of an oscillator connected to an antenna. Additional power can be supplied by the use of power amplifiers between the oscillator output and the antenna. An m-o-p-a is a transmitter consisting of a master oscillator and a power amplifier. To prevent loading effects from disturbing the oscillator frequency, a buffer stage is used between the oscillator and the amplifier. The purpose of the buffer is to provide isolation of the oscillator. Power can be increased by the use of intermediate power amplifiers between the buffer stage and the final power amplifier. When the frequency of the output must be greater than that provided by the oscillator, frequency multipliers are used.

Parasitic oscillations can occur at random frequencies, usually much higher than the operating frequency of the transmitter. They are caused by resonance of circuit leads and components in r-f amplifiers. Parasitics can be suppressed by the insertion of resistors in the grid and plate circuit of the offending section. Harmonic radiation, or multiples of the operating frequency, can be prevented by the use of proper shielding and filtering, and by proper adjustment of the amplifier stages.

Transmitter keying, used in c-w transmission, can be accomplished in either the grid, plate, or cathode of one or more stages of a transmitter. Of these, grid keying is most often preferred, since high plate voltage is removed from the key. Key clicks and chirps can be eliminated by proper filtering. When higher voltages or currents must be keyed, a keying relay or keyer tube is often used.

Modulation is the process of varying an r-f carrier at a rate proportional to the variations in intelligence to be transmitted. When the r-f carrier is varied in amplitude, the result is an amplitude-modulated wave.

When the modulation of the r-f wave takes place in the final r-f amplifier of a transmitter, the process is called high-level modulation. When it occurs at one of the low-level, or intermediate amplifier stages, it is referred to as low-level modulation. High-level modulation requires a high level of modulating power, whereas low-level modulation requires very little power. However, r-f amplifiers subsequent to the modulated stage must be linear to preserve the modulated waveshape. The modulation may be applied in the plate, screen, grid, or cathode circuit of the r-f amplifier stage. Of these, plate modulation is the most preferred, since 100-percent modulation can be achieved.

A suitable means of determining the frequency of a transmitter is by the use of a calibrated receiver. Greater accuracy can be achieved by the use of a heterodyne frequency meter. The power output can be computed by the use of Ohm's law. Modulation levels are best observed by the use of an oscilloscope.

Four easy-to-follow steps form a simple procedure to find faults or troubles in electronic equipment. These are: determine the symptoms, localize trouble to a major function, isolate trouble to a unit or circuit, locate specific fault in unit.

REVIEW QUESTIONS

1. What is the simplest transmitter?

2. What is an m-o-p-a transmitter?

3. Why is a power amplifier necessary?

4. Why is neutralization necessary?

5. What are the basic coupling systems, and what are the advantages of each?

6. Draw the two methods of blocked-grid keying and explain the advantage of each.

7. What is the purpose of a key click filter?

8. What are parasitic oscillations, and how can they be prevented?

9. How can harmonics be prevented?

10. What is the purpose of a buffer?

11. What is amplitude modulation?

12. Define *sideband*.

13. What effect does the percentage of modulation have on the performance of an AM transmitter?

14. What are the effects of overmodulation on the radiated signal?

15. What is the ratio between sideband power and carrier power for 100 percent modulation?

16. Is there a major difference between the r-f circuits in c-w and high-level AM transmitters of the same carrier power?

17. Define *high-* and *low-level modulation* and explain the methods used to obtain each.

18. Why is transformer coupling used between the modulator and the plate-modulated r-f amplifier?

19. What is A3 emission?

20. Give four advantages of c-w over AM transmission.

21. Explain one method of determining the frequency of a transmitter.

22. How is the effective radiated power of a transmitter computed?

23. Describe two methods of modulation monitoring.

24. What is the best test of vacuum-tube performance for tubes used in transmitters?

25. Outline a simple procedure for trouble shooting a transmitter.

CHAPTER NINE

Transmission of Radio Waves

9-1 Introduction

Many types of electronic circuits are capable of producing alternating voltages whose frequency of occurrence is such that they are classified as radio-frequency generators. By placing the proper r-f circuits in a correct sequence, a complete radio transmission device is produced. Since efficiency and power output are important to circuit-operation considerations, the electronic system must also have an efficient means of transferring the radio energy from the transmitting location to the receiving device.

The *antenna system*, so-called, of a radio transmitter is the means used to transfer the intelligence (modulated radio-frequency energy) to a distant receiver for conversion into voice or other types of information. The subject of antennas is an extensive topic; however, to gain a sufficient practical understanding of the subject to enable solving the problems of maintenance, a knowledge of only the basic facts of antenna theory, design, and construction is required.

9-2 PROPAGATION OF RADIO WAVES

Radio waves propagated (transmitted) into space are thought to be a radiant form of energy, similar to light and heat. Radio waves travel at a speed of approximately 300,000,000 meters (or 186,000 miles) per second. The theory of wave propagation can be explained, in relatively simple terms, by associating the effects of the electric and magnetic fields of force which exist about a current-carrying conductor.

The radio-frequency spectrum extends from 0.01 megacycle (very low frequency) to 30,000 megacycles (super high frequency) and beyond. Table 9-1 outlines the various divisions of the over-all frequency spectrum with respect to frequency coverage and their respective designations. The table represents the radio-frequency spectrum in terms of the frequency of the signals, in millions of cycles per second. Another way of classifying radio waves is according to wavelength. *Wavelength* can be defined as the distance the wave travels in the time required to complete one cycle. Since the speed of radio waves is known (300,000,000 meters per second), the wavelength of any radio wave can be found by the following mathematical relationship:

$$\text{Wavelength (in meters)} = \frac{\text{Velocity}}{\text{Frequency}} \quad (9\text{-}1)$$

where:

Velocity = 300,000,000 meters per second

Frequency = cycles per second

For example, a 10 kc or 0.01 mc radio wave has a computed wavelength of 30,000 meters, while a 30,000 megacycle radio wave has a wavelength of 0.01 meter or 1 centimeter. Sometimes the terms *long*, *short* and *microwave* are used to broadly classify the frequency of operation into low, high, and ultra-high frequencies, respectively.

TABLE 9-1. RADIO-FREQUENCY SPECTRUM

Frequency In Megacycles (MC)	Description	Abbreviation
0.01 to 0.03	very low frequency	v.l.f
0.03 to 0.3	low frequency	l.f.
0.3 to 3	medium frequency	m.f.
3 to 30	high frequency	h.f.
30 to 300	very high frequency	v.h.f.
300 to 3,000	ultra high frequency	u.h.f.
3,000 to 30,000	super high frequency	s.h.f.
30,000 to 300,000	extreme high frequency	e.h.f.

Wave Propagation

If an alternating current within the radio-frequency range is applied to a suitable conductor, such as an antenna, it produces changing electric and magnetic fields about the conductor. These periodic changes in field intensity produce a *moving-field wave* which travels away from the antenna. The components of this moving-field wave are called the *induction field* and the *radiation field*. A detailed discussion of the makeup of the induction and radiation fields will be presented, but first, a general concept of the action resulting from the radiation field should be understood.

Referring to figure 9-1, a transmitter, tx, is shown connected to an antenna, which in this case is equal in length to exactly a half wavelength

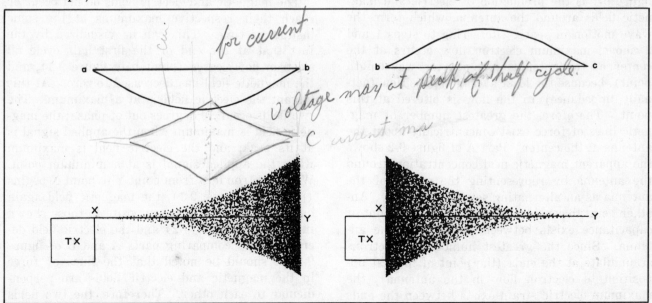

Figure 9-1. Development of Radiation Fields

at the frequency of the applied wave. When this wave is applied to the antenna, the following actions occur in the order given:

1. Electrons immediately begin to flow from point X, at one end of the antenna, to point Y at the other end of the antenna.

2. During the first half cycle of the applied wave, a to b, most of the electrons from point X crowd toward point Y.

3. Point Y, the open end of the antenna, forms a barrier to the further travel of the electrons and they come to a complete stop.

4. As the alternating current enters its second half cycle, b to c, the electrons immediately start flowing back from point Y on the antenna toward point X at the input end.

5. During the second half cycle, b to c, all the electrons from point Y on the antenna crowd toward point X.

6. The electrons which have piled up at point X, begin to travel back toward point Y as soon as a new alternation of the input wave, a to b, arrives at the antenna input, point X.

7. This periodic action continues as long as the transmitter supplies a-c power to the antenna.

The preceding discussion has served to illustrate the motion of electrons within the antenna as a result of applied radio-frequency energy. This motion of electrons can be compared to the ocean waves breaking on a beach front.

The result of the electron motion described in figure 9-1 is the production of electric and magnetic fields around the antenna, which form the wave motion in space. Referring to steps 1 and 2 above, maximum electron flow occurs at the center of the antenna (one-quarter wavelength point), because the least average opposition (actually impedance) to the flow is offered at this point. Therefore, the greatest number of magnetic lines of force exist concentrically about the antenna at the center. Part A of figure 9-2 shows the apparent magnetic-field concentration around the antenna by representing the center of the antenna as an alternating source of energy. Another point to consider is that a certain amount of capacitance exists between the ends of the antenna. Since the greatest number of electrons accumulate at the ends (the point of highest opposition to electron flow in the antenna), the maximum electric strain exists between the ends of the antenna. The resultant apparent electric

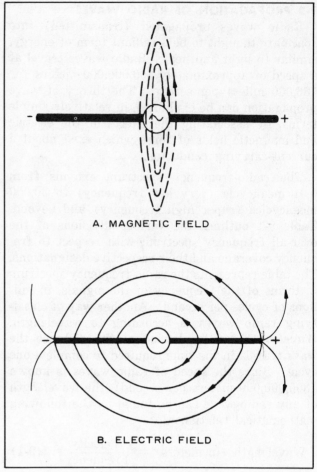

A. MAGNETIC FIELD

B. ELECTRIC FIELD

Figure 9-2.   Magnetic and Electric Fields Around a Wire

field is represented as illustrated in part B of figure 9-2.

The magnetic and electric fields do not occur or reach their respective maximums at the same instant of time. This can be visualized by the fact that at the end of the first half cycle all electron flow ceases (point b in figure 9-1), and the magnetic field has decreased to zero. At this instant the electric field is at a maximum. The two fields occur 90 degrees out of phase; the magnetic field is maximum when the applied signal is at its peak, and the electric field is maximum when the applied signal is at a minimum point. When electron flow from point Y to point X begins (part B of figure 9-1), the magnetic field again builds up (lines of force opposite to those shown in part A of figure 9-2) and the electric field decreases. By comparing parts A and B of figure 9-2, it should be noted that the lines of force in the magnetic and electric fields are perpendicular to each other. Therefore, the two fields are 90 degrees out of phase in space. Summarizing the action of the magnetic and electric fields for any one cycle of input radio-frequency energy to an antenna, the fields occur 90 degrees apart in direction and time. In formal language, the electric and magnetic fields are, at all times, *in space and time quadrature.*

Radiation and Induction Fields

The theoretical computation of the electromagnetic fields that result from current in an antenna is a highly complex operation involving advanced mathematical concepts. The results, however, may be simplified and explained without the use of mathematics, if certain assumptions are made. The electric and magnetic fields at any point in space (around the antenna) are given by a set of six equations, which can be found together with their derivations, in most engineering textbooks covering antenna theory. It can be shown by these equations — but must be assumed for this discussion — that the electric and magnetic fields are at right angles in space (space quadrature). It can also be shown — and again must be assumed — that the total magnetic field is composed of two components which are in phase in time:

One component is inversely proportional to the *distance* from the antenna; the other component is inversely proportional to the *square of the distance* from the antenna.

These two components, when added vectorially, produce the total effective magnetic field. The total electric field is composed of three components as follows:

One component is inversely proportional to the *distance* from the antenna, another inversely proportional to the *square of the distance*, and the third inversely proportional to the *cube of the distance.*

In the case of the electric field, however, all the components are not in phase in time as was the condition with the magnetic field. The electric-field component which is inversely proportional to the cube of the distance has a 90-degree phase relationship with respect to the other two components. The characteristics and relationships between the electric and magnetic fields, when combined, provide an insight into the two electromagnetic fields, the radiation and induction fields.

In the *radiation field,* the electric and magnetic fields are at right angles in space and are in phase in time, as illustrated in part A of figure 9-3. The *induction field* is composed of electric and magnetic fields which are at right angles in space

but are 90 degrees out of phase in time, as illustrated in part B of figure 9-3. The induction field contains the electric component which is proportional to the cube of the distance; therefore, this field may be neglected whenever the distance is more than a few wavelengths. When dealing with the energy radiated close to the antenna, the effects of the induction field must be considered.

In order to gain a better understanding of the phase relations and the power dissipation in the

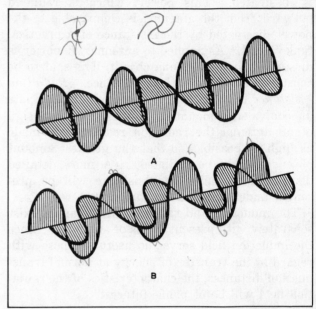

Figure 9-3. Electric and Magnetic Fields About an Antenna

electromagnetic fields, they may be compared to the familiar concepts of the power and phase angle in an a-c circuit, such as a resonant tank. It should be recalled that, in an a-c circuit, $P = EI_{cos} \theta$, where θ is the phase angle. In an ideal tank circuit the voltage and current in each element are 90 degrees out of phase, and no power is delivered to the circuit by a generator ($I_{circulating}$ maximum, I_{line} minimum). Power delivered to either element at any time is supplied by the other element. In this ideal tank circuit the oscillation peak amplitude remains constant, and no power is lost. The total power dissipation over a complete cycle is therefore zero. The antenna may be thought of as a tuned circuit, and the magnetic field, which is directly proportional to the current, may be used to compute the power dissipated. Therefore, the induction field, in which the electric and magnetic fields are 90° out of phase in time, dissipates no power. Any power delivered to the field during one part of a cycle is returned during another part. As mentioned before, the effect of the induction field is negligible at d i s t a n c e s greater than a few wavelengths from the antenna. Thus, at high frequencies, where wavelength is short, the induction field extends effectively only a few feet from the antenna; at low frequencies, however, where a wavelength is much longer, the induction field is apparent at a considerable distance.

In the radiation field, the electric and magnetic fields are in phase in time, and therefore power is dissipated. This power, which is radiated outward from the antenna, is comparable to the power dissipated by the resistance of a practical tank circuit. As applied to antennas, if power is dissipated in the antenna circuit, it is said to be consumed in the radiation resistance. *Radiation resistance* is the resistance which would dissipate an equivalent amount of power. In the design of an antenna the radiation resistance is made as high as possible, so that the greatest amount of energy will be radiated. (A more detailed discussion of radiation resistance will be presented under antenna fundamentals.)

The induction and radiation fields cannot exist separately with present forms of antennas. Since the induction field serves no useful purpose with regard to the transfer of energy at normal transmission distances, the characteristics of the radiation field will be of prime interest.

Polarization

The term *polarization* as applied to antennas, refers to the direction of the electric and magnetic fields. As previously mentioned, the magnetic and electric fields about a radiating conductor exist each in a particular plane as *plane waves,* and are perpendicular to each other. It has been established that the polarization of an antenna is d e t e r m i n e d by the direction of the *electric* plane wave. An antenna erected so that the radiating element is horizontal to the earth's surface produces plane waves as illustrated in part A of figure 9-4. Notice that the electric field E is horizontal; therefore, the antenna is said to be *horizontally polarized.* An antenna erected so that the radiating element is vertical with respect to the earth's surface, produces the plane waves illustrated in part B of figure 9-4, and is said to be *vertically polarized.* Vertical and horizontal polarization are two cases of a form of polarization known as *linear* polarization. The term *linear* means that (except for the 180-degree phase reversal during a cycle) the direction of the electric field does not change. In other words, the

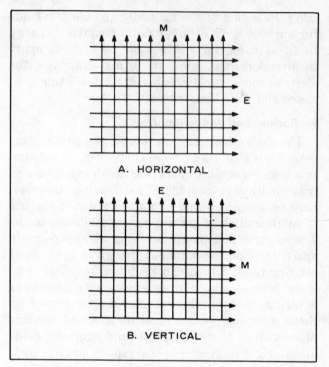

Figure 9-4. *Representation of Magnetic and Electric Fields in Horizontally and Vertically Polarized Wavefronts*

electric field of a horizontally polarized wave always remains horizontal, and the electric field of a vertically polarized wave always remains vertical.

There is another form of polarization, *circular polarization,* but its application is limited to a special purpose. Circular polarization is used in some radar equipments to reduce the amount of returned energy from rain, fog, and cloud formations. In order to gain a concept of circular polarization, assume that the plane waves of part A of figure 9-4 are tilted at a 45-degree angle, as shown in part A of figure 9-5, and further assume

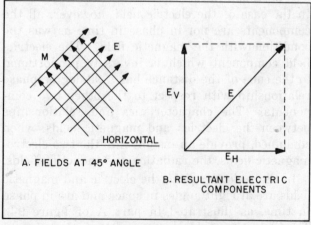

Figure 9-5. *Resultant Electric-Field Components of a Tilted Electromagnetic Wave*

Gain oppisite from Attenuation

that by the use of some device it is possible to resolve the electric field into its horizontal (E_H) and vertical (E_V) components, as illustrated in part B of figure 9-5. These two components would still be in phase; that is, measured at a given point, both E_H and E_V would have the same relative amplitude at any given time. If, now, either component, E_H or E_V can be shifted in phase by 90 degrees (one quarter wavelength), a new type of polarization becomes possible. If it is assumed that the horizontal component E_H has been retarded 90 degrees in phase, then when E_V has maximum amplitude, E_H is zero, and vice versa. The E vector is shown in figure 9-6 for several

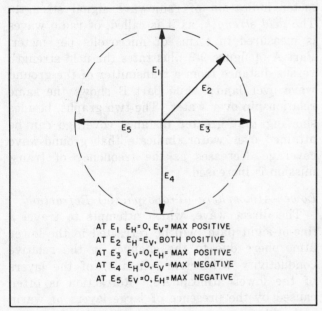

AT E_1 $E_H = 0$, $E_V =$ MAX POSITIVE
AT E_2 $E_H = E_V$, BOTH POSITIVE
AT E_3 $E_V = 0$, $E_H =$ MAX POSITIVE
AT E_4 $E_H = 0$, $E_V =$ MAX NEGATIVE
AT E_5 $E_V = 0$, $E_H =$ MAX NEGATIVE

Figure 9-6. Successive Directions of Electric Field in Circularly Polarized Electromagnetic Field

different conditions of E_H and E_V. The representation is an end view of the resultant E vector; it must be visualized that these vectors occur at different instants of time, moving into the page. To an observer standing in one spot and able to *see* the electric field, the field would appear to have a circular motion and a constant amplitude. The circular motion may either be clockwise or counterclockwise, depending on which component is shifted in phase and the direction of the shift.

In the development of a circularly polarized wave, any attenuation introduced by the phase-shifting device must produce the same effect on both E_H and E_V. If this condition is not obtained, the peak amplitudes of E_H and E_V will not be the same; as a result, the electric field as *seen* by the observer previously mentioned will vary in both amplitude and direction, and will describe an ellip-

tical path. Hence, the resultant polarization is known as *elliptical polarization*.

Linear polarization is of prime importance for the transmission of radio waves for communications purposes. The choice of a horizontally or vertically polarized wave, for a particular application, is dependent upon the frequency of operation and the resultant effects of the ground and sky-wave modes of propagation.

Ground-Wave Propagation

The radiation-field waves from the antenna travel into space in all directions. Those waves which travel along the surface of the earth are generally affected by the earth's presence and its terrain features, and are called *ground waves*.

It was pointed out previously that the behavior of radio waves is similar to that of light waves. From a study of light, it is an established fact that light waves may be absorbed, refracted, and reflected, and that the degree of absorption, refraction, or reflection depends upon the medium (air, water, etc.) through which the waves travel, and the frequency of the wave. These same basic facts are generally true for the propagation of radio waves.

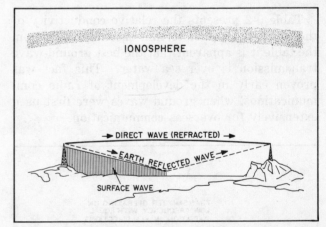

IONOSPHERE

← DIRECT WAVE (REFRACTED) →

EARTH REFLECTED WAVE

SURFACE WAVE

Figure 9-7. Components of Ground Waves. A radiated ground wave from an antenna located on the surface of the earth follows three radiation paths — a direct path to the receiving site, a rebounding path from the antenna to the surface, and a path along the contour of the earth

The part of the radiation-field w a v e which passes along the surface of the earth is called the *ground wave*. The ease with which the ground wave may travel is mainly affected by characteristics of the earth's surface and not by the changing conditions in the upper atmosphere of the earth. The main factors in determining the transmission characteristics of the ground wave are its frequency, the different surface conditions over which it passes, and the conditions of the lower atmosphere. The ground wave consists of three components: a surface wave, a direct wave, and an earth-reflected wave, as illustrated in figure 9-7.

Attenuation of Ground Wave

The earth's surface may be considered as a conductor. This idea is supported by the facts. Since it is known that radio waves travel along a conductor, and that surface waves move along the earth's surface, it is evident that the earth's surface must have some degree of conductivity. The conductivity varies with the nature of the conducting path; thus, the attenuation of the surface wave, due to absorption, depends upon the relative conductivity of the surface over which the wave travels.

TABLE 9-2. RELATIVE CONDUCTIVITY OF VARIOUS MEDIA

MEDIUM	RELATIVE CONDUCTIVITY
sea water	good
flat, loamy soil	fair
large bodies of fresh water	fair
rocky terrain	poor
desert	poor
jungle	unusable

Table 9-2 presents the relative conductivity of the common types of terrain encountered. From the table it is apparent that the best ground-wave transmission is over sea water. This fact was proven early in the development of radio communications, when ground waves were first used extensively for overseas communication.

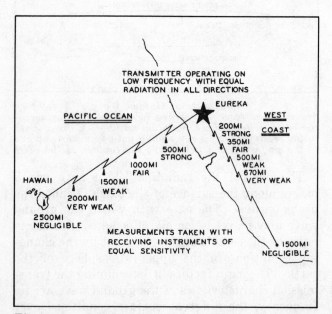

Figure 9-8. Effectiveness of Ground-Wave Propagation over Land and Sea Water

For a comparison of transmission capability over two different surfaces, refer to figure 9-8. The figure shows the relative effectiveness of ground-wave propagation over the Pacific seaboard and the Pacific Ocean. Notice the relative intensity of the radio signals at corresponding distances over land and water.

In order to gain a further insight into the effects of attenuation of the ground wave by the surface of the earth, refer to the graphs shown in figure 9-9. Radio-wave intensity at various points from a transmitting site can be measured by a receiving instrument designed to provide a meter indication of radiowave signal strength. The *field strength*, as it is called, of radio waves is measured in terms of microvolts per meter. Part A of figure 9-9 illustrates the field strength versus distance from a transmitter of the ground wave over land; while part B shows the same relationship over water. The two graphs, besides showing that greater distance coverage can be attained over water, indicate that ground-wave coverage decreases as the frequency of transmission is increased.

Lower-Atmosphere (Tropospheric) Refraction

The direct wave, which attempts to travel a line-of-sight path, will be refracted in the lower atmosphere due to the changes in the relative conductivity (dielectric constant) of the layers of the lower atmosphere. Refraction is often caused by the presence of large layers of warm and cold air masses near each other, by the water-vapor content of the atmosphere, and by sudden temperature differences at the surface of cloud banks due to direct heating by the sun's rays. The refraction due to changes in density and relative conductivity is also dependent upon the frequency of the wave; hence, low-frequency waves are refracted to a greater degree than high-frequency waves. This refraction factor offers one explanation for the fact that at low frequencies greatly extended ranges for ground-wave transmission are realized, whereas at very-high and ultra-high frequencies only slight extension of the transmission range is possible.

V-H-F and U-H-F Considerations

When dealing with v-h-f and u-h-f frequencies, the direct-wave component of the radiated field tends to t r a v e l in practically a *line-of-sight* manner, with minor refraction due to the lower atmosphere. However, a portion of the wave

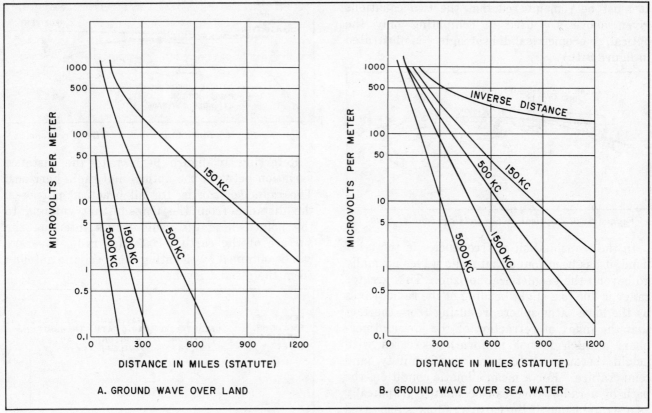

Figure 9-9. Comparison of Strength of Ground Wave Radiated over Land and Sea Water from the Same Transmitter

front strikes the earth at some distance from the antenna, and is reflected upward. The earth-reflected wave lags b e h i n d the direct-wave component in arriving at the distant point. At certain distant points the reflected wave arrives 180 degrees out of phase with the direct wave and a cancellation of signal energy results. To minimize the effects of the earth-reflected wave over the desired coverage area, an increase in antenna h e i g h t will suffice. Increasing the antenna height will tend to decrease the phase angle between the direct- and reflected-waves arriving at a distant point from 180 degrees to a lower value, thus reducing the degree of signal cancellation, which effectively increases the field strength.

The field strength at v-h-f and u-h-f frequencies, as a general rule, increases directly as the transmitting- and receiving-antenna heights increase, and as the square root of the antenna power. Field strength decreases as the square of the distances between the transmitting and receiving antennas.

Since radio transmission above the very-high frequency region is, for all practical purposes,

line-of-sight, consideration must be given to the antenna heights, and the distances of transmission with respect to the earth's surface. A clear line-of-sight transmission distance (d) is illustrated in figure 9-10. This distance is representative of the direct-wave component, neglecting the effect of refraction caused by the lower atmosphere. The direct distance from the transmitting antenna to an intersection point with the earth's surface, over level terrain, can be computed through the use of the following formula:

$$d = 1.23 \sqrt{h} \qquad (9\text{-}2)$$

where:

    d = distance to point of intersection with the earth in miles

    h = height of transmitting antenna in feet

    1.23 = mathematical constant derived from the radius of the e a r t h with respect to points on the earth's surface

Using these same terms, another formula is used to determine required transmitting antenna height to cover a specified direct line-of-sight coverage.

$$h = \frac{d^2}{1.51} \qquad (9\text{-}3)$$

It must be remembered that the two equations given above are used in computing only the optical, or geometrical, line of sight (as illustrated in figure 9-10).

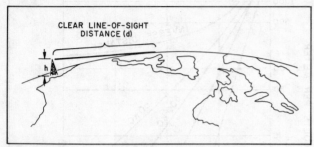

Figure 9-10.   Optical or Geometrical Line of Sight

In the transmission of frequencies in the u-h-f band, it has been found that radio waves normally go beyond the geometrical horizon. This greater range is due to a slight bending of the radio waves by the lower atmosphere, resulting from the fact that the index of refraction of the lower atmosphere (which is not uniform) decreases with height because of changes in humidity and temperature. For a mean climatic condition, the path of a radio wave can be plotted graphically as a straight line, if the earth's radius is increased by a factor of 4/3 (1.33). This factor, known as k, may vary from 1.1 in cold, dry climates to 1.6 in hot, humid climates. Unless otherwise specified, however, the value of k is assumed to be 1.33. The use of this factor, in connection with antenna height, and the earth's radius will provide an approximate distance to the radio horizon (figure 9-11). This approximate distance, over level terrain, can be computed using the following equation:

$$D = \sqrt{2Hrk} \qquad (9-4)$$

where:

  D = distance to radio horizon, in feet
  H = height of antenna, in feet, above surrounding ground level
  r = earth's radius, in feet
  k = 1.33

Since the earth's radius is approximately 3960 miles, 4/3 of this gives the quantity rk a value of 5280 miles, or 5280^2 feet. Converting the value of D from feet to miles, both sides of the equation are divided by 5280; therefore, the equation would simplify to:

$$D = \sqrt{2H} \qquad (9-5)$$

where:

  D = distance to radio horizon, in miles
  H = height of antenna, in feet, above surrounding ground level

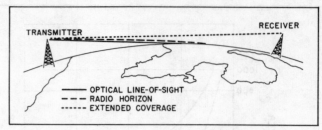

Figure 9-11.   Distance Coverages at UHF Frequencies

Referring to figure 9-11, note the distance variation between the optical and radio horizons. The *radio horizon* is, for all practical purposes, the distance from the transmitting antenna to the point where the radio waves intercept the surface of the earth. Extended radio coverage can be obtained by elevating the receiving antenna from the ground level.

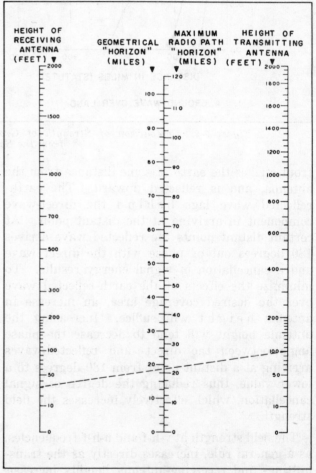

Figure 9-12.   Line-of-Sight Transmission Ranges

The nomograph shown in figure 9-12 can be used to determine the maximum radio line of sight that can be obtained when the transmitting and receiving antenna heights are known, or to determine the antenna heights when the distance to be traversed is known. The quotes about the word "horizon" in the nomograph indicate that when the receiving antenna is elevated, with respect to earth, a new radio distance coverage is established, but it is not the true radio horizon. An example for antenna heights of 30 feet and 100 feet is shown by the dashed line in the graph. Notice the difference in distances to the geometrical and radio "horizons."

In general, most short-distance field communication is carried on by means of v-h-f ground waves. For frequencies of 3 to 30 megacycles, ground-wave transmission is practical for ranges of 5 to 15 miles over land and approximately 75 miles over water.

In the line-of-sight transmission of v-h-f signals, only the direct-wave component is involved. In recent years the accepted theory that only line-of-sight transmission was possible at these frequencies has been disputed. Extension of v-h-f and u-h-f transmission beyond the line-of-sight range has been found possible. The new concepts which explain this action are related to radio-wave transmission utilizing *scatter* and *obstacle gain* techniques of propagation.

Sky-Wave Propagation

In the preceding discussion of ground-wave propagation, attention was directed toward the travel of radio waves on or near the surface of the earth. As was mentioned, the radiation-field waves from an antenna travel into space in all directions. Expanding this statement, the radiation field extends vertically, horizontally, and at all angles of coverage in-between (unless the antenna system is designed to be directive in a particular plane). Sky-wave propagation deals with the radio waves which travel out from the surface of the earth into space. Some of the radiated energy is acted upon by the composition of the gases present in the earth's upper atmosphere so that the transmitted radio energy is reflected back to earth and can be picked up by receiving devices. The following subject material explains the principles of sky-wave propagation in terms of the resultant action of the earth's atmosphere upon transmitted radio-frequency energy.

The Ionosphere and Its Composition

The earth's atmosphere is subject to radiation from the sun, causing considerable ionization of the various constituent gases. These gases are mainly oxygen, nitrogen, hydrogen, and helium.

The oxygen and nitrogen mass extends to approximately 50 miles above the earth, and is highly rarified in the upper regions. Beyond the oxygen and nitrogen region lies the hydrogen and helium mass. The existence of the latter has been verified by spectrographic analysis of meteors set aflame in the earth's atmosphere, and by space-probe rockets.

Ionization begins at a height of approximately 20 to 30 miles above the earth. In the ionizing process, both positive and negative ions and also free electrons are produced. The density of the free electrons is believed to be the most important factor affecting sky-wave transmission. Ordinarily, the m a x i m u m concentration of free electrons occurs at a height of about 250 miles above the earth.

It is a generally accepted fact that the ionization is distributed in stratified layers, as depicted in figure 9-13. The *D layer* exists at heights of 30 to 55 miles above the earth during daylight hours. It has a tendency to absorb sky waves of frequencies less than 30 megacycles. The absorption effect is particularly pronounced at frequencies below 2 megacycles.

The *E layer* is the ionized region between 55 and 90 miles above the earth. Its highest electron density is attained at a height of 65 miles. The E layer becomes highly ionized during daylight hours, so that considerable absorption of sky waves below 1.5 megacycles takes place. During hours of darkness, the electron density is reduced sufficiently to allow the passage of sky waves with minimum attenuation.

The *F region* extends from approximately 100 to 250 miles above the earth, with two well-defined layers present during daylight hours. The lower region is called the F_1 *layer*, while the upper region is called the F_2 *layer*. Over areas of the earth in total darkness, the F_1 and F_2 layers converge to produce a single layer, the maximum density of which occurs at a height of about 200 miles above the earth. This layer is referred to as the *nighttime F layer*. The F_2 layer attains the highest degree of electron density of any of the ionospheric layers.

The ionospheric layers are commonly referred to as the *Kennelly-Heaviside* layers, in honor of the two men who were the first to advance the idea of the existence of the ionosphere.

The ionospheric layers undergo considerable variations in effective altitude, electron density, and layer thickness, due mainly to varying degrees

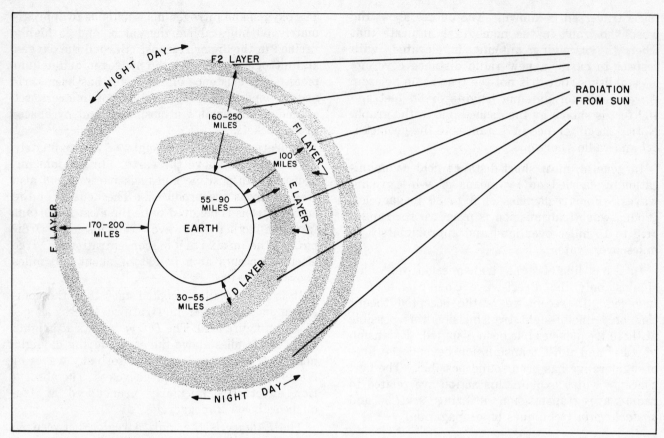

Figure 9-13. Relative Distribution of the Ionosphere Layers about the Earth

of solar ultra violet radiation. Solar disturb-ances, called *sunspot activity,* cause the greatest variation in the F_2 layer. These disturbances occur in varying degrees over an 11-year cycle (minimum 1955, maximum 1966). Figure 9-14 illustrates the effects of F layer sunspot maximum and minimum upon the sky-wave *skip distance.* When sunspot activity is at its maximum, there is a greater concentration of ultraviolet radiation in the earth's atmosphere. The position of the F layer, with respect to the earth, is also affected, but to a lesser degree, by daily and seasonal variations which also follow a predictable pattern.

Refraction of Sky Waves

The preceding discussion gives some idea of the media encountered by radio waves traveling in free space. The waves propagated in free space travel in straight lines, so long as the medium through which they pass has a constant density. Thus, as a wavefront enters the D layer, its path is immediately altered. Lower-frequency waves are readily affected by this layer, so that a scattering, or dispersal, of the wavefront results. Consequently, most of the signal energy is dissipated or absorbed.

High-frequency waves, however, are not so readily affected by the D layer, and hence they continue, along their original path, up to the E layer. As the high-frequency wavefront pene-trates the E layer, it begins to follow a gradual curved path. The influence of the free-electron field is such that the velocity of the wavefront is slightly reduced, thus causing a refraction of

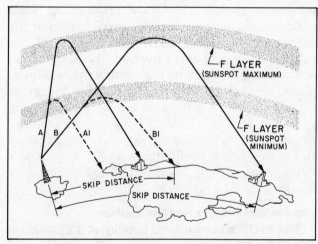

Figure 9-14. Effects of Sunspot Maximum and Minimum on Transmission of Radio Waves (Note the variation in skip distance with variation in sunspot conditions)

the signal. Therefore, the path of the wavefront is bent back toward the earth, so that considerable energy is returned to the earth as a usable signal.

If the frequency of the radio waves being transmitted vertically is gradually raised, a frequency will be found beyond which the waves will not be refracted sufficiently to curve their path back to earth. Consequently, these waves continue on up to the next layer, or in the case of the F layer, on out into space.

The highest frequency which will be returned to earth when transmitted vertically under given ionospheric conditions is called the *critical frequency*. The critical frequency will vary with the time of day, the season, and the sunspot cycle, as mentioned before. The d e n s i t y of free electrons, the layer heights, and the wavelength determine the degree of refraction. In general, the lower the frequency, the more easily the signal is refracted; conversely, the higher the frequency, the more difficult the refracting or bending process. An example of the refraction which occurs at two different frequencies is shown in figure 9-15. The refractive power of the ionosphere

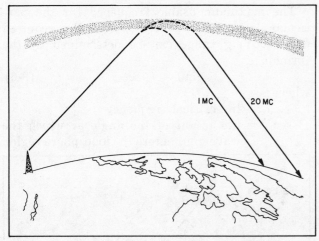

Figure 9-15. Relationship of Frequency of Radiated Wave to Refraction by Ionosphere

increases with the density of the free electrons. The degree of ionization of the ionosphere is greater in summer than in winter, and also greater during the day than at night. It follows, therefore, that the critical frequency will be the highest at noon, and the highest in midsummer. Abnormally high critical frequencies will result during times of peak sunspot activity.

Another factor closely related to the critical frequency is the *critical angle*. Above a certain frequency, waves transmitted vertically will not be returned to earth. However, by lowering the

angle of propagation (the angle the wave path makes with a line tangent to the earth at the transmitting point), a portion of the high-frequency waves will be returned to earth. The highest angle at which a wave can be propagated and still be returned to earth from the ionosphere is called the *limiting angle*, for that particular frequency. For purposes of calculation, the critical angle is the angle which the wavefront, refracted tangentially to the earth's surface, makes at incidence with the ionosphere, with a line extended to the center of the earth, as shown in figures 9-18 and 9-19.

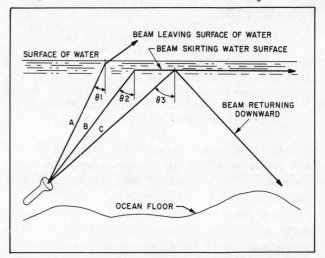

Figure 9-16. Light-Wave Analogy, Showing the Effect of Refraction and the Critical Angle

The light-beam analogy in figure 9-16 demonstrates the critical angle concept. The figure illustrates a light source located well below the surface of a body of water. Light beam A in passing through the w a t e r, undergoes little refraction. Upon tilting the light source slightly to the right, light beam B is refracted a considerable amount and the beam skims the surface of the water. Tilting the light source farther to the right, light beam C is reflected back to the bottom.

The action of a radiated wave from an antenna is very similar to that described above, in that an electromagnetic wavefront entering the ionosphere region is effectively speeded up and follows a curved path due to refraction, as indicated by the dotted line in figure 9-17.

Maximum Usable Frequency (MUF)

From the previous discussion it is apparent that for each communication problem there must be a "best frequency". Referring to figure 9-18, it can be seen that, with a given ionosphere con-

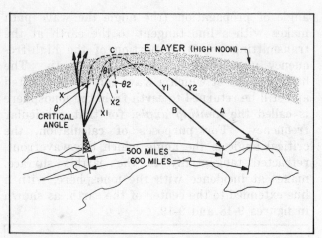

Figure 9-17. Radio Waves Entering the Ionosphere at Various Angles, Showing the Depth of Penetration and the Degree of Refraction

(Notice that wave A is refracted or bent, more gradually than wave B. The waves are speeded up as they enter the ionosphere at points X, X₁, and X₂. Wave A travels through a greater arc and, consequently, returns to the earth at a more distant point than wave B.)

dition, the distance between the transmitter and the point at which the wave returns to earth depends upon the angle of propagation, which in turn is limited by the frequency.

The highest frequency which is returned to the earth at a given distance is the *maximum usable frequency* (muf) for that distance, and it has an average monthly value for any given time of the year. The *optimum working frequency* (owf) is that frequency from which most consistent communication can be expected. Operation at frequencies near the muf will usually result in excellent communication over the greatest possible distance.

It was stated that waves above the critical frequency (f_c) entering the ionosphere at steep ver-

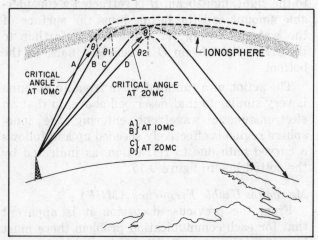

Figure 9-18. Relationship of Frequency to the Critical Angle, and Resultant Path of the Radiated Wave

tical angles (angles smaller than the critical angle) will not be returned to earth, but will continue on into space and will be dissipated there. However, frequencies higher than the critical frequency can be returned to earth, if they enter the ionosphere at an oblique angle, or at an angle greater than the critical angle, as illustrated in figure 9-19.

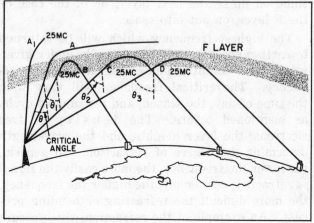

Figure 9-19. Radio Wave Entering the Ionosphere at Various Angles, Showing the Effect on Range

The maximum usable frequency for the particular layer (E, F₁ or F₂) and the required o p e r a t i n g range can be determined by the formula:

$$muf = f_c \sec \theta \qquad (9-6)$$

where:

f_c = the critical frequency

sec θ = the secant of the angle at which the wavefront enters the ionosphere region

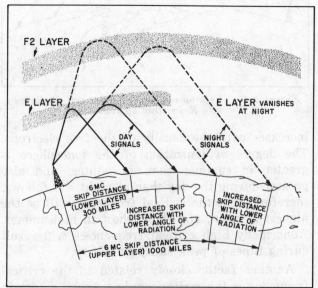

Figure 9-20. Day and Night Signals at Different Angles of Propagation, Showing the Effect on Skip Distance

Optimum Transmission Characteristics

Since most long-distance communication is carried on by sky-wave transmission methods, optimum working frequencies, and optimum angles of transmission are chosen. In common usage, the vertical radiation angle is the angle prescribed by the portion of the electromagnetic wave, with respect to the earth, which provides best transmission characteristics at a given frequency.

The following tabulation indicates the approximate vertical angles of radiation most suitable for radio waves of different frequencies and for different distances between the points of communication.

1.5 to 3 mc	Low-angle of radiation for long distances. High-angle radiation may cause cancellation of ground-wave reception.
3.0 to 6.5 mc	Good sky-wave ground return at any angle of radiation. High-angle radiation can be used for short to moderate distances, but low-angle radiation should be used for long-distance communication.
7.0 to 12 mc	Angle of radiation of 45 to 30 degrees for short to moderate distances. Lower angles should be used for long-distance communication. Higher radiation angles can be used to overcome ionospheric variations at the height of sunspot activity.
13 to 30 mc	Not useful for short-distance sky-wave transmission. Maximum useful angle when operating on a frequency of 13 to 16 mc is about 30 degrees. As the frequency increases above 14 mc, the angle of propagation is progressively decreased from 20 to 10 degrees.

Skip Distance

Of the several layers, D, E, F_1 and F_2, that compose the ionosphere, at night the D and E layers are practically non-existent and the F_1 and F_2 layers combine into a single layer effectively lower in altitude and of reduced electron density. Referring to figure 9-20, it is seen that the points at which the waves traveling through the ionosphere return to earth will vary, depending on the existing layers, their height and density, and angle of wavefront propagation. A wave of given frequency and propagation angle will be returned to earth at a more distant point, if it is reflected from the F_2 layer rather than the E layer, as shown in figure 20. For instance, if in the daytime a 6 mc wave at a 20-degree propagation angle is returned to earth from the E layer at a point approximately 300 miles from the transmitter, the same wave under the same conditions may be returned from the F_2 layer at a point approximately 1000 miles away at night (assuming that the 6 mc wave could not reach the F_2 layer in daytime because of absorption by the D and E layers). The distance between the transmitter and the nearest point where a usable refracted wave is returned to earth is called the *skip distance*.

Another term associated with the skip of radio waves is the *skip zone*. Figure 9-21 illustrates

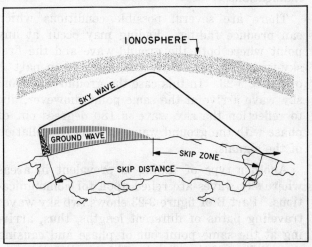

Figure 9-21. Skip Zone

the area designated as the skip zone. As can be seen, the area between the point where the ground wave diminishes and the first sky wave returns is incapable of receiving the transmission.

Since radio waves are propagated at all angles into space it is possible to obtain a condition where the sky-wave signal is reflected back as a result of two different vertical angles. Such a condition is shown in figure 9-22. The two signals are reflected not only by the ionosphere, but also by the earth's surface. Use of the sky wave in this fashion is called *multiple-hop transmission*. Wave B is illustrated as a heavy line with respect to wave A to indicate the relative signal strength; the more hops, the less signal at the point of reception.

Fading

When a received signal varies in intensity over a relatively short period of time, the effect is

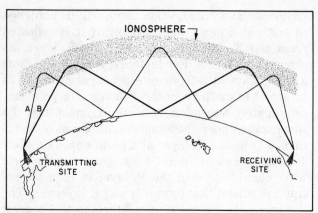

Figure 9-22. Multiple-Hop Transmission

known as *fading*. This can be one of the most troublesome problems encountered in radio communications.

There are several possible conditions which can produce fading. Fading may occur at any point where both the ground-wave and the first sky-wave returns occur, as illustrated in part A of figure 9-23. In this case the ground wave and sky wave arrive at the same point; however, due to reflection the sky wave is 180 degrees out of phase with the ground wave, causing cancellation of the signals.

Another type of fading is prevalent in areas where sky waves are relied upon for communications. Part B of figure 9-23 shows two sky waves traveling paths of different lengths, thus, arriving at the same point out of phase and causing cancellation of the signal. This condition occurs due to reflections from two ionospheric layers.

One method of overcoming fading on important communications channels is to place two antennas feeding two separate receivers one or two wavelengths apart, and combine the output information. This equipment arrangement is known as *diversity reception*.

Scatter Propagation

Scatter propagation of usable radio energy has been made possible through advancement in the design of transmitting and receiving equipments. The theory relating to scattering of radio energy by irregularities in the upper atmosphere has been known for several years. Scattering of radio waves occurs due to the action of both the troposphere and ionosphere. It has been determined that the largest percentage of scattered energy is propagated in the forward direction, or the direction in which the electromagnetic energy is radiated from the transmitting antenna. Since

radio waves are scattered by the troposphere and ionosphere and are propagated mainly in the forward direction, the term *tropospheric and ionospheric forward scatter* is commonly used.

The use of forward scatter propagation enables communication networks in the v-h-f region to be used for long-distance transmission. As was explained earlier, v-h-f transmission was believed possible at only line-of-sight distances. Forward scatter enables radio signals to be transmitted and

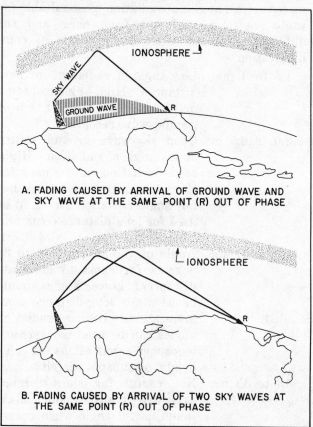

A. FADING CAUSED BY ARRIVAL OF GROUND WAVE AND SKY WAVE AT THE SAME POINT (R) OUT OF PHASE

B. FADING CAUSED BY ARRIVAL OF TWO SKY WAVES AT THE SAME POINT (R) OUT OF PHASE

Figure 9-23. Causes of Fading

received in the skip-zone area between the ground wave and the first reflected sky wave. The use of tropospheric forward scatter enables transmission of v-h-f frequencies and above, up to 600 miles from the transmitting site; ionospheric forward scatter permits transmission of frequencies in the low v-h-f frequency range over distances extending from approximately 600 to 1200 miles.

From figure 9-24 a general concept of transmission by ionospheric scatter can be obtained. The figure represents a comparison of the sky wave of conventional short-wave transmission and the effect of scatter propagation. Note that, with the use of scatter propagation, energy can be received in an area which is without signal under

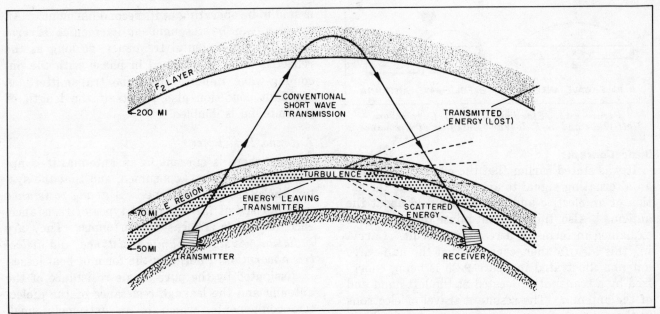

Figure 9-24. Comparison of Conventional Ionospheric Reflection of Radio Waves and Ionospheric Scatter of Radio Waves

ordinary sky-wave propagation. The turbulence area of the lower ionosphere, as illustrated, is responsible for the scattering of radio waves due to irregular variation of the ionosphere. The scatter waves go in all directions (primarily forward), some returning to earth and some traveling on into space. The signal strength of the portion of scattered waves which return to earth as compared to the reflected sky wave is very small. The full usefulness of reliable forward-scatter propagation today has been achieved by the use of extremely powerful transmitting s t a t i o n s, high-gain directional transmitting- and receiving-antenna systems, and very sensitive receiving devices.

This discussion has merely introduced the subject of scatter propagation and its general concepts. A detailed coverage is beyond the scope and intent of this text.

9-3 ANTENNA FUNDAMENTALS

The introduction to the propagation of radio waves presented a method of determining the

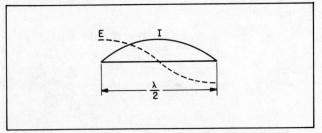

Figure 9-25. Standing Waves of Voltage and Current on a Half-Wave Antenna

wavelength, in meters, of any alternating wave. If an antenna is constructed to be the same physical length as the calculated wavelength, the antenna is said to be one wavelength or λ (lambda) long at the desired frequency. Antennas may be designed to have a length equivalent to one-half wavelength ($\lambda/2$), one-quarter wavelength ($\lambda/4$), or some other sub-multiple of a wavelength. The formula for determining wavelength, or antenna length in feet instead of meters, is as follows:

$$\text{Wavelength } (\lambda) \text{ in feet} = \frac{984}{f \text{ (in megacycles)}}$$

$$(9\text{-}7)$$

The function of an antenna is to transfer, in the form of an electromagnetic wave, the radio-frequency energy generated by the transmitter through distances in space. A portion of the radiated wave, in traveling through space, is intercepted by the receiving antenna, and a voltage is induced in the antenna. The amount of voltage induced in the receiving antenna depends primarily upon the intensity of the radiated wave, which, in turn, depends mainly upon the transmitting antenna length and height, and the current in the antenna. The current in the transmitting antenna, for a given frequency and power input, is greatest when the antenna reactance at that particular frequency is approximately zero. When the above condition exists, the antenna is said to be *resonant* to the frequency of the applied wave.

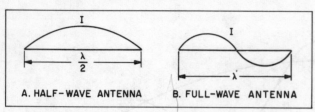

*Figure 9-26. Standing Wave of Current on
Half-Wave and on Full-Wave Antennas at Resonance*

Basic Concepts

It was stated earlier that the effect of applying an alternating signal to an antenna is the formation of an electric and a magnetic field about the antenna. Also, the resultant phase relations were explained in terms of a resonant circuit. Carrying this idea farther, consider that the half-wave antenna illustrated in figure 9-25 is being energized by a transmitter located at the left-hand end of the antenna. The resultant travel of electrons in the antenna conductor causes points of voltage maximums to occur at the ends, and a current maximum at the center. Referring back to figure 9-2, this concept coincides with the generation of the electric and magnetic fields. Returning to figure 9-25, the distributions of current and voltage are referred to as *standing waves* of current and voltage; the point of maximum current or voltage is called a *loop*, and the point of minimum current or voltage is called a *null*.

The half-wave antenna shown in part A of figure 9-26 has one standing wave of current upon it at resonance. If the frequency of the applied wave is doubled, two standing waves will appear as shown in part B of figure 9-26 and the antenna

is said to be operating at its second harmonic. An antenna can be resonant at harmonics several times the fundamental frequency, so long as the reflected wave is returned in phase with the oncoming-wave impulse from the transmitter. A resonant condition also results if the length of the antenna is doubled.

Antenna Resistance

Since there is current in an antenna, it is apparent that power is consumed, and that the system therefore has resistance. *Antenna resistance* is comprised of *three* distinct types of resistance, each of which is measured in ohms. They are *radiation resistance, ohmic resistance,* and *dielectric absorption*. Energy in the form of heat losses, is dissipated by the pure ohmic resistance of the antenna and the leakage resistance of the dielectric components, which is an extremely small value.

The energy dissipated by the radiation resistance is the resultant energy which is radiated as the electromagnetic field. Radiation resistance is not a measurable resistance by standard means, such as an ohmmeter. The radiation resistance of an antenna depends upon its effective height (in wavelengths), its shape, and the operational frequency. Therefore the radiation resistance varies from antenna to antenna.

For proper operation of a transmitting system the load the antenna reflects into the transmitter must be matched for maximum transfer of energy into space.

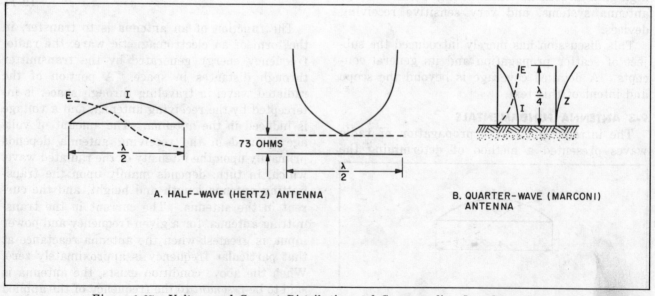

*Figure 9-27. Voltage and Current Distribution and Corresponding Impedance Curves
of Half-Wave and Quarter-Wave Antennas*

Antenna Impedance

Any antenna at resonance presents a specific impedance at every point along its length. This can easily be seen by comparing the voltage and current values distributed along an antenna, as shown in part A of figure 9-27. Since the impedance of any electrical circuit is equal to the voltage divided by the current, the impedance curve represented in the figure can be constructed. The highest impedance occurs where current is minimum, and the lowest impedance occurs where current is maximum.

The voltage and current distribution along an antenna in free space (a theoretical situation) depends upon whether it is resonant or non-resonant at the frequency of the applied power. Since it is impossible to entirely isolate an antenna from ground, surrounding objects, etc., the voltage and current distribution is changed by the inductive and capacitive effects introduced. This, in turn, changes the impedance values along the length of the antenna.

The impedance value represented in part A of figure 9-27 is the low impedance point on the half-wave antenna. This value of 73 ohms is generally accepted as the radiation resistance of a half-wave antenna in free space. The maximum impedance of this antenna, at the ends, is approximately 2400 ohms. Part B of figure 9-27 shows the impedance curve of a vertical quarter-wave antenna. The low-impedance point is located at the end illustrated as ground and varies around 36 ohms, whereas the high-impedance point (open end) is approximately 4800 ohms. It is important to know the relative antenna impedance along the antenna in order to provide the correct matching between transmitter and antenna for efficient power transmission. For example, if the output impedance of a transmitter is low, energy should be coupled to a low-impedance point on the antenna; this point would be where maximum current exists and the antenna would be a *current fed* device. If the transmitter output impedance is high, a high-impedance point on the antenna must be selected; this would be a high-voltage point and therefore the antenna would be *voltage fed.*

Antenna Radiation Patterns

The following discussion aims at a visualization of the resultant pattern formed by the radiated electromagnetic energy from a half-wave (or Hertz) antenna and from the quarter-wave vertical (or Marconi) antenna.

The basic radiation pattern of an antenna depends primarily upon the distribution throughout its length of the current, which in turn, is affected

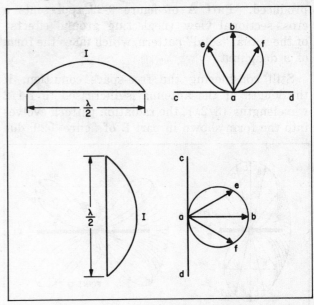

Figure 9-28. Basic Radiation Patterns

by the antenna length, height, shape, polarization, etc. Since the current distribution along the length of any antenna is uneven, the resulting electromagnetic wave distribution in space is also uneven; maximum intensity extending f r o m points on the antenna where the current is at maximum, and minimum intensity where the current is at minimum. This accounts for the characteristic radiation pattern of each type of single-element antenna. For example, the radiated-field intensity for a single-wave, horizontally-polarized, voltage-fed half-wave a n t e n n a, which is located in free space, is maximum in the direction *ab* (as illustrated in parts A and B of figure 9-28) broadside to the center of the antenna and minimum in the directions *ac* and *ad* from the ends of the antenna, corresponding to the loop and nodes of the current-distribution pattern. Parts C and D of figure 9-28 illustrate, similarly, the current distribution and corresponding radiation pattern on a vertically-polarized half-wave antenna in free space.

The relative intensity of radiation in parts B and D of figure 9-28 is proportional to the length of the line drawn from the center of the configuration to the perimeter. Lines *ae* and *af*, in both cases, indicate points of lower intensity than lines *ab* or *ac*.

It is important to remember that a simple transmitting antenna radiates in all directions, but with varying intensities in different directions. The radiation patterns shown in figure 9-28 are only a cross-sectional slice of the actual "solid" pattern produced. Part A of figure 9-29 represents a cross-sectional view (neglecting ground effects) of the actual "solid" pattern, which takes the form of a doughnut.

Still considering the free-space condition, if the length of the antenna is increased to 1-1/2 wavelengths (3/2λ), the radiation pattern evolves into the form shown in part B of figure 9-29, due

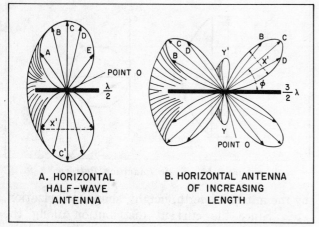

Figure 9-29.   Cross Section of Radiation Pattern

to the vector addition of the individual radiation components from all portions of the antenna. This causes a change in the angle of maximum radiation from that shown for the half-wave antenna.

Several important differences in the character of the field pattern become readily apparent in part B of figure 9-29. The so-called doughnut-shaped intensity pattern is remolded into three distinct envelopes or lobes. The major lobes have shifted from directly broadside, as in the half-wave antenna, to a direction approximating a 45-degree angle with respect to the antenna. The width X[1] of the major lobe has decreased; also, the angle made by lines *oc*, the maximum intensity point, has decreased. Note that as antenna length increases, minor lobes appear and the power in the direction of the major lobe increases; this is an important factor in antenna design. The ability of an antenna to concentrate power in a given direction is called *directivity*. In general, the narrower the major lobe is at its maximum width (X[1]), the greater is the directivity of the radiated pattern. Increasing antenna length is not the only means of obtaining directivity, as will be pointed out later.

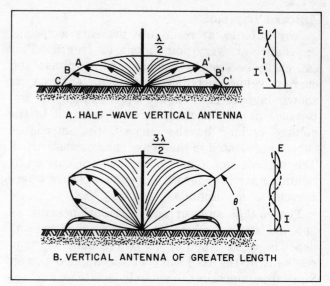

Figure 9-30.   Cross Section of Radiation Pattern

Parts A and B of figure 9-30 show the radiation pattern of a vertically-polarized half-wave antenna (neglecting ground effects), and the resulting action when antenna length is increased. Again, notice that increasing length will change the radiation angle of the maximum intensity point of the major lobe.

In the previous discussion of the development of basic field-intensity patterns, all descriptions were based on the assumption that the antenna was in free space. Obviously, an antenna cannot be suspended in free space, and is always relatively close to the ground. The presence of ground causes the reflection and absorption of the radiated wave (known as *ground effects*), modifying the antenna radiation pattern.

Reflections take place because the electromagnetic waves leave the antenna at such angles that some of the radiation strikes the earth's surface. Figure 9-31 shows how the resultant radiated waves would appear at different points in space (P1 and P2) with respect to their phase relationships. Thus, some signals are cancelled, and others are reinforced by reflections from the ground plane.

The height of the antenna above ground determines, to a large extent, the amount of distortion of the free-space pattern by ground effects. The ground-reflection factors of antennas are usually expressed graphically to indicate the relative field-intensity patterns. Figure 9-32 illustrates two typical field-intensity patterns of a horizontally-polarized, half-wave antenna, one-quarter wavelength above a perfectly conducting ground. Part

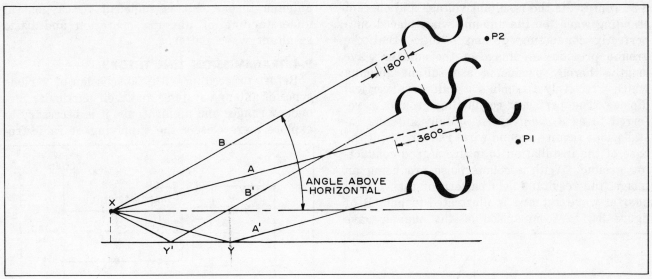

Figure 9-31. Signal Energy Traveling Multiple Paths,
Showing the Possibility of Cancellation with Resulting Variation in Field Intensity

A of the figure represents the field intensity as viewed looking down the length of the antenna, while part B illustrates the intensity as viewed at right angles to the wire. By placing the antenna at different points above ground, many varied

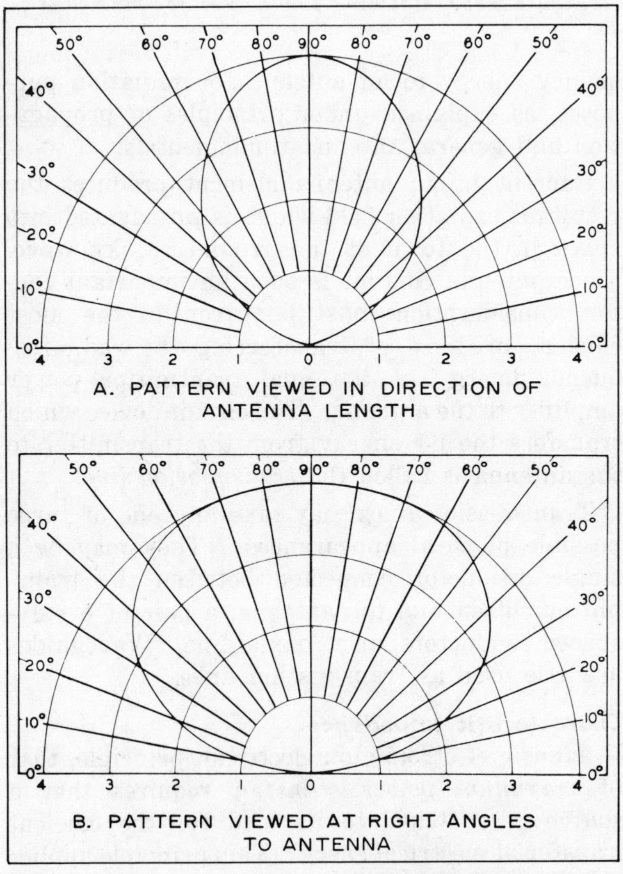

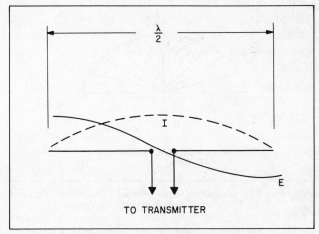

Figure 9-32. Vertical-Plane Radiation Pattern of a Horizontal Half-Wave Antenna One-Quarter Wavelength above a Perfectly Conducting Ground

types of patterns can result; consequently, their use is dependent upon a specific application.

The field patterns just discussed assume a half-wave antenna which is end-fed from a transmitter. Making a new assumption, consider that the antenna is to be fed at a low-impedance point. Figure 9-33 illustrates a common half-wave antenna known as a *dipole*. The antenna is divided

Figure 9-33. Half-Wave Dipole

at the one-quarter wave point to facilitate coupling the antenna to the transmitter at a maximum-current point. Notice that the current and voltage standing waves are for all practical purposes the same as for the end-fed half-wave antenna. The half-wave dipole will have the same radiation pattern (doughnut at the center), as represented in part A of both figures 9-29 and 9-30.

Another type of antenna often used is the one-quarter wave vertical antenna. Part A of figure

9-34 represents the resultant voltage and current standing waves on the antenna when placed on a perfectly conducting ground. Notice that the ground provides an image of the quarter wave length, thereby producing a resultant antenna which effectively resembles a half-wave vertical dipole. The perfectly conducting ground is referred to as a *counterpoise*. Many antenna installations require ground wires radially about the base of the installation to insure a good conducting ground. With a counterpoise producing an image, the resultant field pattern of the vertical quarter-wave antenna is illustrated in part B of figure 34. A comparison of the quarter-wave

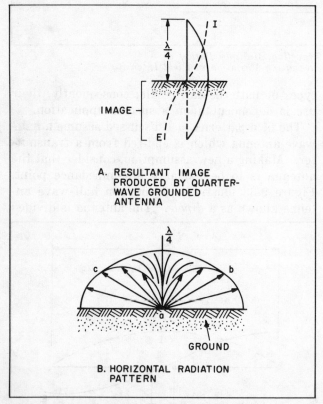

Figure 9-34. *Resultant Image and Radiation Pattern of Quarter-Wave Vertical Antenna*

vertical pattern should be made with the pattern of the half-wave vertical (part A of figure 9-30) and notice taken that the angle of maximum radiation intensity with respect to ground of the quarter-wave antenna (line *ab*) is greater than that for the half-wave.

The various antenna radiation patterns, which are multiples of half- and quarter-wave antennas located at various wavelengths above ground, can be found in almost any text dealing specifically with antenna theory. The information presented herein has actually only scratched the surface of

antenna theory, but is sufficient for a general understanding of antenna operation and basic resultant wave patterns.

9-4 TRANSMISSION LINE THEORY

Before proceeding with a discussion of various types of antenna systems and their particular frequency ranges and applications, it is necessary to explore more closely the supplying of radio-fre-

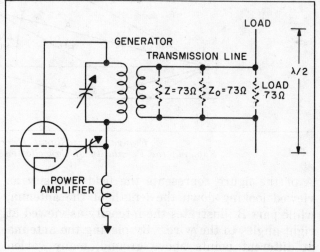

Figure 9-35. *Matching Impedances for Maximum Transfer of Power*

quency energy to an antenna for radiation purposes, as explained under principles of propagation and general antenna fundamentals.

Current in an antenna element produces the resultant radiation field which is propagated into space in the form of the ground or sky wave. Since antenna current is such an important factor, consideration must be given to the most efficient m e a n s of transferring the radio-frequency energy of the final transmitter power amplifier to the antenna. The circuit device which transfers the r-f energy from the transmitter to the antenna is called the *transmission line*.

Transmission lines may take any one of three possible physical appearances: They may be a single conductor connected between the transmitter output and the antenna, a pair of evenly-spaced conductors, or a coaxial line. Waveguides are also used as transmission lines.

Characteristic Impedance

A basic electronic, or electrical, principle, that of *maximum power transfer*, requires that a source be matched to its load for the efficient transfer of electrical energy. This principle applies also to antenna systems, as indicated previously. Referring to figure 9-35, the output circuit of a

ratio Max/min 12/10 = 1.2

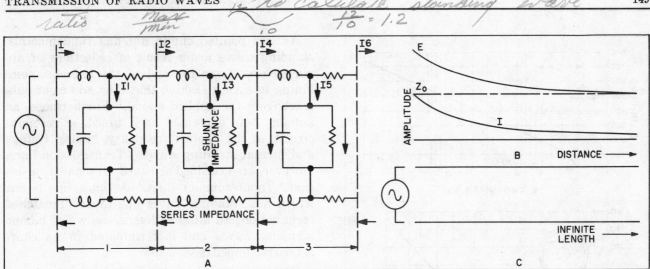

Figure 9-36. Equivalent Circuit of Transmission Line and Development of Characteristic Impedance

transmitter is matched to the impedance of the transmission line, which, in turn is matched to the load the half-wave dipole represents. In this case all the energy sent down the line from the generator (transmitter output) is absorbed by the load, and no energy is reflected back to the generator from the load. This condition is true because the load impedance is equal to the *characteristic impedance* of the transmission line. Every transmission line has a certain characteristic impedance, usually designated Z_0. In order to achieve proper impedance matching of a transmitter to a load, a knowledge of the theory of transmission lines is necessary.

The transmission line of figure 9-35 is a pair of evenly-spaced conductors. These conductors exhibit properties of inductance, capacitance, and resistance. A representation of a transmission line can be developed as illustrated in part A of figure 9-36. The inductive, capacitive, and resistive qualities of the line are shown distributed evenly along the length of the line, since the placement of lumped quantities at any specific point on the line would be incorrect. A generator is shown connected to an assumed infinitely long line (no termination), of which three representative sections are illustrated. Considering the first section, the conductors are represented as having an equivalent inductance and resistance in series; also the spacing between the wires is represented by equivalent capacitance and leakage resistance of the insulating medium. The current in the line is assumed to be in each representative small section, producing a voltage drop, due to the inductive and capacitive reactances and the resistance of the line. The voltage drop in each succeeding section is proportionally smaller, but a

constant ratio of voltage to current (impedance) is maintained, as illustrated in part B of figure 9-36.

In the infinitely long line, the impedance finally approaches a constant value. This final value of impedance, which is "seen" by a generator "looking" into an infinitely long line, is the characteristic impedance of the line. It follows from this discussion that the characteristic impedance of a finite line is a definite value.

The characteristic impedance of transmission lines can be computed through the use of the following formulas. For two-wire type lines the characteristic impedance is determined by:

$$Z_0 = 275 \log_{10} \frac{2D}{d} \qquad (9\text{-}8)$$

where:

Z_0 = characteristic impedance
D = spacing between wire centers, in inches
d = diameter of wire, in inches

For coaxial-type transmission lines the formula for characteristic impedance is:

$$Z_0 = \frac{138}{e} \log_{10} \frac{D}{d} \qquad (9\text{-}9)$$

where:

D = inside diameter of outside conductor
d = outside diameter of center conductor
e = dielectric constant of dielectric material

In comparing these formulas, the main factor (aside from the dielectric of the coaxial line) is the spacing of the conductors, or the ratio D/d. Characteristic impedance can easily be computed by s o l v i n g the given formulas; also, graphs

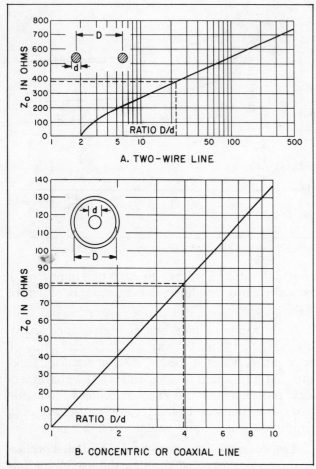

Figure 9-37. Graphs for Determining the Characteristic Impedance of Parallel Open-Wire and Coaxial Transmission Lines

As was pointed out in antenna fundamentals, standing waves are a result of reflections of applied power from the end of the antenna, combining in such a fashion that they add to or subtract from the applied signal. Furthermore, an antenna was explained as a tuned or resonant circuit, at the applied frequency, having voltage and current standing waves. Transmission lines, however, are classified as *tuned* (resonant) or *untuned* (nonresonant) lines. A *tuned line* is one which has standing waves due to an unmatched termination; an *untuned line* is one which has no standing waves and is terminated in its characteristic impedance.

Since the impedance presented by an antenna is different for different frequencies, a perfect matched condition is possible at only one frequency. At this frequency, the transmission line is untuned, and is very efficient because of negligible radiation; such lines are widely used for fixed-frequency applications.

The tuned type of transmission line is widely used because, by comparison with the untuned line, it is simple to adjust, and provides satisfactory transfer of power over a relatively wide-frequency band. Also standing waves on a tuned line which is connected to an antenna conform to those on the antenna, that is, the transmission line acts like an extension of the antenna.

Terminations

As stated, a transmission line terminated in its characteristic impedance has no standing waves. Refer to figure 9-38 for two conditions which would be representative of extremes of transmission line termination. Part A of the figure illustrates an open line as terminated in an extremely high impedance, and part B a shorted line as terminated in a low impedance. Notice that voltage standing waves are present, and the variation of impedance shown along the line.

Several very important facts can be gathered from a careful analysis of the voltage and impedance curves of figure 9-38. It is common practice to characterize transmission lines according to their termination. For this reason, the wavelength indicators on the figure are with respect to the termination. At half-wave points from the termination the generator would "see" identical impedances. In part A of the figure the generator "looks" into a high impedance, as reflected by the high-impedance termination; however, if the generator were moved to the half-wave point it would still meet a high impedance.

similar to those presented in figure 9-37 are provided in data handbooks for determining characteristic impedance where the ratio D/d is known. As a general rule, if the wire size is large with respect to the spacing, the Z_0 is low, and vice versa.

Standing Waves on Transmission Lines

Referring back to the transmission line illustrated in figure 9-36, if the line were to be terminated at any point along its length by a load equal to the characteristic impedance of the line, any radio-frequency wave sent down the line would arrive at the load with the same relative voltage and phase angle with which it left the generator.

If the line is terminated by a load different from the characteristic impedance of the line, a *mismatch* occurs which results in signal distortion due to phase changes. A mismatch results in the presence of standing waves of voltage and current on the line.

Comparing part A with part B, the voltage standing waves are displaced by 90 degrees in the direction of the load. If, for example, it were possible to display the standing waves of the open line, then short the termination, the voltage null at *a* would shift to *a*.

Considering another condition, if the transmission line were terminated in a pure resistive load, whose resistance is greater or less than the

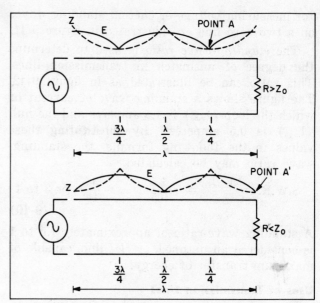

Figure 9-39. *Voltage and Impedance Curves on Full-Wave Transmission Line with Pure Resistive Load*

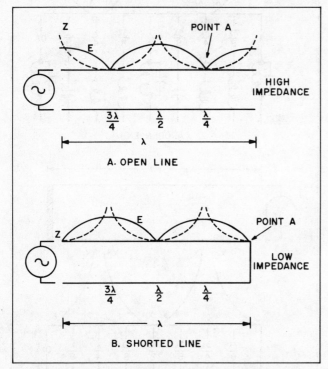

Figure 9-38. *Voltage and Impedance Curves on Full-Wave Open and Shorted Transmission Lines*

characteristic impedance of the line, the resulting voltage standing wave and impedance curve would be illustrated as in figure 9-39. Notice that the voltage maximums and nulls occur at the same points as those shown in figure 9-38 for open and shorted lines. Therefore, a transmission line terminated in a pure resistance greater than the Z_0 of the line produces the same voltage and impedance points; however, the maximum and minimum points are reduced. Similarly, a pure resistive termination less than the characteristic impedance of the line appears as a shorted line with reduced amplitude of standing waves.

In practical applications, transmission lines are connected to antennas which represent a resistive load (at the resonant frequency) or a reactive load (either capacitive or inductive). The effect of capacitive or inductive reactance in the load of a transmission line shifts the standing wave

in one direction or the other along the length of the line. The resultant shift tends to change the impedance of the line as "seen" by the generator. This effect is illustrated by figure 9-40. Part A of the figure represents the load seen by a generator placed at various fractions of a wavelength away from a transmission line terminated in an open circuit. Notice that the open (or high impedance) termination is represented as a parallel resonant circuit. If the generator were placed $\lambda/8$ away from the termination, it would see a capacitive load, and $\lambda/4$ wavelength away from the termination it would see a resistive load represented by a series-resonant circuit. The representations of how a transmission line looks to a generator placed at various wavelengths from a high or low impedance termination can be seen by a close study of figure 9-40.

Standing-Wave Ratio

In the preceding topic the standing waves and resultant impedance at various points along a transmission line were presented in terms of a very high (open) or a very low (shorted) termination impedance. Actually, the load impedance offered by an antenna varies with the degree of mismatch between the generator and line, and between the line and the load. This degree of mismatch is indicated by the magnitude of standing waves on the transmission line. Measuring instruments are available which indicate the value of the current or voltage standing waves present on a transmission line. Two simple instruments for measuring voltage or current standing waves on a two-wire line are illustrated in figure 9-41.

The *standing-wave ratio* is used to determine the degree of mismatch in transmission lines. This ratio can be illustrated as in figure 9-42. The figure shows a standing wave of current of which the loop (I_{max}) is 1.5 amperes and the null (I_{min}) is 0.5 amperes. By substituting these values in the following formula, the standing-wave ratio may be calculated.

$$\text{S.W.R.} = \frac{I_{max}}{I_{min}} = \frac{1.5}{0.5} = \frac{3}{1} \text{, or 3 to 1}$$
(9-10)

A standing wave-ratio of approximately 1.5 to 1 is considered an untuned, or *flat* line, capable of maximum transfer of energy.

Uses of Transmission Lines

Transmission lines are used to feed antennas, correct impedance mismatches, and to act as step-up or step-down transformers.

Methods of Feed at Antenna

The most important factors in determining the method of feed at the antenna are the type of antenna and its impedance characteristics at resonance. The standing-wave distribution on a resonant antenna conforms to the various impedances presented along its length. Equivalent impedances must be realized at the junction of the transmission line and the antenna feed point.

An untuned transmission line is properly terminated at the antenna; therefore, it can be extended to any reasonably practical length between the transmitter and the antenna. Figure 9-45 represents a means of feeding a half-wave antenna with a single-wire feed line. The figure shows that the connection from the single-ended tank is to an off-center position (the distance D) from the center of the antenna. This point would represent the proper impedance match of approximately 600 ohms. Note that the dotted capacitance is the return path for the r-f energy. An untuned coaxial line would be connected to a half-wave antenna in a manner similar to that illustrated in figure 9-46. As can be seen, the line would match the impedance of the antenna at a current feed point; therefore, the coupling network to the line would be a series-tuned circuit to provide some adjustment for an accurate match.

A tuned line can be converted into an untuned line by impedance-matching techniques. Assume a situation wherein the only available materials

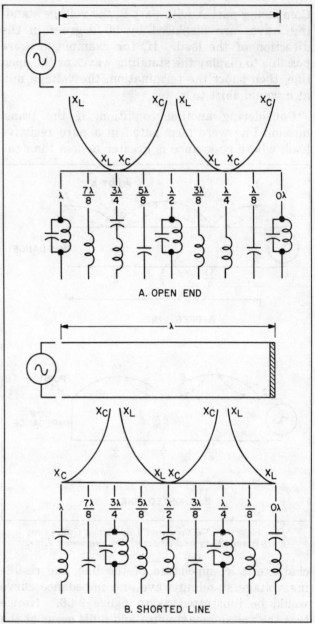

Figure 9-40. *Equivalent Impedance Presented to Generator Connected at Intermediate Points along One-Wavelength Transmission Line Terminated in an Open and a Short Circuit*

are a half-wave antenna and a 600-ohm transmission line. Figure 9-47 illustrates the method used to match the line and antenna. In many instances, the proper match is made by trial and error in connecting the line to the antenna for maximum transfer of power.

Coupling Transmitter to Transmission Line

A coupling circuit is used to transfer the energy from the transmitter to the transmission line. Several common types of coupling networks are illustrated in figure 9-48. These circuits have

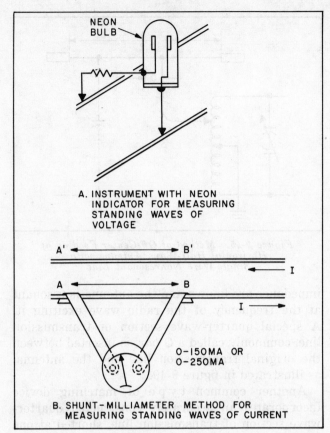

Figure 9-41. Simple Standing Wave Measuring Devices

been illustrated in the discussion on transmission lines but are grouped together here to show their application. Direct, inductive, and link coupling circuits are used primarily with untuned lines. For the most part, they are rather critical in their construction, since no compensation components are included. Series- and parallel-tuned coupling can be used with either tuned or untuned lines with low- or high-impedance inputs. These circuits can be adjusted to compensate for variations in impedance, thus insuring maximum power transfer.

For all practical purposes, a tuned line is connected to an antenna at the highest or lowest impedance point (point of voltage or current feed, respectively). A tuned line will provide efficient transfer of power, if it is kept under one wave-

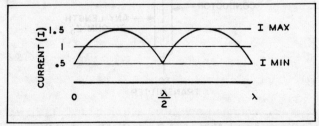

Figure 9-42. Determining Standing-Wave Ratio

length. Untuned lines should be used where the transmission line length exceeds one wavelength.

An important consideration in tuned-line construction is to maintain structural and electrical symmetry to insure that corresponding points on the conductors have opposing fields of equal magnitude, and therefore result in a minimum of

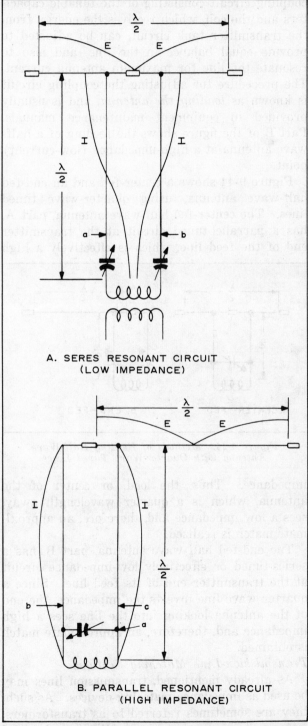

Figure 9-43. Methods of Feeding Half-Wave Antennas with Tuned Feeder Lines

radiation. Two methods of feeding a half-wave antenna using a half-wave tuned transmission line are illustrated in figure 9-43. Part A of the figure shows a series-resonant circuit as the impedance the transmitter sees, looking into a line connected to a low impedance (high-current) point at the center of a half-wave antenna. The coupling circuit consisting of the tunable capacitors and the coil, which receives the energy from the transmitter tank circuit, can be adjusted to provide equal balance in the line, and also to resonate the line for maximum antenna current. The procedure for adjusting the coupling circuit is known as *loading the antenna,* and is usually provided in equipment maintenance manuals. Part B of the figure shows the feeding of a half-wave antenna at a high-impedance (low-current) point.

Figure 9-44 shows a center-fed and an end-fed half-wave antenna, using quarter-wave tuned lines. The center-fed half-wave antenna, part A, has a parallel-tuned circuit at the transmitter end of the feed line, which is effectively a high

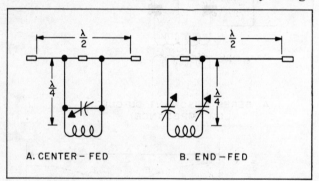

Figure 9-44. Methods of Feeding Half-Wave Antenna with Quarter-Wave Tuned Lines

impedance. Thus, the load, or center of the antenna, which is a quarter wavelength away, sees a low impedance and, therefore, an approximate match is realized.

The end-fed half-wave antenna, part B, has a series-tuned or effectively low-impedance circuit at the transmitter end of its feed line. Since a quarter wave line inverts the impedance, the end of the antenna looking into the line sees a high impedance and, therefore, an approximate match is obtained.

Transmission-Line Matching Sections

As already mentioned, transmission lines may be used as impedance matching-devices. As such, they are sometimes referred to as transformers.

A quarter-wave matching section may be used if both the line impedance and antenna input

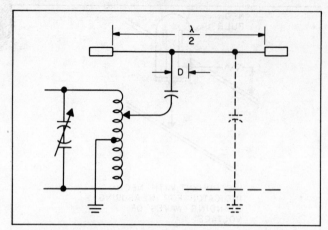

Figure 9-45. Method of Off-Center Feeding of Horizontal Half-Wave Antenna with Single-Wire Nonresonant Line

impedance are known and the antenna is resonant at the frequency of the radio wave exciting it. A special quarter-wave section of transmission line, commonly called a *Q bar,* is inserted between the original transmission line and the antenna, as illustrated in figure 9-49.

Another common type of matching device incorporates an accurately constructed quarter-wave section of transmission line, shorted at one end, with one leg of the other end attached to an end of the antenna, as shown in part A of figure 9-50. The transmission-line feeders are attached along the length of the quarter-wavelength line at the points which provide the proper impedance match. When used in this manner the quarter-wave section is called a *matching stub.* A matching stub may also be used in coupling a center-fed, half-wave dipole to a high-impedance line, as shown in part B of the figure. These two matching stubs can be considered as step-up and step-down transformers, respectively, since the low Z

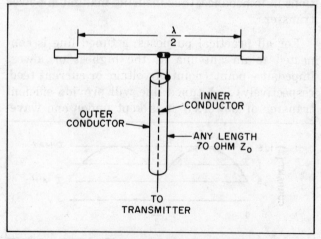

Figure 9-46. Method of Center-Feeding Half-Wave Antenna with Coaxial-Type Feed Line

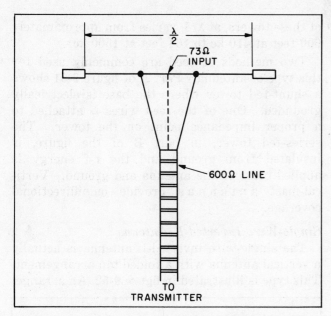

Figure 9-47. Impedance Matching of High-Impedance
Line to Low-Impedance Input

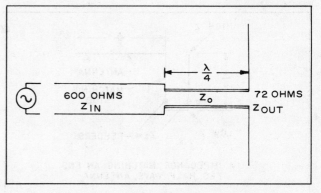

Figure 9-49. Q-Bar Matching Section

(in part A) represents a low-voltage, high-current point and the high Z (in part B) represents a high-voltage, low-current point.

9-5 TYPES OF ANTENNAS

There are numerous types of antenna systems in use for communications and other applications. Antenna systems are designed to provide efficient service at various frequencies and for different areas of coverage. Some antenna systems provide

radiation of energy in all directions from the transmitting site, while other arrangements are made directive for the beaming of radio energy to a specific area.

In the following paragraphs several of the many possible types of antenna are presented. These antennas are classified into the standard types of low, high, and very high frequencies.

Low-Frequency Antennas

Low-frequency antennas are those serving the band of frequencies ranging from .01 to 3 megacycles. Three of the most common types of this class are described below.

Vertical-Tower Antennas

The vertical mast, or tower, radiator is a Marconic-type antenna which is approximately one-

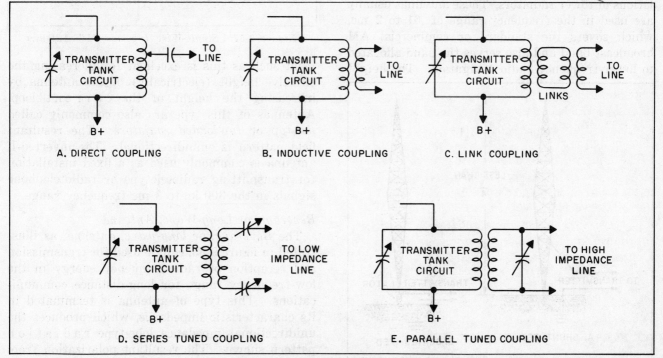

Figure 9-48. Typical Types of Coupling

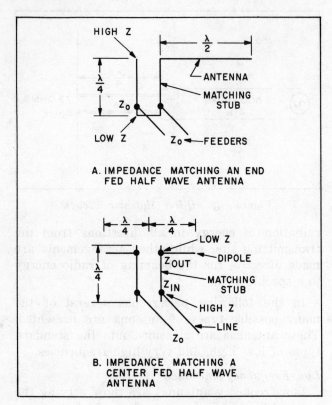

Figure 9-50. Use of Corrective Stubs for Impedance Matching

quarter wavelength long. In this type of antenna, the tower structure itself or a vertical wire placed inside the structure may be the radiating element. Figure 9-51 illustrates typical installations of tower radiators. These antennas usually are used in the frequency range of .01 to 2 mc, which covers the standard or commercial AM broadcast band and also serves the band allocated to lower-frequency radio navigation. The height

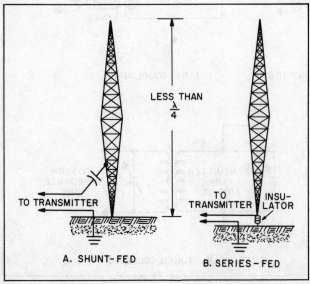

Figure 9-51. Vertical Tower Antennas

of these towers, at λ/4, varies from approximately 600 feet at 410 kc to 164 feet at 1500 kc.

Two methods of feed are commonly used for this type of antenna. Part A of figure 9-51 shows a shunt-fed tower where the base is electrically grounded. One of the feed wires is attached to a proper impedance point on the tower. The series-fed tower, in part B of the figure, is insulated from ground and the r-f energy is applied between the antenna and ground. Vertical-mast antennas provide omnidirectional coverage.

Single-Wire Inverted-L Antenna

The single-wire inverted-L antenna is actually a vertical antenna with a folded top arrangement. This type is illustrated in figure 9-52. An arrange-

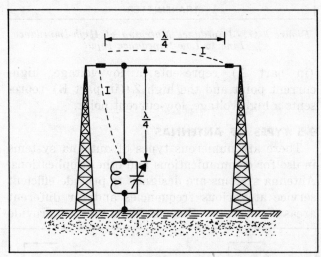

Figure 9-52. Single-Wire Inverted "L" Antenna

ment such as this is excellent for increasing the effective height (electrically) of the antenna by increasing the height of the current loop. Antennas of this type are also commonly called *flat-top* or *top-loaded radiators*. The resultant field pattern is omnidirectional. The inverted-L antenna is commonly used as a fixed installation for transmitting radioteletype or radiotelephone signals in the 300 kc to 3 mc frequency range.

Beverage, or Long-Wave, Antenna

The *Beverage, or long-wave, antenna,* as illustrated in figure 9-53, can be used for transmission and reception of radio-frequency energy in the low-frequency range for long-distance communications. This type of antenna is terminated in its characteristic impedance, which produces the unidirectional-impedance lobe-type radiation pattern shown. The resultant polarization from the transmitting antenna is a horizontally polari-

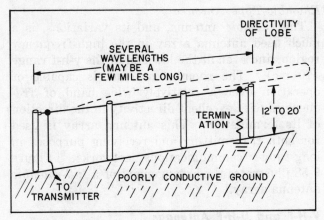

Figure 9-53. Beverage or Long-Wave Antenna

zed wave. A requirement of this type of antenna for good directivity is that it be constructed over ground which has poor conductivity.

High-Frequency Antennas

The high-frequency range can be considered to cover the band of frequencies from 3 to 30 mc. Both horizontal and vertical a n t e n n a s are commonly used. In the case of h o r i z o n t a l antennas, they are located at a point greater than one-quarter wavelength above ground, and have varying degrees of directivity. For the most part, vertical antennas use ground as a counterpoise to provide a desired angle of radiation or as an integral part of the antenna system. There are many antenna arrays used in high-frequency applications; several of which are treated in the following paragraphs.

Vertical Antennas

The vertical antennas in the high-frequency region can be constructed similar to the tower, or mast, antenna used for low-frequency applications. They may have a length equal to a quarter wave, some multiple of a quarter wave, or some fraction of a quarter wave. The vertical high-frequency *whip* antenna for either permanent or mobile use is illustrated in figure 9-54. In vehicular applications, a principle which is common to all vertical antennas is u s u a l l y employed. That is, if the physical length of the antenna is shorter than a quarter wavelength at the operating frequency, the antenna will reflect a capacitive load. To compensate for this, an inductance of the proper value is placed in series with the antenna to cancel, or resonate, the capacitive load; this effectively increases the electrical length of the antenna, thus allowing efficient operation (see part A of figure 9-55). If the physical length of the antenna is too long, it will reflect an induc-

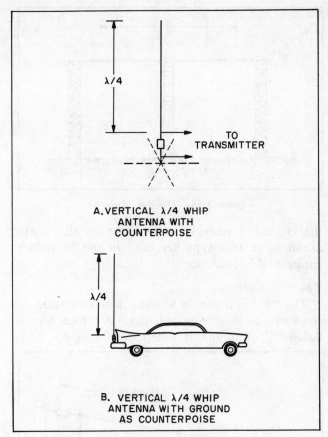

Figure 9-54. Vertical "Whip" Antennas

tive load; therefore, to shorten the antenna electrically, a capacitance is inserted in series with the antenna, as illustrated in part B of figure 9-55.

The Doublet Antenna

The *doublet antenna,* shown in figure 9-56, is s i m p l y a center-fed, half-wave, horizontally-polarized dipole antenna. This antenna arrangement can be used equally as well for receiving or transmitting.   The radiation pattern is bi-

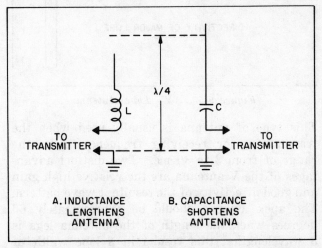

Figure 9-55. Method of Obtaining Desired Effective Vertical Antenna Length

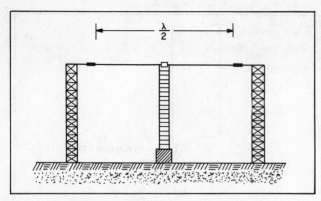

Figure 9-56. Doublet Antenna

directional, broadside to the antenna. Half-wave antennas of this type are used in the frequency range of 2.5 to 20 mc.

The "V" Antenna

The *"V" antenna* is actually a modification of the wave, or long-wire, antenna. A typical terminated "V" antenna is illustrated in figure 9-57.

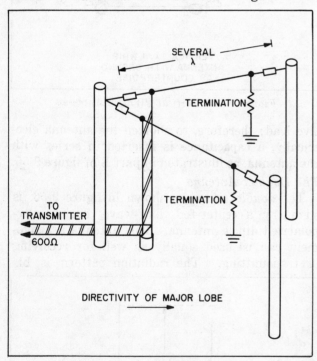

Figure 9-57. "V" Type Antenna

This type of antenna is usually used when the transmitting or receiving frequency is in the range of from 3 to 30 mc. Two distinct advantages of the V antenna are the relative high gain and good directivity of the resultant wave pattern. The apex a n g l e should be approximately 60 degrees when the length of the antenna legs is 3 wavelengths; this results in a lobe width of around 23 degrees at the half-power points.

Rhombic-Type Antenna

The *rhombic* antenna, and its variations, is a much used antenna array in the high-frequency region, and even at the low end of the v-h-f range (70 mc). The rhombic antenna is capable of operation over a relatively wide band of frequencies with excellent directivity in the direction of its termination. This antenna array is used for both transmitting and receiving purposes in long-range communications networks. Figure 9-58 illustrates the arrangement of a *full-rhombic* antenna array.

V-H-F and U-H-F Antennas

Very-high, and ultra-high-frequency antennas operate in the frequency range well above 30 megacycles. These antennas conform to the types previously discussed in relation to vertical and horizontal arrangements. As known, in the v-h-f region and above, transmission and reception of radio waves is restricted, for all practical purposes, to line of sight. This limitation is therefore a contributing factor to the design of both transmitting and receiving antennas. The over-all physical size of the antennas operating in this frequency range is small, due to the fact that the wavelength is extremely short in comparison with the long waves at the low frequencies.

Vertical Antennas

The vertical antennas in the v-h-f region physically appear similar to the vertical whip antennas illustrated in figure 9-54, except that the physical length is appreciably decreased. Many times the vertical *whip* or *post* antenna in a vehicular installation is mounted on the roof of the vehicle, permitting the use of the roof as a counterpoise for the omnidirectional antenna.

Another type of vertical antenna commonly used is the *blade* antenna, illustrated in figure 9-59. This antenna uses a formed metal sheet as the radiating element instead of a straight piece of wire. The result of this construction is an effective broad-banding characteristic, w h i c h permits the antenna to be used efficiently for both transmitting or receiving over several hundred megacycles. As an example, the height of a quarter wave at 200 mc would be approximately 14.4 inches.

Directive Half-Wave Antenna

The most commonly used antenna in the v-h-f region for reception and transmission for some uses is the *half-wave dipole* antenna. The directive characteristics of this antenna, and thus the

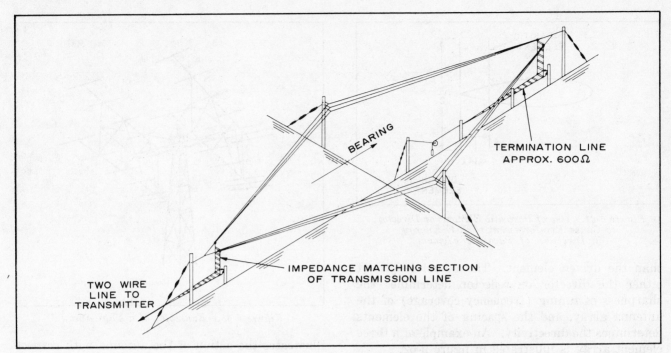

Figure 9-58.   Full-Rhombic Antenna Installation

resultant concentration of radiated or received energy, can be increased by adding *parasitic elements* to form an antenna array.

To understand the development of the directive effect, consider first the fact that if two conductors of equal length are placed parallel to each other and one of them is excited with r-f energy at its resonant frequency, a current is induced in the other conductor which, in turn, produces a radiated wave. Thus, both conductors radiate energy and, if they are sufficiently separated (greater than 0.14 wavelength apart) the secondary radi-

ated wave from the parasitic element is in phase with the incident wave from the so-called *driven* element. These two waves combine and reinforce each other in the direction of the driven element, as illustrated in figure 9-60. This effect is possibly more easily understood by considering the parasitic element as a reflecting mirror for the waves traveling in its direction from the half wavelength driven element.

Another fact, which has been determined, is that if two elements are separated by less than 0.14 wavelength, the radiated wave is reinforced in the direction toward the parasitic element, as shown in figure 9-61.

In common application the director is cut slightly shorter and the reflector slightly longer

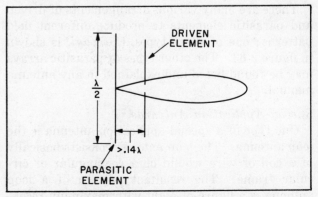

Figure 9-60.   Use of Parasitic Element or Reflector to Cause Reinforcement of R-F Energy in Direction of Driven Element

Figure 9-59.   Blade-Type Vertical Antenna

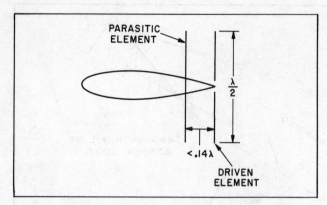

Figure 9-61. Use of Parasitic Element or Director
to Cause Reinforcement of R-F Energy
in Direction of Parasitic Element

than the driven element. The actual length of either the director or reflector determines the sharpness of tuning (frequency coverage) of the antenna array, and the spacing of the elements determines the directivity. An example of a three element array is illustrated in figure 9-62.

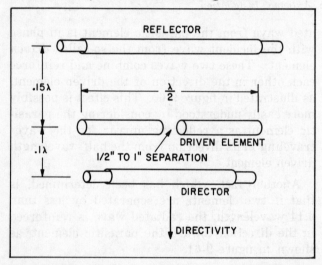

Figure 9-62. Physical Arrangement of Three-Element
Parasitic Array

There are many various arrangements of driven and parasitic elements to produce different field patterns; one of these types, the *Yagi*, is shown in figure 9-63. The other types of parasitic arrays may be found listed and explained in any antenna manual.

Special-Application Antennas

One type of a special-application antenna is the *loop* antenna. The loop antenna consists basically of a coil of wire wound on a rectangular or circular frame. The resultant pattern of a loop antenna is a figure-of-eight with maximum reception occurring when one leg of the loop is pointed toward the received signal. Part A of figure 9-64

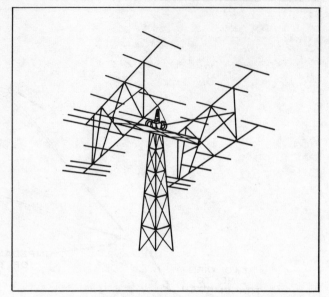

Figure 9-63. Example of a Yagi Array

illustrates the action of the antenna with respect to signal strength and orientation of the loop. Part B of the figure shows why the loop antenna produces no signal input to a receiver when the loop is facing the direction of arrival of received energy. Note that the induced voltage in the "legs" of the antenna are in such a direction that the resultant output from the loop is zero.

The loop antenna is very useful in a direction-finding installation to determine the direction from which the received radio energy is arriving for navigational purposes. When the loop is used with a vertical antenna known as the *sense* antenna, a pattern similar to that illustrated in figure 9-65 is formed. From use of this pattern, along with the knowledge of what side of the loop is facing the station, accurate bearings can be obtained.

9-6 SUMMARY

The propagation of radio waves is dependent primarily upon the effects of the earth, the earth's atmosphere, and the frequency of the electromagnetic energy being radiated. Propagation is accomplished through the action of ground, sky-reflected, and direct waves.

Antenna theory deals with the radiation of electromagnetic waves from an antenna system into free space. In order to accomplish the efficient radiation of energy, the tuning and effective impedance of the transmitter output, transmission line, and the antenna itself, must be taken into consideration. For the most part antennas are designed to operate on specific frequencies or, by

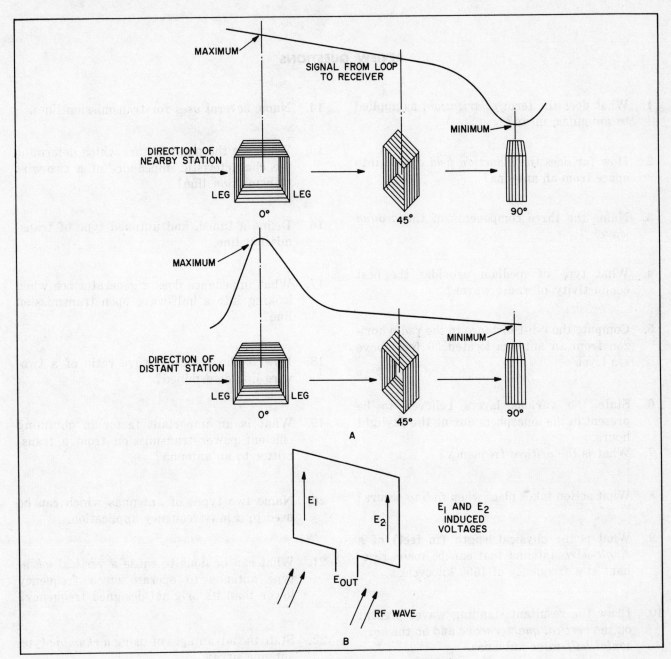

Figure 9-64. Loop Antenna Characteristics

the addition of inductance and capacitance, over a band of frequencies.

The various types of antennas available and their applications are many; however, antenna characteristics conform mainly to modifications of the basic half-wave horizontal or the quarter-wave vertical antennas. Electronic technicians should have at least a basic knowledge and understanding of antennas and antenna systems, sufficient to make repairs or effect temporary measures necessary to maintain effective communications.

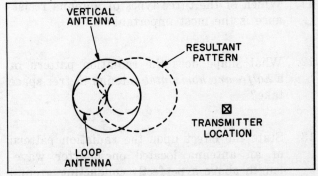

Figure 9-65. Resultant Loop and Vertical Antenna Pattern

REVIEW QUESTIONS

1. What does the term *polarization,* as applied to antennas, mean?

2. How far does the *induction field* extend into space from an antenna?

3. Name the three components of the *ground wave.*

4. What type of medium provides the best conductivity of radio waves?

5. Compute the v-h-f distance to the radio horizon from an antenna located 30 feet above sea level.

6. State the various layers believed to be present in the ionosphere during the daylight hours.

7. What is the *critical* frequency? *frequency that doesn't return to earth.*

8. What action takes place when *fading* occurs?

9. What is the physical length (in feet) of a *single-wire* antenna that can be made resonant at a frequency of 1600 kilocycles.

10. Draw the resultant standing waves present on the *vertical quarter-wave* and on the *horizontal half-wave* antennas.

11. Which of the three types of antenna resistance is the most important?

12. What shape does the radiation pattern of a *half-wave horizontal* antenna in free space take?

13. State the effect upon the radiation pattern of an antenna located one-quarter wavelength above a perfectly conducting ground surface.

14. Name several uses for transmission lines.

15. What are the main factors which determine the characteristic impedance of a two-wire transmission line?

16. Define a tuned, and untuned type of transmission line.

17. What impedance does a generator see when looking into a half-wave open transmission line?

18. How is the standing wave ratio of a two-wire line determined?

19. What is an important factor in obtaining efficient power transmission from a transmitter to an antenna?

20. Name two types of antennas which can be used in a low-frequency application.

21. What can be done to cause a vertical *whip*-type antenna to operate on a frequency lower than its original designed frequency?

22. State the advantages of using a *rhombic*-type antenna array.

23. What effect would shortening the length of a director element of a parasitic antenna array have on antenna performance?

24. Describe the directive qualities of a *loop*-type antenna.

25. At what points on the radiation pattern of the loop antenna would the received signal be at a null? *Broad side or side with hole*

CHAPTER TEN

Reception and Detection of Radio Waves

10-1 Introduction

The purpose of the transmission of radio-frequency energy is to convey some kind of information to a distant point in space. When the radio-frequency signals reach the desired area, a device must intercept and convert the information into a usable form.

Since radio waves decrease in amplitude rapidly as the distance from the transmitting antenna increases, the receiving device must be capable of intercepting this very small signal and amplifying it to a usable level. Also, since many radio waves of different frequencies are radiated by other transmitters, the receiving device must be capable of selecting the desired signal. Once the desired signal has been selected and amplified, a process known as *detection*, or *demodulation*, must be performed in order to reproduce the transmitted information.

10-2 BASIC RADIO RECEIVERS

A device used to intercept, or receive, a radio signal and convert the informational content into its original or desired form is called a *radio receiver*.

Essentially, a receiver must be able to perform the following five reception functions: signal interception, selection, amplification, detection, and reproduction. Although there are many other considerations governing the choice of the actual circuitry employed in receiver d e s i g n, these functions must be accomplished in any receiver; the only possible exception is the function of amplification, which can be omitted in the simplest form of receiver.

Crystal Receiver

The simplest radio receiver consists of a tuned circuit, a crystal detector, and a headset. It must, of course, be connected to an antenna. Such a receiver is the crystal set shown in figure 10-1. The block diagram in part A shows the functions of the respective portions of the circuit presented in part B. The antenna intercepts the transmitted radio w a v e s, the variable-tuned L-C circuit making possible the selection of the desired signal. Detection is performed by rectifying and filtering the r-f signal, effectively removing one-half of the wave envelope. The varying d-c voltage is then applied to a headset, where the original modulation is reproduced.

Antenna Circuit

The receiving antenna, although not necessarily considered a part of the receiver itself, performs the function of intercepting the transmitted radio-frequency energy. In some applications, such as t w o-w a y communications systems, the transmitting and receiving antennas are actually the same device.

When a receiver is to be operated in an area where the signal strength of the transmitted wave is relatively great, the construction of the antenna system is not critical. Often a piece of wire, whose length is no particular wavelength will provide adequate signal input to the receiver.

However, maximum efficiency, or maximum transfer of energy to the antenna, is possible only when the antenna circuit is tuned to resonance at the frequency of the desired signal. It is therefore necessary, in weak signal areas, that the antenna be resonant at or near the desired receiver frequency. Also, the effective physical dimensions of the antenna should be such that a greater area of signal is intercepted. This is often accomplished by properly phasing or beaming the antenna and its associated elements in the direction of the transmitting antenna, when multi-element antenna arrays are employed.

The signal voltage, induced in the antenna, is applied to the antenna coil, L1, as shown in part B of figure 10-1. L1 and L2 form an impedance-matching transformer to match the low impedance of the antenna to the high-impedance detector circuit.

Signal Selection

The p h y s i c a l dimensions of the antenna generally favor its response to a specific frequency band within the total r-f spectrum. Within this given frequency band, some means must be provided to select the desired signal from all of the r-f signals intercepted by the antenna.

Signal selection, or tuning, is most easily accomplished by the use of tuned L-C circuits. According to the theory of resonant circuits, a series-tuned circuit will provide minimum total impedance and maximum voltage across each component at its resonant frequency. In part B of fig-

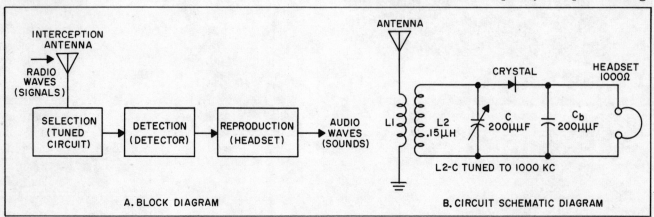

Figure 10-1. Simple Crystal Receiver

ure 10-1, L2 and the variable capacitor C form the series tunable circuit required for signal selection. If the L-C circuit is adjusted to be resonant at one of the radio frequencies which are inducing a signal voltage in the antenna, maximum transfer of energy is accomplished in the transformer, and maximum voltage produced across the tuned circuit, at that frequency. If the tuned circuit is slightly misadjusted, the voltage is reduced accordingly as the impedance curve rises. The ability of the tank circuit to select just one frequency depends on the sharpness of resonance, which, in turn, is determined by the losses in the tank circuit.

Detection

The output of the tuned circuit is the desired r-f carrier and its modulation envelope. Examination of part A of figure 10-2 reveals that the

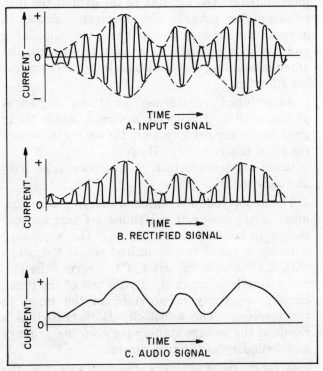

Figure 10-2. Waveshapes of Amplitude-Modulated Signal Before and After Rectification and Filtering

audio, or modulating signal, is not present as such in an amplitude-modulated wave, but rather appears as variations in the amplitude of the modulated wave, with equal positive and negative excursions of the r-f envelope. If this envelope were applied to a reproducer such as a headset, the device would not respond to the r-f wave at an audio rate, since the positive excursions would be cancelled by the negative excursions of the r-f wave. Some method m u s t therefore be

employed to remove the modulation from the carrier. Several methods can be used, but the most common is simply that of rectification.

Crystal sets employ galena crystals, although others, such as carborundum and silicon, are also quite suitable. The crystal, a semiconductor, favors current in only one direction; thus, only the positive or negative portions of the wave envelope (depending on the polarity of the crystal) appear at the detector output. This output, shown in part B of figure 10-2, consists of the modulating audio signal superimposed on positive (or negative) pulses of dc. In order to keep the r-f component from the audio circuit or headset, a bypass capacitor (C_b in figure 10-1) is connected across the output of the detector. The action of the capacitor is that of an r-f filter, and its capacitive value should be such that it bypasses only the rf without causing a loss of the audio voltage. The resultant signal is therefore a d-c voltage varying at the modulation, or audio, rate.

Reproduction

The audio output of the detector and its filter could be applied to any reproductive device such as a headset or loudspeaker. However, a loudspeaker requires considerable power. Since there is no amplification in the crystal set, the only power available is that supplied by the signal at the antenna. Unless the set is in very close proximity to the transmitting antenna, the available power is at a very low level, usually only a few microwatts. This power is sufficient to operate only a sensitive headset. Amplification at the output of a crystal set becomes impractical, since the poor selectivity of the single tuned circuit and the inherent characteristics of the crystal result in a very low signal-to-noise ratio. The *signal-to-noise ratio* is the level of the desired signal divided by the level of unwanted signals or noise. Thus, amplification at this point would result in increased noise nearly as great as the increased audio signal.

Disadvantages

Several disadvantages r e n d e r the crystal receiver useless for present-day applications. First, the single-tuned circuit does not provide sufficient selectivity. Since there is no amplification in the receiver, only signals of large amplitude can provide a usable output, resulting in poor sensitivity, and consequently a limited range of communication. Further, any attempts to improve fidelity would result in the insertion of

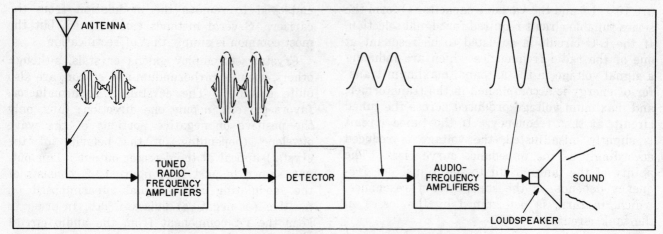

Figure 10-3. Block Diagram of T-R-F Receiver

losses in the circuit, impairing the strength of the already weak signals. At best, the output is sufficient to operate only a headset.

10-3 TUNED R-F RECEIVER

Amplification is necessary in order to increase the strength of received radio energy to a practical, usable level. The ability of a receiver to provide a given output from a very weak signal is a measure of the *sensitivity* of the receiver. The sensitivity, t h e n, can be increased by amplification.

The ability to select only the desired signal and reject the unwanted other frequencies is a m e a s u r e of the *selectivity* of a receiver. Additional tuned circuits in the r-f section before detection increase the selectivity.

In a tuned-radio-frequency (t-r-f) receiver one or more stages of tuned r-f amplifiers are included in the signal circuit before the detector. Also, since it is desirable to increase the audio output to a level high enough to operate a loudspeaker, one or more stages of audio amplification subsequent to the detector stage are added. Such a receiver is shown in block form in figure 10-3, along with the input and output waveforms from each section. The signal intercepted by the antenna is shown as an r-f carrier amplitude-modulated by two cycles, of an audio-frequency tone. It is selected and amplified by the t-r-f amplifiers. The amplified output is applied to the detector stage, where the modulation is extracted. The output of the detector stage is only the audio-frequency variation of the carrier. The a-f signal is strengthened by one or more stages of audio amplification until its amplitude is of sufficient value to drive the loudspeaker.

Antenna Coupling

The antenna coupling transfers the signal intercepted by the antenna to the grid of the first r-f amplifier tube in the receiver. Since, in general, the antenna circuit has a low impedance and the grid circuit has a high impedance, the antenna coupling serves also an impedance-matching function.

An untuned transformer, as shown in part A of figure 10-4, if properly designed, has a fairly good frequency response over the entire frequency range of the receiver. However, compared with a tuned r-f transformer, it has poor selectivity and sensitivity.

The most common antenna-coupling arrangement is the conventional tuned r-f transformer shown in part B of the figure. The secondary winding is tuned to the desired signal frequency with the variable capacitor, C1, whereas the primary usually is untuned. By the use of the tuned circuit, selectivity is provided in the input to the receiver. The sensitivity is increased as a result of the voltage step-up between the primary and secondary of the transformer.

Greater coupling may be desirable for the reception of very weak signals. Such increased signal transfer can be obtained with some sacrifice of selectivity by capacitive or direct coupling, as in C or D of the figure, respectively. Another variation of direct coupling is the use of a loop antenna, with the loop actually forming the antenna coil in the grid circuit of the first r-f amplifier.

R-F Amplifier

R-F amplifiers used in radio receivers provide amplification of the radio signal as received at the antenna. Essentially, the circuitry and circuit

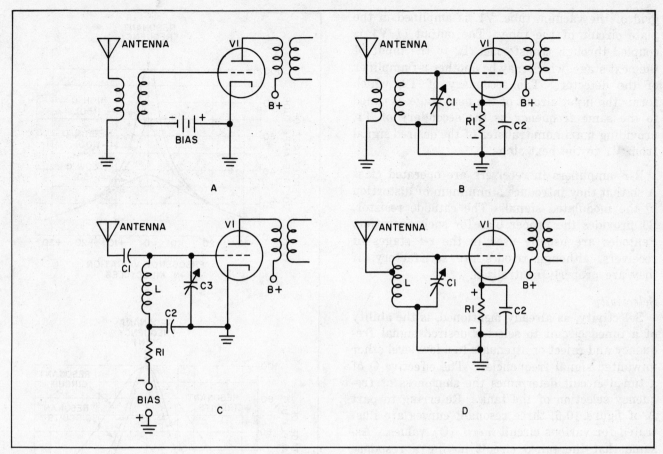

Figure 10-4. Antenna Coupling Methods

features are those common to all r-f amplifiers. A few additional factors, however, must be considered in order to obtain the desired results in receiver applications. Among these are sensitivity, selectivity, noise, fidelity, and the methods of obtaining and/or controlling each factor.

Operation

A typical tuned r-f amplifier circuit is shown in figure 10-5. The selection of the desired r-f signal is made in the tuned grid circuit, L1 and C1. The signal input from the antenna or a preceding amplifier is applied to the untuned primary of the r-f transformer, T1. The tuned secondary in the grid circuit passes the input signal frequency to which it is tuned, but suppresses all other frequencies. This signal, applied to the

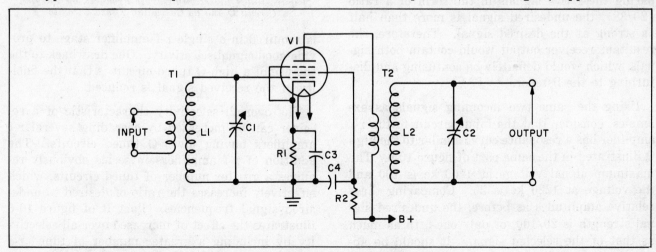

Figure 10-5. Typical T-R-F Amplifier Circuit

grid of the vacuum tube, V1, is amplified in the plate circuit of the tube. The output of V1 is coupled through transformer T2 to the input of the next stage, which may be another r-f amplifier or the detector. The secondary of T2, which forms the input circuit of the next stage, is tuned to the same frequency as the secondary of T1, providing maximum transfer of the desired signal from V1 to the next stage.

R-F amplifiers in receivers are operated class A so that they introduce a minimum of distortion in the modulated signal. The cathode resistor, R1 provides the proper bias for such operation. Pentodes are usually used in the r-f stages of receivers, although triodes are satisfactory, if they are properly neutralized.

Selectivity

Selectivity, as already mentioned, is the ability of a tuned circuit to select a desired signal frequency and reject or attenuate to a low level other unwanted signal frequencies. The effective Q of a tuned circuit determines the sharpness of frequency selection of the tank. Referring to part A of figure 10-6, three resonant curves are ilustrated for various circuit *merit* (Q) values. Assume that the tuned circuit having a response curve represented by the low Q value is the input circuit of a tuned r-f amplifier and that the resonant frequency point of 1200 kc is the desired signal frequency: then, the maximum signal voltage across the tuned circuit has a relative value of approximately 38 percent. If another signal of equal strength but at a frequency of 1220 kc were present at the input, it would have a relative voltage value of approximately 20 percent. Comparing these two signals in the form of a ratio (20/38), the undesired signal is more than half as strong as the desired signal. Therefore, the resultant receiver output would contain both signals, which would definitely be confusing and disturbing to the listener.

Using the same two incoming signals as examples, consider that the input circuit to the r-f amplifier has a resonance curve similar to the high Q illustrated in the same part of figure 10-6. The maximum signal voltage at 1200 kc is 100 and the voltage at 1220 kc is 20. Comparing these relative amplitudes as before, the undesired signal strength is 20/100, or only one-fifth as much as that of the selected signal. It should be apparent, then, that a relatively high-Q tuned circuit

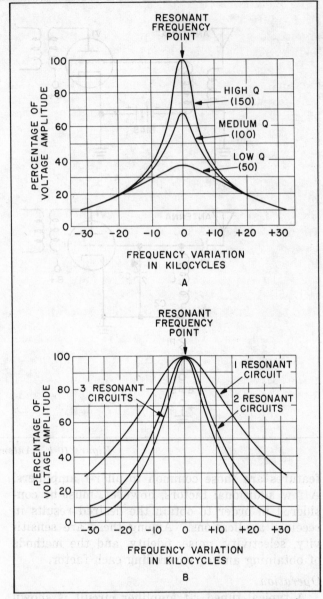

Figure 10-6. *Selectivity Curves Produced by Varying Circuit Q and by Cascading Tuned Circuits*

is required in a single r-f amplifier stage to provide good signal selectivity. One drawback to the the use of a high-Q tuned circuit is that the fidelity of the received signal is reduced.

The over-all selectivity characteristic of a receiver can be increased by cascading several r-f amplifiers having lower-Q tuned circuits. The addition of r-f amplifiers in series obviously requires a greater number of tuned circuits, which effectively increases the ratio of desired to undesired signal frequencies. Part B of figure 10-6 illustrates the effect of increased over-all selectivity by including a greater number of tuned r-f amplifier stages in a receiver.

To explain how the increased selectivity of part B of figure 10-6 is obtained, assume that equal-amplitude signals of 1200 and 1220 kc are applied to the selective input circuit of an r-f amplifier. If the tuned input circuit is resonant to 1200 kc, maximum signal voltage is produced across the tank circuit, and a lesser percentage (dependent upon the circuit Q) at 1220 kc, as a result of the selectivity characteristic. This resultant percentage of voltage is illustrated by the one resonant circuit curve as 100. Again establishing a ratio of desired to undesired signals, it is 100/50 or 2 to 1. In the first amplifier vacuum tube the signals are amplified in this ratio of 2 to 1. If the amplified 2-to-1 ratio signals are applied as an input to a second 1200-kc tuned circuit (having the same Q as the first), the resultant output voltage, due to the selectivity characteristic, is in the ratio of 4 to 1 with respect to the original input signals. As illustrated in part B of 10-6, the resultant selectivity curve of two resonant circuits is 100/25, or 4 to 1.

The third curve of part B of figure 10-6 (three resonant circuits) is the result of amplifying a 4-to-1 ratio of signal strengths and applying them as an input to a third 1200-kc resonant circuit having the same Q factor as the preceding tuned circuits. The resultant ratio of the desired signal (1200 kc) to the undesired signal (1220) kc of the cascaded tuned amplifiers has been reduced from 1 to 1 at the input to 8 to 1 at the output of the r-f amplifier string. Thus, over-all selectivity has been increased by increasing the steepness of the selectivity curve of a single-tuned circuit without affecting to any great extent the peak of the resonance curve.

Sensitivity

The sensitivity rating of a receiver is effectively a relationship of the r-f input signal required to produce a desired audio output signal. Sensitivity is usually expressed in terms of microvolts input (r-f) to watts of audio power output. From the above statement it can be concluded that sensitivity is a measure of the over-all gain capability of a receiver. As applied to a trf, the sensitivity is mainly dependent upon r-f amplifier gain factors.

Signal-to-Noise Ratio

It has been pointed out that the r-f amplifier circuits of a radio receiver must have good selectivity and sensitivity for proper operation. One factor, not mentioned before, which limits the gain of a receiver is the signal-to-noise ratio.

Noise may be generally divided into two kinds insofar as receiving systems are concerned. Noise generation may be external or internal to the receiver. If the sensitivity of the receiver is made too high, the "hash", "buzz", or "crackle" heard in the output may drown out the desired signal.

Before proceeding with the discussion of the signal-to-noise ratio, an examination of the causes of receiver noise should be made. The most common external noise sources are atmospheric and man-made disturbances. Atmospheric noise is produced by static, or electrical discharges caused by electrical storms. Noise generated by man-made devices may be the result of any device which produces electric arcs, including electric motors and spark plugs in automobile engines.

Noise is therefore any electrical disturbance which radiates random impulses of electromagnetic energy. Noise is generally composed of many frequencies which tend to modulate the carrier wave of radio signals and interfere with amplitude-modulated communications.

Internal noise, produced by the r-f amplifiers of the receiver itself, results from tube noise, thermal agitation, and hum. *Tube noise*, or *shot effect*, is generated within the electron stream of vacuum tubes by random fluctuations in the plate current. *Thermal agitation* is a form of random noise caused by temperature differences between the terminals of resistors and other components, thereby producing random motion of electrons. *Hum* is often present in a-c operated receivers, usually because of improperly filtered power supplies and stray inductive pickup from coils and transformers.

Internally generated noise in the receiver is the least important factor of the signal-to-noise ratio. The externally generated noise, which appears along with the desired signal at the receiver input, is the limiting factor of the weakest signal the receiver is capable of reproducing. This fact is readily apparent when it is recalled that the noise and signal both are amplified equally by the over-all receiver. The maximum sensitivity of any receiver is limited by the ratio of the desired signal strength to the strength of all interfering noise rather than as the receiver's capability of amplifying a very weak signal. The signal-to-noise ratio can be improved by reducing the bandwidth of the tuned coupling circuits between r-f amplifiers.

Bandwidth, Bandpass, and Fidelity

When a receiver is to be used for the reception of voice-modulated radio signals, the bandwith of the tuned circuits must be sufficient to pass the highest modulating frequency.

As explained in the discussion of the principles of amplitude modulation, the sidebands generated by modulating the carrier contain the intelligence. In order to receive the desired information, the r-f amplifiers must be capable of passing and amplifying signal frequencies equal to twice the modulating frequency.

A practical bandpass curve is illustrated in figure 10-7. Observe that the bandpass of a receiver circuit is the width of the band of frequencies that are passed with almost equal amplitude.

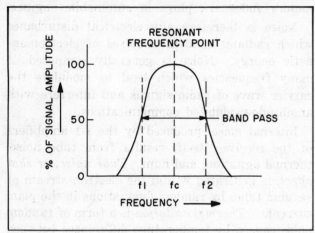

Figure 10-7. Bandpass Curve

The over-all bandpass is effectively dependent upon the bandpass of all the individual receiver r-f stages. As shown in part B of figure 10-6, bandpass and selectivity are directly related.

The term *fidelity*, as defined in the audio-amplifier section, means the accurate reproduction of an input signal. In receivers the output fidelity is only as good as the bandpass of the selective circuits allows. If the tuning of the resonant circuits is quite sharp (high Q), the high-frequency modulating signals are greatly attenuated, resulting in a loss of fidelity.

Summary of R-F Amplifier Characteristics

The several general radio receiver characteristics depend mainly upon the operational characteristics of the r-f amplifier circuit: selectivity, bandpass, and fidelity are all dependent upon the sharpness of tuning of the r-f amplifier coupling circuit; sensitivity is dependent upon the r-f amplifier circuit signal-to-noise ratio.

All these factors must be taken into account in designing a receiver for a specific application. C-W receivers have more selective circuits, since only a narrow band of frequencies above and below the carrier is used; commercial receivers must have broad-band circuits to allow good fidelity, but must still maintain proper selectivity.

Principles of Detection, or Demodulation

To obtain the required output from a receiver, a circuit must be included to extract the modulation from the amplified AM carrier wave. The circuit used to demodulate, or remove the impressed information from the carrier, is the *detector*.

A detector circuit must be capable of reproducing the original modulating signal impressed upon the carrier at the transmitter site. Many types of electronic circuits are used to perform this function, the type used being dependent upon the requirements of the particular receiver system.

Linear Detection

Detection, or demodulation, is essentially the process of rectification. This process was mentioned briefly in the discussion of the crystal receiver. The galena crystal provided the unidirectional current when the received modulated carrier wave was impressed across it.

A vacuum-tube diode replaces the crystal in almost all low-, medium-, and high-frequency receiving equipments. The crystal and the vacuum-tube diode are classified as nearly linear devices. A *linear detector* is one that produces an output whose amplitude is directly proportional to the amplitude of the input.

Essentially, the output of a diode detector is a nearly linear reproduction of the modulation envelope, with either the positive or the negative excursions of the carrier removed. The remaining half of the radio-frequency carrier is then removed by a filter circuit, leaving only the modulation component as the desired output from the circuit. The diode detector is often referred to as an *envelope detector*.

Square-Law Detection

A *square-law detector* is a circuit that produces an output the amplitude of which is proportional to the square of the amplitude of its input. Square-law detectors are usually used to detect very weak applied signals, since the slight changes in amplitude will result in an effectively large output signal (the square). Vacuum-tube triodes may be

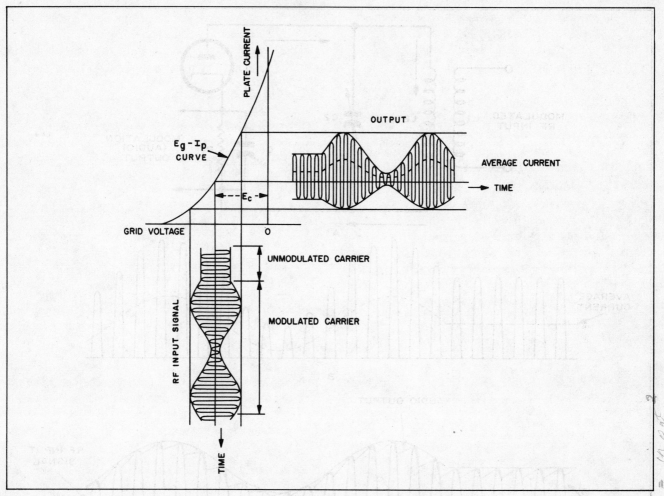

Figure 10-8. Square-Law Detection by a Triode

used to provide square-law detection. The essential requirement of square-law detection is that the vacuum tube be biased to operate over the curved portion of its E_g-I_p characteristic curve, as shown in figure 10-8. Any vacuum tube or similar device satisfying this condition of non-linearity can be used.

The non-linear characteristic causes the positive portion of the applied signal to be amplified more than the negative excursion. The resultant average plate current then resembles one-half of the modulation envelope. Square-law detectors suffer two serious disadvantages: one is that the non-linear characteristic of the E_g-I_p curve causes the generation of additional frequencies in the plate circuit of the tube, some of the generated frequencies possibly falling in the same range as the modulation signal and producing distortion; the other serious disadvantage is that a large decrease in output voltage results from a very small decrease in the applied signal strength.

Detector Circuits

Various types of detector circuits are in general use, each having certain advantages and limitations, which determine its application. A linear detector is normally used where a relatively high input-signal level is available. The square-law detector, as mentioned, can be used where relatively low modulated r-f input signals are expected.

The most important and commonly used detector circuits are the diode detector, the plate detector, the infinite-impedance detector, and the grid-leak detector.

Diode Detector

The basic diode detector circuit is shown in part A of figure 10-9. Since the diode conducts only when the plate is positive with respect to the cathode, the current in the circuit is directed as illustrated in part B of the figure. On each half-cycle of the r-f signal there is enough current to charge capacitor C1 to the peak r-f volt-

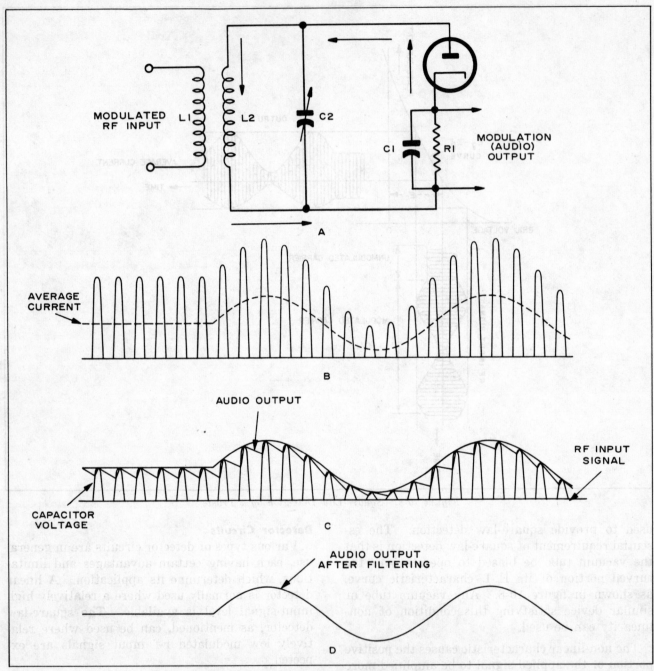

Figure 10-9. Basic Diode Detector Circuit and
Associated Waveforms

age, less a small drop lost across the tube. Between these p e a k s the capacitor discharges through resistor R1. The voltage across the capacitor is shown in part C of the same figure.

Except for the r-f variations, the voltage across the capacitor is a replica of the audio-modulating signal. The ratio of this voltage to a peak r-f signal is called the *efficiency of rectification*. The rectification efficiency becomes higher as the value of load resistor R is i n c r e a s e d, the power

absorbed by the diode decreasing. On the other hand, R must be small enough to discharge C at a rate that follows the modulation envelope as it decreases in amplitude. Thus, R1 and C1 form an R-C filter which removes the r-f variations from the audio output. The resultant output is shown in part D of the figure.

Although they have excellent linearity characteristics, diode detectors need a strong signal voltage for efficient operation, having low sensitivity. Their use is confined chiefly to highly sensitive receivers, where high amplification takes place before demodulation.

Plate Detector

Triodes and pentodes biased approximately to cutoff can also serve as detectors. If an r-f signal is applied to the circuit shown in figure 10-10, the output will consist of half-cycles provided the tube is biased very close to cutoff. The operation of this circuit is equivalent to class B operation, in which there is plate current for slightly more than one-half of the a-c cycle. The average value of the current is proportional to the magnitude of the r-f signal and is utilized as the audio output. A capacitor, or preferably a filter section, eliminates the r-f fluctuations of the output. The advantages of this strong-signal detector are high input impedance (if the grid is not driven positive) and good sensitivity. However, the distortion of the output signal is greater than that of the diode detector.

In a square-law plate-circuit detector, the operating voltages are chosen so that the tube characteristic is curved, satisfying the condition for square-law detection. Numerous frequencies are present in the output current when a weak signal is applied to the tube, the most important, of course, being the modulating frequency. Other frequency components include the sums and differences of the modulating frequencies, if more than one modulating frequency is present. For modulation percentages under 50, the distortion present in the output is not serious.

A compromise can be reached when the tube is operated in the portion of the E_g-I_p curve as shown in figure 10-11. For weak signals, the plate detector operates essentially in the curved (square-law) portion of the E_g-I_p characteristic. As a result, considerable distortion of the output

waveform occurs. For strong input signals, operation takes place over the more linear portion of the characteristic curve, and less distortion occurs in the output. The maximum signal-handling ability of the plate detector is limited, however, since the signal voltage must be below the value that would cause the grid to draw current. If the grid draws current, the sensitivity and the selectivity of the detector are lowered. Pentodes usually are preferred as plate detectors because they provide a larger audio-output voltage than do triodes.

Infinite-Impedance Detector

The infinite-impedance detector is essentially a cathode follower biased nearly to cutoff. The voltage produced by rectification appears across the cathode resistor and capacitor. As the name of the detector implies, the input impedance is extremely high, because even for strong-signal inputs there is a negative bias between grid and cathode. The grid cannot be driven positive, regardless of signal strength, and consequently it never draws current. As a result, the selectivity of the circuit is excellent. A further characteristic of the infinite-impedance detector is its good linearity (low distortion), and its ability to handle high signal-input voltages.

The circuit, shown in figure 10-12, resembles that of the plate detector, except that the audio load resistor, R_k, is connected between the cathode and ground and thus is common to both grid and plate circuits of the tube. Therefore, negative feedback from the plate-to-grid circuit takes place at audio frequencies, further improving the linearity and reducing distortion at all signal levels. Since the output is taken from the cathode circuit, there is no amplification, and the sensitivity of the circuit is consequently low.

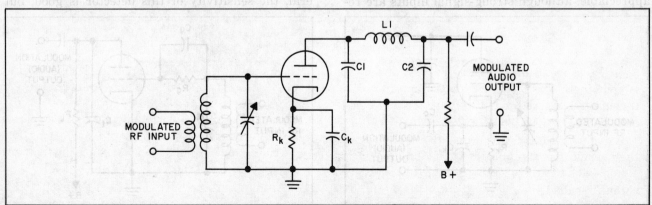

Figure 10-10. Plate-Detector Circuit

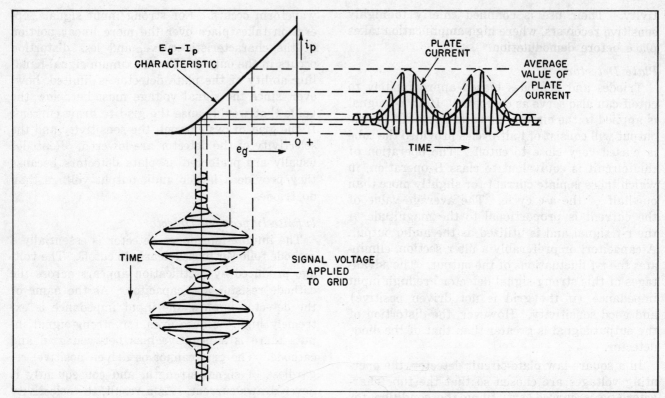

Figure 10-11. Optimum E_g-I_p Operating Point for Plate Detection

The main advantage of the infinite-impedance detector is that the grid cannot be driven positive, since the grid bias is automatically adjusted by the value of voltage, produced across the cathode resistor, R_k by the applied signal. The value of capacitor C_b is such that the capacitor bypasses both the r-f and modulation frequencies to ground.

Grid-Leak Detector

The basic grid-leak detector circuit is shown in figure 10-13. By proper choice of circuit-component values this detector can be adjusted for two modes of operation — *power detection* and *square-law detection*. In power detection the output is appreciable, although strong-signal inputs are re-

quired. The distortion is relatively low, but greater than that in diode detection. During the positive half-cycle of r-f signal, grid current charges the capacitor shunting the grid-leak resistor. Some of this charge is lost through the resistor during the remainder of the cycle when grid current ceases. The time constant of the resistor and capacitor must be short enough to allow the capacitor charge to follow the amplitude variations of the r-f signal faithfully. These variations are amplified in the plate circuit of the tube. Unless the plate-circuit characteristic is linear, considerable distortion results. In general, the sensitivity of this detector is good, but

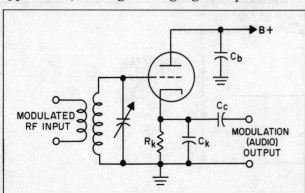

Figure 10-12. Infinite-Impedance Detector Circuit

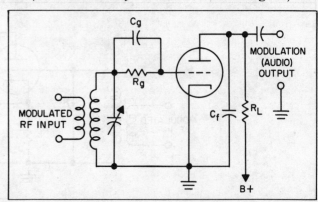

Figure 10-13. Grid-Leak Detector Circuit

the distortion is higher than that occurring in diodes, particularly for very strong input signals. A weak signal causes square-law conditions to be approached.

For square-law detection, the second mode of grid-leak detector operation, the grid-leak resistance, which is returned to the cathode, determines the operating point of the grid-voltage, grid-current characteristic. In the absence of a signal, contact current produces a small negative voltage that becomes the operating bias of the stage. Since the grid current is non-linear with respect to the applied grid voltage, an r-f signal applied to the grid is detected by square-law action. The composite signal present in the grid-cathode circuit is amplified in the plate circuit of the tube. This action differs from plate detection in that the average plate current is decreased rather than increased in the presence of grid excitation. Although the distortion is high and the sensitivity

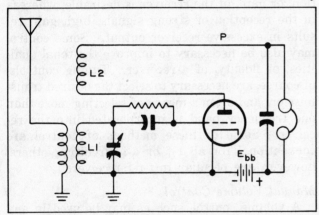

Figure 10-14. Regenerative Detector Circuit

low, especially when the percentage of modulation exceeds 50, this type of grid-leak detection is stable and sensitive to weak signals.

The choice of circuit values for operation as a weak-signal, or square-law, detector requires that the tube plate voltage be relatively low. Also, the grid-leak resistor-capacitor arrangement must have a long time constant (R_g of several megohms and C_g of 200 to 300 micromicrofarads). When the circuit is to be operated as a power detector, plate voltage is increased and the grid-leak circuit time constant is reduced by lowering the value of R_g to several thousand ohms and C_g to approximately 100 micromicrofarads.

Regenerative Detector

The amplification of a detector circuit can be increased materially by returning some of the output voltage in the plate circuit, in the proper

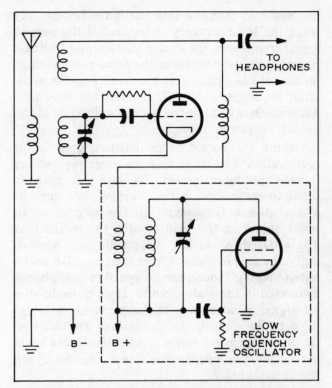

Figure 10-15. Superregenerative Detector Circuit

phase, to the input circuit. This process is known as *regeneration*, and is fundamental to all oscillatory circuits. In this application, however, the amount of regeneration is restricted so that oscillation does not occur. A regenerative circuit based on grid-leak detection is shown in figure 10-14. Here the regenerative voltage is produced in a plate inductance, and is coupled back by mutual induction. The actual voltage to be amplified by the tube is therefore increased. A severe drawback to regenerative detection is a tendency toward instability; careful design, however, can minimize this tendency.

Superregenerative Detector

If the circuit of figure 10-14 is modified somewhat as shown in figure 10-15, another type of detector, called a *superregenerative detector*, is formed. Since the operation of this circuit is alternately oscillatory and non-oscillatory, the action of this detector differs from ordinary regeneration. In particular, the sensitivity is much greater.

Superregeneration results if the coupling in the circuit of figure 10-14 is considerably increased, and if another oscillatory voltage is introduced at point P. Such a circuit is shown in figure 10-15. The frequency of this signal must be slightly above the audible range. Adjustments are made so that the tube oscillates briefly only when the low-frequency signal, called the *quench signal,* reinforces the steady plate-supply voltage. Shortly afterwards, when the total plate voltage on the tube begins to fall, the conditions for oscillation no longer exist. Therefore, the tube produces a series of high-frequency oscillations at the quench-frequency rate.

During the period of oscillations, grid-circuit rectification o c c u r s, and the negative voltage thereby produced across the grid-leak resistor tends to cause dips in the average plate current at the quench frequency. In the absence of an input signal in the grid circuit, the oscillations are initiated by random noise voltages. Accordingly, the dips in plate current are irregular, and a harsh "frying" sound can be heard in headphones connected in the plate circuit. If an unmodulated r-f signal greater than the noise voltages is applied to the circuit, the oscillations are initiated by the uniform r-f signal. As a result, the plate current fluctuations become steady and the frying sound disappears.

The action of a modulated signal is somewhat different. Since the envelope of the incoming signal varies at an audio rate, the instants at which oscillations begin in the circuit also occur at an audio rate. Therefore, the dips in plate current occur at the audio-frequency rate of the modulating signal.

It is possible to operate a superregenerative detector in certain ways, or *modes.* One of these is the *logarithmic mode,* which occurs when the audio output is proportional to the logarithm of the r-f signal. In this mode the output for strong inputs is not much greater than that for weak inputs. Unfortunately, the fidelity of such a detector is poor. Operation in the *linear mode* decreases distortion, but strong signals result in much greater output than do weak signals.

A superregenerative detector that is provided with two tuned circuits, so that it can generate its own quench-signal as well as the high-frequency oscillations, is said to be *self-quenching.*

Heterodyne Detector

When an unmodulated signal is applied to any of the preceding detector circuits, rectification of the signal occurs, but no audio output is produced. Reception of c-w signals therefore requires a provision for generating an audible tone. Consequently, a local oscillator, called the *beat-frequency oscillator,* is used to generate a signal at a slightly different frequency (within the audio range) from that of the transmission. By applying both the transmitted signal and the local signal to a nonlinear device such as a detector, sum and difference frequencies, in addition to the original frequencies, are produced. Suitable filters in the output circuit then pass the audio difference frequency on to the following stages. When the transmission is tone-modulated, the usual methods of detection previously described are satisfactory, and heterodyne detection is unsuitable. Tone modulation is employed when stabilization of the transmitter frequency is difficult.

Control Circuits

Since selectivity and sensitivity are improved in the t-r-f receiver, some methods of control are necessary in order to limit the output signals to reasonable or desirable limits. In the presence of weak received signals, all the possible amplification, or gain, of the receiver is desirable, whereas in the reception of strong signals, high gain results in excessive receiver output. Some control may also be necessary to improve the tonal qualities, or fidelity, of a receiver. Tuning controls, of course, are necessary to select the desired transmission, and often a means of selecting more than one frequency band is incorporated into the receiver. Some of these methods of control are conventional for all r-f or a-f circuitry; others, however, are peculiar to t-r-f receivers.

Manual Volume Control

A volume control, such as may be used in any audio amplifier, is equally well suited for use in the audio circuits of a radio receiver. Such a control consists of a potentiometer across which the input signal is applied. In a receiver, the audio output of the diode detector is impressed across the diode load resistor. By inserting a potentiometer in place of the resistor, a voltage-divider circuit is formed. The variable-amplitude output available at the center arm of the potentiometer is then applied to the grid of the first audio amplifier. The disadvantage of this type of volume control, used alone, is that the amplifiers are operated constantly at maximum gain, introducing additional tube noise, especially in the r-f stages.

An r-f gain control is often used in the receiver as a means of controlling the output level. This can be done by varying one of the controlling potentials applied to one or more of the r-f stages, such as the grid-bias, plate, or screen volt-

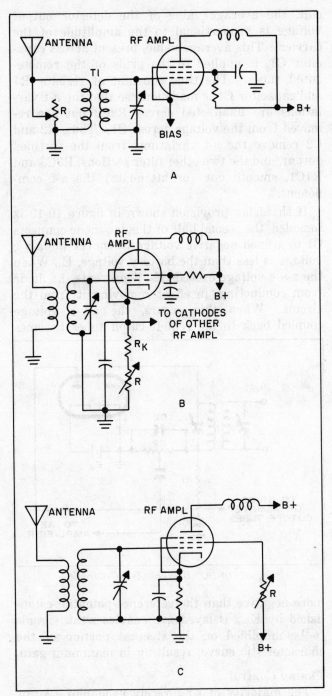

Figure 10-16. Manual R-F Gain-Control Circuits Used in T-R-F Receivers

first tuned circuit is lowered. The gain of the r-f stages is unaffected in this system.

A more desirable method, a true gain control, is presented in part B. The variable resistor, R, permits changing the bias and thus the gain of the r-f amplifier stage. A remote-cutoff, or variable-mu pentode, is used for this purpose. Varying the bias of a variable-mu tube causes the tube amplification factor and c i r c u i t gain to change smoothly. A limiting resistor, R_k, prevents the bias of the r-f amplifier from becoming zero when R is adjusted to a minimum value. By increasing the value of R, the bias is increased and the amplification is reduced. When using this method, the bias voltages of all the r-f amplifier stages are usually controlled simultaneously by connecting the cathodes of the tubes together.

In still another method, shown in part C, the gain of the r-f amplifier stage is controlled by varying the screen-grid current (and thus the screen-grid voltage), as by varying the variable screen resistor, R. The same effect can be produced by means of a variable resistor in the plate circuit of the amplifier.

Automatic Volume Control (AVC)

As its name suggests, an automatic-volume-control, or a-v-c, system maintains the signal applied to the detector of a receiver at a nearly constant amplitude. This condition can be attained only if the amplifying ability of the tubes used in the r-f stages of the receiver can be diminished in the presence of a strong signal. Accordingly, remote-cutoff tubes (also named *variable-mu* or *super-control* tubes) have been developed. Figure 10-17 shows a graphical comparison of the E_g-I_p characteristic of an ordinary sharp-cutoff pentode with that of a typical remote-cutoff type. For sharp-cutoff tubes there is only one region of linear operation. The tapering characteristic of remote-cutoff tubes, however, enables low-distortion operation over any region of the curve. The gain of the tube depends upon the steepness of the curve at the region selected. Consequently, at low values of negative bias the gain is relatively high, and at high values the gain is low, because the plate-current change produced by grid-voltage variations near the cutoff point is small. The use of these tubes in a-v-c applications has effectively eliminated crosstalk, a form of distortion which otherwise occurs when the variations of a strong signal extend into nonlinear regions of a sharp-cutoff characteristic.

ages. In figure 10-16, a few commonly used r-f gain control systems are shown. In part A, a variable resistor, R, is connected in parallel with the primary winding of the antenna transformer, T1. The lower the value of this resistor, the greater is its shunting effect and the lower the volume of the receiver. The disadvantage of this arrangement is that by shunting the primary of T1, the Q, and therefore the selectivity, of the

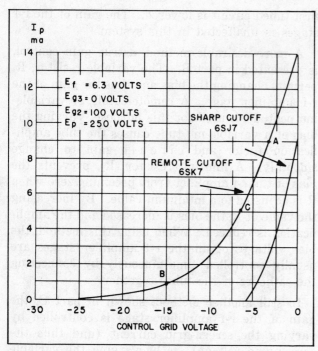

Figure 10-17. Comparison of Characteristic Curves of Sharp- and Remote-Cutoff Tubes

To maintain the carrier signal applied to the detector at a constant amplitude, it is necessary to vary the bias of remote-cutoff tubes in a suitable manner. Figure 10-18 shows a typical diode detector circuit with provision for a negative voltage that varies with the magnitude of the received signal. The filter composed of resistor R2 and capacitor C2 yields a varying voltage, which is a replica of the modulating intelligence of the carrier. This a-f signal is at all times negative with respect to ground, because the diode conducts in one direction only. In a properly designed cir-

cuit, the average value of the detector output voltage is proportional to the amplitude of the carrier. This average value, present across capacitor C1, is applied to the grids of the remote-cutoff tubes. The time constant of resistor R1 and capacitor C1 is made long so that the a-f variations are unaffected across R2C2 but are removed from the voltage across C1. Thus, R2 and C2 remove the r-f variations from the rectified output, and the two other filter sections, R3C3 and R1C1, smooth out (or attenuate) the a-f component.

If the delay provision shown in figure 10-19 is included, the second half of the duo-diode connects C1 to a fixed negative voltage whenever the a-v-c voltage is less than the battery voltage, E_d. When the a-v-c voltage exceeds E_d, it prevents the diode from conducting, in effect removing it from the circuit. When this occurs, the a-v-c voltage coupled back to the remote-cutoff tubes becomes

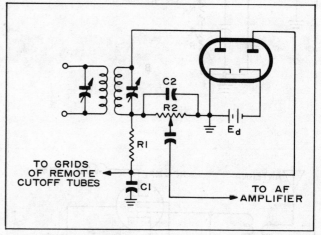

Figure 10-19. Delayed A-V-C Circuit

more negative than the reference potential established by E_d. Delayed avc enables weak signals to be amplified on the steepest portion of the characteristic curve, resulting in maximum gain.

Tuning Control

The majority of t-r-f receivers employ two or three stages of r-f amplification. In order to effect simultaneous tuning of all stages, the various tuning capacitors are constructed as a single unit using a common shaft. The capacitors are then said to be *ganged*. This feature necessitates identical stages, so that all will be tuned to the same frequency over the frequency range covered. A small *trimmer* capacitor, which serves as a compensating device for irregularities, is connected across each tuning capacitor. The process of adjusting the trimmers so that tuning will be con-

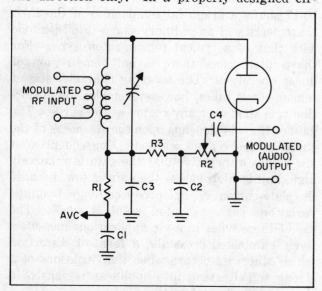

Figure 10-18. Diode Detector Circuit with AVC

tinuously accurate is known as *alignment*. When alignment has been accomplished successfully, the stages are said to be *tracking*.

When the frequency spectrum of the tuning range is crowded, it is frequently helpful to "spread out" a small section of the tuning range over the entire scale of a separate tuning dial. This can be done in two ways. The *bandspread dial* may be geared mechanically to the *main dial*, so that the former moves considerably during only a small movement of the main dial. Another expedient is to connect a small tuning capacitor in parallel with the main one. If the small capacitor is connected to a tap on the coil, its tuning range will be an even smaller fraction of the band.

When more than one band of frequencies must be covered, the receiver includes an arrangement for using different sets of coils. One method is to mount the coils in the receiver, and switch in the appropriate set by means of a multicontact rotary switch (*band-switch*). Another method is to plug in the appropriate set.

10-4 TYPICAL T-R-F RECEIVER CIRCUIT

A typical 5-tube t-r-f receiver is shown in figure 10-20. In this receiver, the antenna is coupled by an r-f transformer to the first r-f amplifier stage. The r-f signal is amplified in three stages of t-r-f amplification. Pentode tubes are used throughout the receiver for high gain. The gain of the receiver is sufficient to take advantage of the highly linear, though relatively insensitive, infinite-impedance detector, to which the last r-f stage is coupled. An audio volume control is used at the input to the a-f stage. A power pentode in the single audio stage provides enough output to drive the loudspeaker.

A tuning capacitor is employed in the input circuit of each r-f stage, and also in the detector. These four tuning capacitors are ganged for single-control tuning, as indicated by the dotted lines in the diagram. A small trimmer capacitor is connected in parallel with each section of the ganged tuning capacitor to permit accurate alignment of the tuned circuits.

Heater and plate voltages for the vacuum tubes are provided by the standard power supply. Since all tubes operate with cathode bias, or self-bias, no separate bias supply is required for this receiver.

To prevent instability and regeneration, each r-f stage must, of course, be well shielded. In addition, an isolating resistor and bypass capacitor are inserted in the plate lead of each of the three r-f amplifiers. These R-C combinations form decoupling filters — the resistor offering impedance to the r-f signal currents, which the associated bypass capacitors shunt to ground. If these filters were not present, the r-f stages would be coupled together through the common plate supply impedance, and regeneration would be likely to result through the common signal path offered by the plate supply leads.

Limitations of T-R-F Receiver

Although a t-r-f receiver is reasonably satisfactory when designed to cover a single band at the lower frequencies, such as the broadcast band, there are a number of disadvantages. The most important one is the variation of selectivity over the tuning range, the selectivity at the high-frequency end being poorer. Related to this effect is the decrease in amplification at the higher frequencies. Crosstalk effects, a form of distortion, are difficult to avoid when a large number of r-f stages are present. Finally, oscillatory tendencies become more serious as the number of stages is increased.

When a group of cascaded stages derives power from the same d-c source, part of the output signal from a particular stage is present across the internal impedance of the d-c power source. Unless preventive steps are taken, this small voltage may be fed back to any prior input circuit except the first. Since the phase of the output signal of an amplifier is the same as that of the input signal applied to the preceding stage, an amplifier consisting of several stages (usually three or more) has a tendency to oscillate. To overcome this tendency, a decoupling filter is placed in series with the load impedance of all amplifying stages but the last two. A typical decoupling filter is simply a resistor-capacitor combination, arranged so as to attenuate the feedback signal between plate and ground from one amplifier stage to the next. By this means the oscillatory tendency of a cascaded amplifier is partially suppressed.

Shielding of the receiver also helps prevent oscillation due to feedback. The added expense of shielding and decoupling filters between stages must be incurred to prevent instability and oscillation. This instability is present because the entire amplification takes place at the same signal frequency, and, therefore, the slightest coupling between output and input results in large feedback. Finally, the t-r-f receiver is not practical

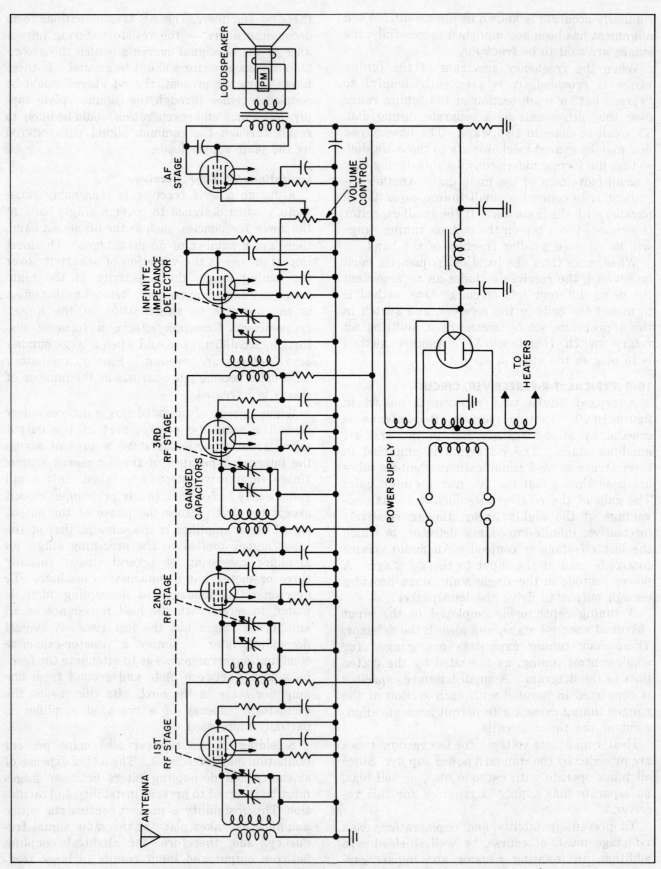

Figure 10-20. Schematic Diagram of a Typical T-R-F Receiver

for use at high frequencies and as a multiband receiver, since its selectivity and amplification fall off rapidly at the higher frequencies.

10-5 SUMMARY

A radio receiver intercepts a tiny portion of the radio energy radiated by a transmitter and recovers the intelligence contained in it. In the process of radio reception a receiver performs five functions: interception, selection, amplification, detection, and reproduction of the desired signal. A crystal receiver consists of an antenna, a tuned input circuit, a crystal detector, and a reproducer. A t-r-f receiver has, besides an antenna, one or more stages of r-f amplification, a detector, an audio amplifier, and a reproducer.

All the tuned circuits of a t-r-f receiver operate at the frequency of the incoming signal. A t-r-f amplifier has a tuned input circuit for signal selection and a vacuum tube for amplification. Successive amplifier stages are usually coupled through r-f transformers. Selectivity is the ability of a receiver to differentiate between the desired signal frequency and all unwanted signal frequencies. The sensitivity of a receiver (ability with which it receives weak signals) is expressed in microvolts for a standard output. Signal-to-noise ratio limits the usable sensitivity of a receiver; it is the ratio of signal strength to noise present at the input of a receiver. Fidelity is the characteristic of a receiver which permits it to amplify a band of frequencies containing the modulation without discrimination or distortion; it is determined essentially by the bandpass of the receiver and its tuned circuits.

The t-r-f amplifier helps to prevent radiation of r-f energy produced in oscillatory circuits when they are incorporated within the receiver. The antenna coupling can be direct, capacitive, or by a tuned or untuned transformer. The tuned transformer is most widely used. Shielding is necessary to prevent direct radiation and to minimize feedback.

Detection, or demodulation, is performed by rectifying the modulated carrier and filtering out the rf. The result is an audio frequency which corresponds to the modulation at the transmitter. A linear detector develops a rectified output proportional to the amplitude of the r-f input voltage, whereas a square-law detector has an output proportional to the square of the amplitude of the r-f input. A weak-signal, or square-law, detector is intended for small r-f inputs, while a power detector is designed to rectify relatively large r-f inputs. The signal-handling capability of a detector is its ability to rectify relatively large signal inputs with a minimum of distortion. Square-law detection is obtained by operation on the curved portion of the characteristic curve of either a vacuum tube or a crystal or metallic diode. Likewise, triodes and pentodes may be operated in this fashion, or operation may be on the linear portion of the curve to provide linear detection.

A t-r-f receiver gives good performance for a single low- or medium-frequency band, but is not practical for use at high frequencies, since its selectivity and sensitivity fall off rapidly with frequency. It is also inherently unstable.

REVIEW QUESTIONS

1. Describe the essential functions of a receiver.
2. How is the signal detected in a crystal receiver?
3. Describe the essential parts of a t-r-f receiver.
4. Define *selectivity*, *sensitivity*, *fidelity*, and *signal-to-noise ratio*.
5. How does a t-r-f stage suppress radiation?
6. What are the various types of antenna coupling, and what are the advantages of each?
7. Why is shielding necessary in t-r-f receivers?
8. What happens in the process of detection?
9. Define the following terms: *linearity*, *weak-signal detection*, *power detection*, and *square-law detection*.
10. Describe the operation of a grid-leak detector, a plate detector, and an infinite-impedance detector.
11. Describe the various methods of obtaining volume control.
12. What is the function of decoupling filters in t-r-f receivers, and why are they necessary?
13. List the advantages and disadvantages of a t-r-f receiver.
14. How are single-control tuning and band selection obtained in a t-r-f receiver?
15. Define *tracking* and *alignment*.

CHAPTER ELEVEN

The Radio Receiver and Special Receiver Circuits

11-1 Introduction

The modern radio receiver possesses circuit arrangement and construction characteristics which eliminate the shortcomings of the tuned-radio-frequency receiver. As mentioned before, the trf receiver permitted a communications system which was more effective and reliable than that previously possible. However, the trf receiver was incapable of producing a high uniform voltage gain of the incoming radio signal because of the likelihood of oscillations occurring between the common-tuned stages. Also, the trf receiver could not provide adequate selectivity of signals in areas where transmitters were operating at close frequencies. The problems of reliable radio reception and of adequate coverage for both communications and entertainment purposes were solved by the use of the superheterodyne principle.

The superheterodyne receiver has become standard in almost all radio communications applications. In this type of radio receiver the incoming r-f signal is mixed with a signal generated within the receiver to produce a resultant signal, which is usually lower in frequency than the received r-f carrier. This lower frequency signal, known as the *intermediate frequency*, is then amplified in constant-gain circuits, demodulated, and applied to a reproducing device such as a loudspeaker. The superheterodyne principle, as first applied, is still used, but through the development of superior components and additional special circuits the modern receiver is c a p a b l e of greatly improved performance.

11-2 SUPERHETERODYNE RECEIVER

Before entering into a detailed discussion of the principles of heterodyne action, or frequency conversion, refer to figure 11-1 for illustration of a basic amplitude-modulated superheterodyne receiver in block diagram form. The radiated wave envelope from the transmitter is intercepted by the antenna and selected in the input circuit of the variable-tuned radio-frequency amplifier. The low signal voltage is amplified and applied to the mixer stage. Also applied to the mixer stage is an unmodulated radio-frequency signal generated in the local oscillator circuit. The resultant action of the mixer stage, through selective tuning in its output, is to produce an intermediate frequency, which is the difference between the carrier and local oscillator frequencies. For the sake of illustration, assume that the r-f amplifier is selecting a frequency of 1200 kc and the local oscillator is tuned to 1655 kc; the difference would be 455 kc. An intermediate-frequency amplifier circuit accepts the intermediate frequency and amplifies it greatly for application to the detector circuit, which, in turn, extracts the modulation component and applies it to the audio amplifier and loudspeaker for conversion into audible sound waves.

One of the important features to be noted is the mechanical tuning link indicated in figure 11-1. This link tunes the output frequency of the local oscillator simultaneously with the fre-

quency selection of the r-f amplifier, thus providing a constant i-f difference frequency from the mixer stage regardless of the carrier frequency selected. With this type of arrangement, the resultant modulated signal applied to the detector is constant over the receiver tuning range.

Intermediate-Frequency Amplifiers

The intermediate-frequency amplifier section of a superheterodyne receiver is equal in importance to the principle of heterodyning, since the i-f amplifier contributes most of the receiver's amplification and selectivity. In this discussion of radio receivers, the i-f amplifier circuit will be presented first; therefore, it should be assumed by the reader that the desired frequency has been selected (in the r-f amplifier stage), and that frequency conversion in the mixer has resulted in the generation of the modulation-bearing i-f signal.

General Considerations

The i-f amplifier section of a superheterodyne receiver may contain one or several stages. These stages usually use high-gain pentode receiving type tubes. Since these circuits are required to amplify only the i-f signal, their coupling circuits can be adjusted once for optimum amplification and selectivity without any need for further tuning during receiver operation. A typical i-f amplifier circuit is illustrated in figure 11-2.

The i-f amplifier must be capable of passing not only the intermediate-frequency, but also the

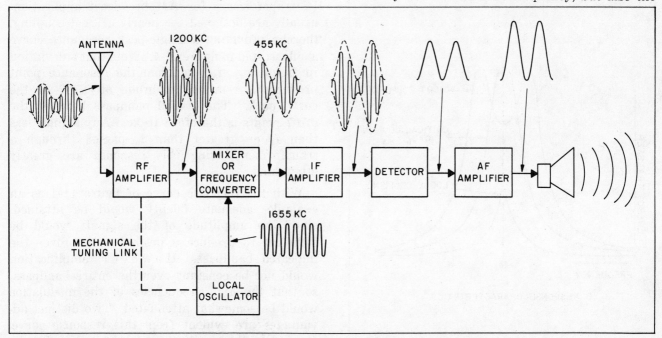

Figure 11-1. Basic Superheterodyne Receiver

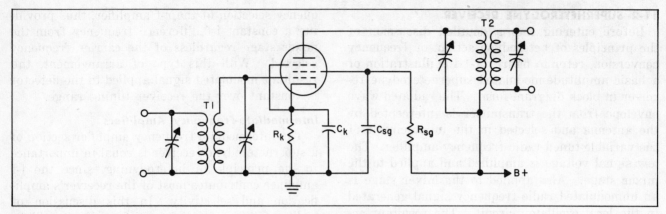

Figure 11-2. I-F Amplifier Circuit

siderbands caused by the modulation impressed on the original carrier at the transmitter. Therefore, the i-f amplifier must have the same fidelity as required for the r-f amplifier in order not to reject any portion of the modulation-bearing sideband frequencies. In standard AM broadcast applications the spacing between channels is 10 kc.

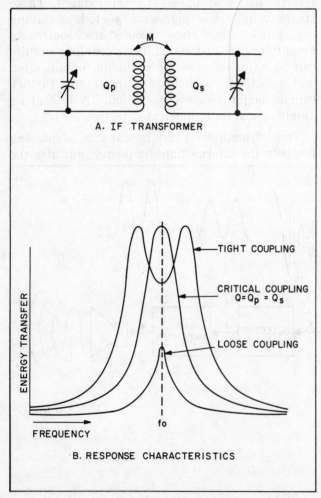

Figure 11-3. Effects of Degrees of Coupling

Bandpass Characteristics

The principles of tuned circuits apply to the i-f amplifier section, since coupling between stages is usually accomplished by means of double-tuned resonant circuits. Recall from the explanation of tuned amplifiers, that the response curve depends mainly upon the degree of coupling. Loose coupling provides a low-efficiency transfer of energy but a sharp resonance point; critical coupling (where the Q of the primary and secondary are equal) allows maximum transfer of energy with a broader resonant point; and tight coupling produces a double-peaked response curve with a wide bandpass. These effects are shown in figure 11-3.

In actual practice the i-f transformers are constructed so that the coupling is fixed. Standard i-f transformers for AM broadcast applications usually are designed for nearly critical coupling, thereby providing a single-peak resonance curve as illustrated in figure 11-4. Note that a deviation in frequency of 5 kc from the resonance point produces a relative amplitude of 0.707 of the curve peak. The overall bandpass between the 0.707 points is therefore 10 kc. Any signals less than f_1 or greater than f_2 passed through a transformer having this response are greatly attenuated.

With the response curve of figure 11-4 as an example, adequate fidelity would be attained, since the amplitude of the signals would be sufficient to produce a desired output over the indicated bandpass. However, amplification would not be constant over the entire bandpass, so that the high frequencies of the modulation would be somewhat attenuated. Two distinct advantages are evident from this response curve. One is that the sensitivity would be high due to the relatively high peak at the resonant frequency, thus allowing maximum transfer of signal and resulting in greater gain per stage. The other is good selectivity, since the frequencies below and above the bandpass limits would be greatly attenuated.

If a broader bandpass were desired from a single resonant-peak circuit, the tuning capacitors in the i-f transformer, as illustrated in part A of figure 11-3, could be adjusted so that the primary would be resonant to a frequency lower than f_o and the secondary resonant to a frequency higher

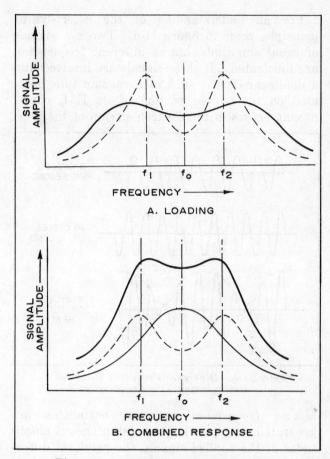

Figure 11-5.   Methods of Reducing Dip in Double-Peaked Resonant Curve

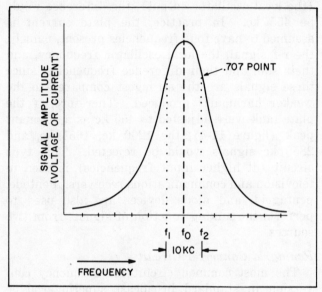

Figure 11-4.   Bandpass as Measured at the Half-Power Points

than f_o. The resultant bandpass would be wider; however, lower sensitivity and poorer selectivity would result. This technique is called *stagger tuning*, a term also applied to the tuning of several interstage transformers to slightly different frequencies for the same purpose.

More elaborate communications receivers may employ double-peaked i-f transformers for constant amplification of frequencies within the required bandpass. One disadvantage of double-peaked, or over-coupled, tuned circuits can be readily seen by noting the dip in the resonance curve illustrated for tight coupling in part B of figure 11-3. There are two common methods used to smooth out the dip in the resonance curve. The first method is to place a loading resistance across the secondary, which lowers the effective Q and produces a resultant response as illustrated in part A of figure 11-5. However, this method greatly reduces the relative signal strength. The second, and possibly the more common, method is

to use the effects of two double-tuned stages of i-f amplification, the first being coupled to produce double peaks and the second being single-peak tuned. The resultant response would be as indicated in part B of figure 11-5.

Intermediate-frequency amplifiers, just as r-f amplifiers, are biased for class A operation, and the gain of an i-f amplifier section is dependent upon the individual amplifier circuit gains.

Frequency Conversion

Conversion of the r-f input signal to an i-f signal, to be amplified by i-f amplifiers with high gain and good stability, is the basic feature that distinquishes a superheterodyne from other types of receivers. The frequency conversion function is usually performed by either a mixer circuit with a separate oscillator or by a pentagrid converter circuit.

Mixer circuits are used to combine two frequencies, the input signal and a local oscillator signal, in order to produce a new frequency, which is usually the difference or beat frequency between the two. This action is called *heterodyning*.

For an understanding of the heterodyning principle, refer to figure 11-6. Two c-w signals of equal amplitude, but of different frequencies, are illustrated. If these signals are inserted into a nonlinear device, such as a vacuum tube operated on the curved portion of its E_g-I_p curve, mixing occurs in the electron stream of the tube.

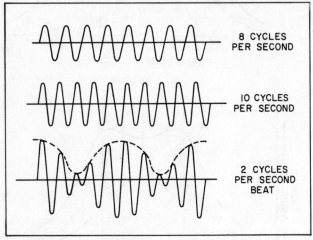

Figure 11-6. Difference Frequency Produced by Heterodyning Two Frequencies

Many frequencies, including harmonics, are generated. By plotting the instantaneous amplitudes of the applied signals, the resultant difference, or *beat* frequency (in this case a two-cycle beat note) is seen. Further, a modulation envelope present on the weaker of the two c-w signals, appears superimposed on the beat frequency as a result of the mixing, or heterodyning, action in the electron stream of the vacuum tube.

In the application of the heterodyne frequency conversion principle to the superheterodyne receiver, attention is directed primarily to the difference frequency between the carrier and the local oscillator signals. Selection of the difference frequency is made in a tuned circuit (tank) in the plate circuit of the mixer tube. The simplest type of mixer circuit, where the two signals are fed to the control grid of a triode amplifier stage, is illustrated in part A of figure 11-7. The bias is such that the tube operates on the nonlinear portion of the E_g-I_p curve to produce heterodyning of the signals. The plate circuit would be tuned so that a resonance curve similar to that of figure 11-4 would occur. Assuming that the input signals are 1200 kc (the r-f signal) and 1655 kc (the local oscillator output), the difference would be 455 kc. In practice, the plate current is assumed to have four frequencies present, namely, the r-f signal, the local oscillator frequency, and their sum and their difference frequencies, since these signals are the strongest compared to the weaker harmonics produced. Therefore, if the plate tank were adjusted to 455 kc as a resonant peak (figure 11-4), the 1200 kc, 1655 kc, and 2855 kc signals would be rejected. This type circuit (at higher input frequencies) is used in television and communications receivers. Pentode, pentagrid, and diode devices are also used to perform the mixing function of signals from two sources.

Pentagrid Converter Circuit

The most common circuit for frequency conversion in standard broadcast superheterodyne receivers is the pentagrid converter. A pentagrid converter (part B of figure 11-7) uses a single stage as both oscillator and mixer. A portion of a multigrid tube acts as the local-oscillator section, while another portion acts as the mixer.

The pentagrid tube is generally used in a single-stage converter circuit. However, various dual

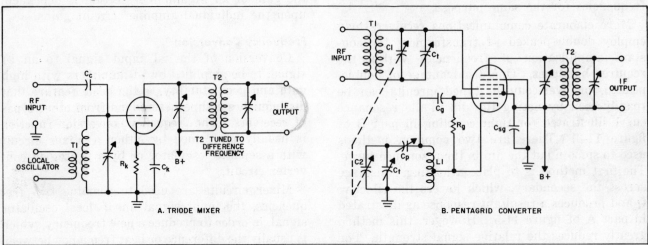

Figure 11-7. Frequency Conversion Circuits

tubes, such as a dual triode or a heptode-triode, may also be used to serve local oscillator and mixer functions.

The pentagrid converter of part B of figure 11-7 uses the cathode, grid 1 as control grid, and grids 2 and 4 as the plate of the oscillator section. A conventional series-fed Hartley oscillator circuit is illustrated in this particular case. This arrangement, in which the oscillator grid is closest to the cathode, provides what is called *inner-grid signal injection*. Between grids 3 and 4 there is a strong tendency for electrons to accumulate and build up a space charge. This space charge acts as a virtual cathode for the mixer portion of the tube, the amount of charge at any instant being dependent upon the instantaneous potential of grid 1. Electrons from this space-charge region are drawn to the plate of the tube in accordance with the potential on grid 3, which is varied by the r-f input signal. The oscillator signal modulates the electron stream from the cathode, while the r-f input signal varies the tube current reaching the plate. Therefore, the two signals are mixed, and the plate tank selects the desired difference frequency.

Choice of Intermediate Frequency

In almost all AM receivers in applications below approximately 10 megacycles, an intermediate frequency of 455 kc is used. This frequency has been chosen as a compromise to provide good selectivity and gain, along with good *image frequency* rejection.

For every frequency to which a superheterodyne receiver may be tuned, there is an image frequency, which is either higher or lower than that of the local oscillator by an amount equal to the intermediate frequency. If the frequency of the local oscillator is lower than the incoming-signal frequency, the image signal is lower in frequency than that of the oscillator, and the difference between the image and the desired signal is twice the intermediate frequency. Similarly, if the frequency of the oscillator is higher than that of the desired signal, the image frequency is higher than the signal frequency by an amount again equal to twice the intermediate frequency.

Unless the circuit selectivity ahead of the mixer is capable of satisfactorily attenuating the image signal, it will be heard in the output of the receiving set. Figure 11-8 illustrates image frequency response in a superheterodyne receiver. The receiver is assumed tuned to 840 kc, and the

response of the resonant circuits preceding the mixer is displayed in part A of the figure. With the local oscillator operating at a frequency of 175 kc above that of the desired signal, the image frequency is 1190 kc. In view of the broad frequency-selectivity characteristic of t h e tuned circuits ahead of the mixer, a strong signal at 1190 kc may not be entirely suppressed. In general, the i m a g e rejection capability of a receiver is stated as the ratio of the input required at the image frequency to the signal

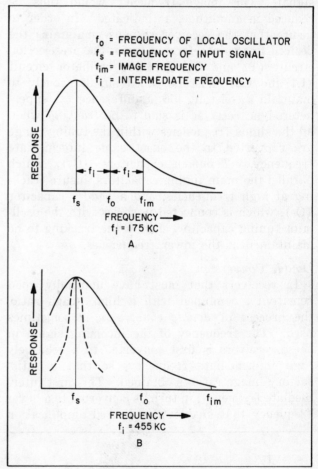

f_o = FREQUENCY OF LOCAL OSCILLATOR
f_s = FREQUENCY OF INPUT SIGNAL
f_{im} = IMAGE FREQUENCY
f_i = INTERMEDIATE FREQUENCY

Figure 11-8. Image Frequency Response of a Superheterodyne Receiver

required at the normal frequency to produce output signals of the same magnitude. This ratio is known as the *image ratio* or *image-interference ratio*, of the receiver. Image interference is greatly reduced when this ratio is sufficiently high.

A receiver with an improved image ratio is shown in part B of figure 11-8. In this case, the intermediate frequency is 455 kc, and the image signal is 1750 kc. With this increased separation from the desired signal (840 kc) there probably will be sufficient attenuation to reject the image. If the separation of the received signal and the local oscillator were further increased (thereby causing a higher i-f frequency), the result would be reduced selectivity and gain of the i-f stages.

Referring to part B of figure 11-7, assume that the tuned input circuit consisting of T1 and C1 has a frequency response similar to that of part B of figure 11-8, and also that the local oscillator portion of the converter is 455 kc above the input signal. The image frequency would thus be reduced in amplitude, as indicated. In order to insure that the receiver response maintains the desired image-interference ratio, the preselection circuit (T1 and C1) and the oscillator circuit (L1 and C2) must be tuned simultaneously to maintain a constant 455 kc difference. A superheterodyne receiver is said to be *tracking* when all the signal frequencies within the tuning range are converted to the exact same intermediate frequency. *Trimmer* capacitors (C_T), which parallel the main tuning capacitors, insure tracking at high frequencies, and a *padder* capacitor (C_P), which is connected in series with the oscillator tuning capacitor, enables the tracking to be maintained at the lower frequencies.

Double Conversion

In receivers that must have unusually good sensitivity, combined with a high image ratio, the process of *double conversion* is sometimes used. The frequency of the incoming signal in these receivers is first converted to a relatively high intermediate frequency, so that a satisfactory image ratio is obtained. This first intermediate frequency, in turn, is converted to a lower frequency that enables the desired amplification

to be obtained. A block diagram of a possible double conversion arrangement is shown in figure 11-9. Note that the second local oscillator operates at a fixed frequency.

Typical Superheterodyne Receiver

A typical 7-tube superheterodyne receiver suitable for AM broadcast reception is shown in figure 11-10. It consists of one stage of tuned r-f amplification, a pentagrid converter, one stage of i-f amplification, a detector and separate a-v-c diode, a first a-f voltage amplifier stage, and a push-pull a-f power amplifier stage. The receiver is operated from the 115 volt a-c power line through a filtered, full-wave rectifier d-c power supply. Understanding of the function of the individual circuits and components can be acquired from a circuit analysis.

Input and R-F Amplifier

A signal intercepted by the receiver antenna is coupled to the grid of the r-f amplifier tube, V1, through the r-f input transformer, T1. The grid input circuit is tuned to the desired signal by a tank circuit consisting of the secondary of T1 and the variable capacitor, C2. C2 is ganged to both the oscillator and converter tuning capacitors. The selected signal, amplified in the plate circuit of V1, is coupled to the converter stage through the r-f coupling transformer, T2. An a-v-c voltage is applied to the grid of V1 through decoupling resistor R1. Decoupling is provided by R1 and C1 in the grid circuit, R3 and C4 in the screen circuit, and R4 and C5 in the plate circuit. R3 also provides a lower screen voltage for the tube. The tube operates class A with cathode bias, produced by the cathode resistor, R2. C3 is the

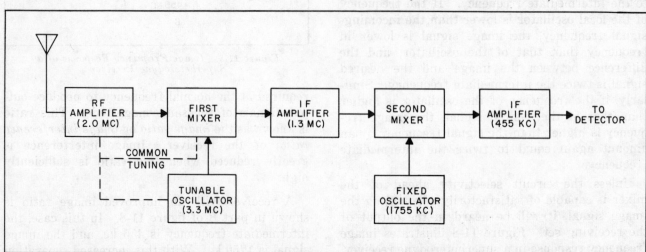

Figure 11-9. Block Diagram of Double Conversion Tuner

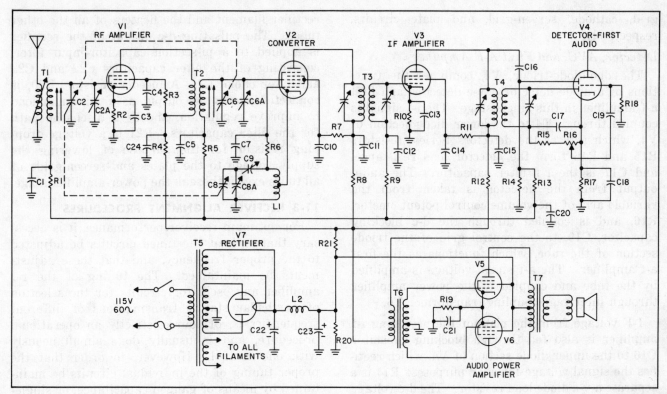

Figure 11-10. Superheterodyne Receiver

cathode-bypass capacitor, and C2A is a trimmer capacitor in parallel with the main tuning capacitor C2.

Converter

The converter performs the combined functions of generating a local oscillator frequency and of mixing this frequency with the received signal to produce the desired intermediate frequency. L1 and C8 form the oscillator tank circuit of a Hartley oscillator. The cathode of V2 is connected to a tap on the oscillator coil, and the cathode path to ground is through the lower end of the coil. Operating bias is provided by the grid-leak resistor R6 and grid capacitor C7. C8A is a trimmer across the oscillator section tuning capacitor, and C9 is the padder that enables oscillator tracking at the low-frequency end of the tuning range. Proper voltage for the screen grid, which forms the plate of the oscillator section of V2, is provided by the screen-grid voltage dropping resistor, R7, and decoupling of the r-f currents is effected by the screen-bypass capacitor, C10. The incoming r-f signal is selected by the tuned secondary of T2, applied to the signal-injection grid (grid 3) of V2, and mixed with the local oscillator frequency signal in the electron stream of the tube. C6, a section of the ganged

or main tuning capacitor, enables tuning of the secondary of T2 to the same frequency to which T1 is tuned. C6A is the trimmer capacitor for C6. A-V-C voltage is applied through R5 to the signal grid. Since the oscillator section is tuned to a higher (or lower) frequency than the selected signal carrier by an amount equal to the intermediate frequency, both of these signals are present at the plate of V2, along with the sum and difference frequencies. However, only the difference frequency is selected by the double-tuned i-f transformer, T3, the primary of which is in the plate circuit.

I-F Amplifier

The i-f amplifier stage is conventional, consisting of the pentode amplifier tube, V3, input i-f transformer, T3, and output i-f transformer, T4. Both double-tuned transformers are tuned to the i-f frequency. The i-f signal is coupled through T3 to the control grid of the tube, and the amplified output in the plate circuit is coupled through the output transformer to the diode-detector stage. Cathode bias for class A operation is produced by R10, and a-v-c voltage is applied to the control grid through R9, C12, C13, C14, and C15 are decoupling, or r-f bypass capacitors, for the grid, cathode, screen-grid, and plate circuits, respectively.

Detector, AVC, and First A-F Amplifier

The duo-diode-triode, V4, combines the functions of a diode detector, a-v-c detector, and first a-f amplifier in this single stage. The i-f signal is coupled through T4 to the lower diode section of V4, which acts as the detector. Series resistors R15 and R16 form the detector load resistance, and C17 is the r-f filter capacitor. The audio output from the detector is taken from the variable arm of the volume control potentiometer, R16, and is coupled through the d-c blocking capacitor, C19, to the control grid of the triode section of the tube, which functions as the first a-f amplifier. The a-f signal voltage is amplified by the tube and coupled to the power amplifier through interstage coupling transformer T6.

I-F voltage from the plate of the preceding i-f amplifier is also fed through blocking capacitor C16 to the upper diode section of V4, which rectifies the signal voltage for a-v-c purposes. R14 is a separate a-v-c diode load resistor. The d-c voltage across this resistor is applied as the a-v-c voltage to the grids of the r-f amplifier, converter, and i-f amplifier through the a-v-c filter (R13 and C20), which eliminates both the audio and r-f components from the a-v-c voltage. Proper bias for the operation of V4 is supplied by the cathode resistor, R17, and its bypass capacitor, C18. R18 is the grid resistor for the first a-f amplifier.

A-F Power Amplifier

The audio voltage output from the plate of V4 is fed to the grids of the pentode power-amplifier tubes, V5 and V6, through the interstage coupling transformer, T6. Since the amplifier is operated push-pull, the secondary of this transformer is center-tapped in order to apply the audio in opposite phase to the two tubes. The power-amplifier output is coupled to the voice coil of the loudspeaker through the center-tapped output transformer, T7. The transformer insures a correct match between the voice-coil impedance and the manufacturer's recommended plate-to-plate load impedance of the amplifier. Bias is supplied by the common cathode resistor, R19, and its bypass capacitor, C21.

Power Supply

The 115 volt, 60-cycle a-c line input is coupled to the plates of the full-wave rectifier tube, V7, through the power transformer, T5. The transformer has additional windings to supply the rectifier filament and the heaters of all the other tubes. The pulsating d-c output of the rectifier is applied to a pi-section capacitor-input filter, consisting of the filter capacitors C22 and C23 and filter choke L2. A bleeder resistor, R20, is connected across the output as a minimum load to improve regulation, and as a discharge path for the filter capacitors. R21 is a voltage-dropping resistor for the purpose of lowering the supply voltage to the plates and screen-grids of all tubes except those in the power-amplifier stage.

11-3 RECEIVER ALIGNMENT PROCEDURES

For optimum receiver performance, it is necessary that each of the tuned circuits be adjusted to the proper frequency, and that these adjustments be maintained. The tuning of the r-f amplifier and oscillator circuits for the selection of particular station transmissions of different frequencies is, of course, strictly an operational procedure, and is usually done simultaneously with one control. However, in order that the proper tuning of the individual circuits be maintained by means of ganged capacitance, or single-control tuning, the capacitors must be trimmed, so that each is adjusted in the same proportion to produce the proper intermediate frequency. This process, called *tracking*, must be included as a part of the over-all alignment of the receiver, in addition to peaking the tuned transformers. The end result of a satisfactory receiver alignment is maximum sensitivity and selectivity with minimum interference and distortion.

The order of procedure for aligning an AM receiver is to align first the i-f amplifiers, then the converter (or local oscillator) next the r-f amplifier (if used), and finally the antenna tuning circuits. The actual test equipment connections may vary from one receiver to another, but the steps always follow the same sequence.

Test Equipment Requirements

One of the most important items necessary for alignment of a modern receiver is a good signal generator. Signal generator requirements vary with the complexity and f r e q u e n c y of the receiving equipment. That is, a multiband communications receiver with variable selectivity and accurate calibration would require a precision signal generator, whereas such a generator would not be necessary to properly align a simple broadcast receiver with only a minimum of tuned stages. Often, the simple receiver can be satisfactorily aligned by tuning to a broadcast station

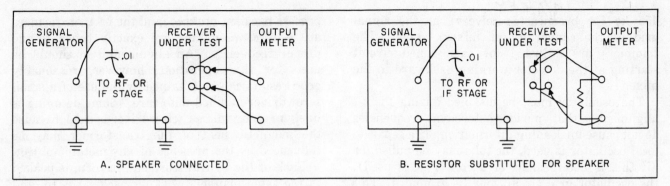

Figure 11-11.   Test Setups for Receiver Alignment

at the desired point in the band and making the necessary adjustments of the tuned circuits for maximum output. Since the frequencies of broadcast stations must be held to very close tolerance, a receiver so tuned may be more accurately calibrated than when an inferior signal generator is used. However, for satisfactory alignment of high-frequency o r multiband communications receivers, a good signal generator is a necessity. Also, a visual output indicator, such as an output meter, a voltmeter, or an oscilloscope is necessary, since a slight change in output may be more readily seen than heard.

Equipment Setup

The manufacturer's specifications should always be consulted, whenever possible, and the recommendations observed. In general, however, the equipment should be given a 15-minute warmup before alignment is attempted. This applies to the receiver, the signal generator, and the VTVM or the oscilloscope, if used.

The output-indicating device may be connected directly across the voice-coil leads of the receiver loudspeaker, or may be plugged into the phone jack (if the receiver is so equipped). In cases where it may be desirable to disconnect the loudspeaker, a suitable resistance must be substituted to provide the proper load for the power amplifier. This resistance should, as nearly as possible, match the impedance of the voice coil, or headset. Some output meters contain such a resistor, which may be inserted by means of a switch.

In figure 11-11 the equipment setup for both methods of output-meter connection are shown. In part A, the meter (or oscilloscope) is connected directly across the voice coil of the speaker, and no resistor is necessary. In part B, one of the leads to the voice coil is disconnected, and a resistor is substituted for the voice coil. The value of voice-coil impedance for most modern receivers is 3.2 ohms; therefore, a 3.2 ohm resistor should be used.

Proper impedance match should be maintained at the output of the signal generator, although this match is not critical for most purposes of alignment. The use of a shielded output lead is important to prevent stray pickup, and a blocking capacitor should be used to couple the signal to the desired point in the receiver. The capacitor must be used, when the signal is injected into the plate circuit of a tube in the receiver, to prevent the plate voltage from damaging the signal generator output-attenuator network.

Mechanical Alignment

During the equipment-warmup p e r i o d, the mechanical alignment of the tuning dial may be performed. The first step in the alignment procedure is to check the position of the tuning-dial pointer relative to the setting of the ganged tuning capacitors. This is done by setting the pointer over the first index mark at the low-frequency end of the dial (or dial backing plate), with the tuning capacitor fully meshed. After the 15-minute warmup period, set the receiver volume control to maximum and the bandswitch, if included, to the lowest band covered (usually the broadcast band). If an output meter is used as an indicating device, set the meter to its lowest range. If the indicator is a voltmeter or vtvm, it should be set on a low-voltage range, such as the 1.5-volt scale. If an oscilloscope is used, the output should be connected to the vertical input of the oscilloscope, and the horizontal gain should be minimized so that only a vertical line appears on the oscilloscope. With a calibrating voltage of 1.25 volts as a reference, a good-sized pattern should be obtained. The vertical-gain control should be left in this position during the rest of the alignment procedure, and the 1.25-volt calibration point noted for reference purposes.

I-F Amplifier Alignment

The i-f amplifier stages are aligned by injecting a signal at the intermediate frequency (usually

455 kc for broadcast receivers) at the signal grid of the converter (or mixer) stage. The trimmers are adjusted for each tuned circuit starting at the detector working backward to the mixer.

The oscillator must be disabled during the i-f alignment so that spurious heterodyne frequencies do not cause misleading information. If a separate local oscillator is used, the tube may be pulled, or (if this is not feasible, or a converter is used), the oscillator grid circuit may be grounded. This is easily done by shorting the variable tuning-capacitor plates of the oscillator section with a small screwdriver or clip inserted between the rotor and stator plates.

The a-v-c circuit must also be disabled during alignment, since a-v-c action would also cause misalignment. The avc is readily removed by grounding any point on the a-v-c bus. In some communications receivers a front-panel switch is provided for this purpose.

A modulated signal must be applied from the signal generator for the alignment process. Most signal generators provide internal modulation at 400 cycles for this purpose. Thirty-percent modulation should be used to avoid the possibility of overmodulation effects. This also reduces the amplitude of the sidebands and results in closer alignment.

The output of the signal generator is applied through a blocking capacitor (usually .01 mf) to the signal grid of the converter. The ground connection may be made at any chassis-ground point of the receiver, but preferably as near to the point of signal injection as practicable.

The signal-generator output level is adjusted until a small indication is noted on the output meter or oscilloscope. The volume control on the receiver should be kept at maximum during the alignment process, and the signal-generator output level reduced as required in order to maintain the output level under the prescribed amount (usually 1.5 volts). The reason for this is to prevent overloading of the amplifier, which causes false selectivity curves of the tuned circuits and hence results in improper alignment.

First the secondary of the last i-f transformer is adjusted for maximum output of the receiver, and then the primary is adjusted in the same manner. The final setting of the capacitors (or inductor slugs of permeability-tuned circuits) is very critical, and the closer to the point of maximum output that the adjustment is made, the better the alignment results. This part of the

process is called *peaking*, and the i-f transformers are *peaked* when they are exactly tuned to the proper frequency. An alignment tool should be used for this operation; however, reasonably good results can be obtained by the use of a small screwdriver handled with care. Some detuning is likely to occur when a screwdriver is used, because the magnetic field of the transformer may be influenced by the presence of any metallic object.

Each of the i-f transformers, in turn, is peaked in the same manner, working backwards to, and including, the output of the mixer or converter. The output of the signal generator m u s t be reduced whenever the output of the receiver exceeds the prescribed level of 1.5 volts.

In the case of a badly detuned receiver, there may be no output when the signal is applied at the converter stage. In such cases, it is preferable to inject the signal at the plate or grid of the last i-f stage. There is, then, only one double-tuned circuit in the signal path, and the desired setting may be more easily reached. When the proper setting is obtained, the signal injection may be made at the preceding stage and its output transformer adjusted in the same manner, working backwards to the mixer, stage by stage.

The entire i-f alignment process should be repeated at least once, since some interaction occurs between primary and secondary adjustments of tuned transformers.

If in doubt about the exact intermediate frequency of a particular receiver, it is best to refer to the manufacturer's data. If this is not possible, the correct frequency may be found by connecting the signal generator as previously described, and rotating the signal-generator frequency d i a l through the common intermediate frequencies until a signal is indicated at the output of the receiver. The most common i-f values for broadcast AM receivers are 175 kc, 262 kc, 455 kc, and 456 kc. Communications-type receivers m a y employ such values as 85 kc, 470 kc, and 1500 kc. If a broad peak is observed at the receiver output in the region of 270 kc, for example, it would be safe to assume that the correct value is 262 kc. It is also important to begin the search for the proper intermediate frequency with the signal generator at the high end of the range of possible i-f frequencies. In the case of broadcast receivers, for example, the signal generator tuning should be started at 500 kc and tuned down in frequency until the output is indicated at the receiver. The purpose of this is to prevent the harmonics of the signal-generator output from giving false indications. For instance, if the signal search were started at the low end of the i-f range, one might be misled by an output indication at the 230-kc setting, and assume the correct intermediate frequency is 262 kc. It would then be difficult to align the receiver. If, however, the search were continued upward in frequency, a greater output would be evident in the 455-kc frequency region. The first (erroneous) indication was caused by the second harmonic of the fundamental signal-generator frequency.

Once the proper i-f has been established, and repeated peaking of each i-f transformer results in no further increase in receiver output, the alignment of the i-f section is accomplished.

Oscillator Alignment

With the i-f amplifier section properly aligned, the next step involves the correct oscillator adjustment. The oscillator should a g a i n be made operative (by replacing the tube or removing the short circuit from the grid tank circuit). The a-v-c circuit, however, should be left inoperative, or grounded, during the entire oscillator alignment procedure.

The oscillator is adjusted first at the high end of the band. This is done by injecting a signal at the receiver dial frequency at the antenna input to the receiver. When a loop antenna is a part of the receiver, a loop antenna should also be used to couple the output of the signal generator to the receiver antenna. Such a loop may be formed by at least two turns about six inches in diameter of insulated wire. The loop is connected to the output of the signal generator, and placed about six inches from the receiver loop antenna and parallel to it. In the case of receivers not equipped with a loop antenna, the signal-generator output may be coupled to the antenna terminal through a 200-$\mu\mu$f blocking capacitor.

The receiver should be tuned to a point at the high end of the dial that is not in use by any local station (between 1500 and 1700 kc). Some receivers have an alignment mark engraved on the dial or dial blocking plate. The proper frequency for this point is usually given in the manufacturer's data as 1620 kc, and this frequency should be used when so specified. The signal generator is therefore set to this frequency and its output modulated. The oscillator trimmer is then carefully adjusted with an alignment tool for maximum indication on the output meter or oscilloscope. The output of the signal generator

should be reduced, if the output of the receiver exceeds the 1.5-volt reference level.

R-F Amplifier and Antenna Circuit Alignment

The r-f amplifier stages, if included in the receiver, are aligned at a slightly lower frequency than the oscillator to insure better tracking at the high end of the band. This is usually done at either 1500 kc or 1400 kc for the broadcast band. The signal generator, still connected to the antenna, is set to the desired frequency, and the receiver is tuned slowly about this frequency until maximum receiver output is indicated. The r-f trimmers of each r-f section of the ganged tuning capacitor are then adjusted, with the alignment tool, for maximum output. In the absence of an r-f stage in a receiver, the mixer or converter input is the antenna circuit. The antenna circuit is tuned in the same manner as an r-f stage.

Tracking

The oscillator and r-f circuits, once adjusted at the high end of the band, must also be aligned at the low end of the band to insure proper tracking.

The receiver dial is set near the low-frequency end, usually 600 kc for the broadcast band. The signal generator is set to this frequency, still connected as before. The oscillator padder is adjusted, by means of the alignment tool, for maximum output of the receiver. If there is no padder, the adjustment on the oscillator coil inductance is used.

Although the dial is set to 600 kc, there is no assurance that the r-f tuned circuits are resonant at 600 kc. The ideal alignment is obtained, when the r-f tuned circuits are resonant at 600 kc, and the oscillator is tuned to the intermediate frequency above 600 kc (1055 kc for a 455 kc intermediate frequency).

The adjustments for the r-f sections will vary, depending on the receiver. Whatever is provided, adjustment is made for maximum output. Possible provisions include padders, variable inductance, or slit rotor end-plates on tuning capacitor sections. The slit end-plates are bent toward the stator plate to increase capacitance (lower frequency) and vice versa. Bending these plates is tricky, tedious, and best avoided, if possible. Variable inductance causes more interaction with the high-frequency adjustment than does a padder capacitor.

After all adjustments are made at the low end of the band, the high end must be readjusted as before. This is because of the interaction of all adjustments. The e n t i r e process should be repeated at both ends of the band at least once, or until maximum output is obtained at all settings of the receiver dial. Final adjustments should always be made at the high end of the band. In some receivers, especially automobile radios, a small antenna trimmer capacitor is included in the antenna circuit. This is adjusted at the high end of the band for maximum receiver output.

In the case of multiband receivers, the i-f adjustments are the same, and the r-f and oscillator adjustments are made starting with the lowest band, and successively for each band up to the highest frequency covered.

11-4 RECEIVER TROUBLE-SHOOTING PROCEDURES

Home-radio and auto-radio broadcast receivers are usually operated without service, repairs, or alignment until they become inoperative. When this occurs, some form of trouble shooting must be employed to determine the defective component, and the repair or replacement then made. Some improvement over past performance is usually observed when the repair is followed by alignment of the receiver.

Communications receivers, on the other hand, are usually subjected to periodic operational checks and submitted for test or repair whenever operational checks show unsatisfactory performance.

Receiver trouble shooting may then be classed into two broad categories: the malfunctioning receiver, rendering reduced performance (where some signal can be heard), and the non-functioning, inoperative, or "dead" receiver.

Trouble Shooting the Malfunctioning Receiver

When any signal can be heard at the output of a receiver, trouble shooting is relatively simple. Usually all that is necessary is to make such tests or adjustments as are required to restore the receiver output to its normal value, level, or quality for a given input signal. Whenever tests or performance checks are made, any deficiencies should be noted on an accompanying tag. In the absence of such records, it may be necessary to make such performance checks before trouble shooting in order to determine the nature of the trouble.

Performance Checks

Performance checks vary with the particular requirements of a given installation, and are performed to determine the quality character-istics of a receiver, such as sensitivity, selectivity, and fidelity. For home-type receivers, such checks are merely an aural comparison with the original quality of each characteristic. In communications-type receivers, however, a calibrated signal-generator frequency is applied to the input, or antenna circuit, of the receiver and the values noted when a standard o u t p u t is obtained. Various tests are also made to determine such characteristics as hum and noise level, image rejection, tracking, oscillator drift, etc. Failure of such tests to reveal satisfactory performance indicates the sections or circuits to be searched for trouble. Poor sensitivity, for instance, accompanied by poor selectivity, may be the result either of misalignment or poor amplification, which in turn, may be the result of tube aging or failure, or the failure of some other component in an amplifier stage. If the selectivity, on the other hand, is not impaired, the alignment may be assumed to be satisfactory, and trouble may be suspected in an amplifier stage.

Naturally, alignment of a radio receiver will restore proper performance only if the rest of the receiver circuitry, including tubes and power supply, are functioning properly.

Signal Tracing and Signal Injection

Two simple methods may be used to find a faulty stage in a radio receiver. These are *signal tracing* and *signal injection* (or *signal substitution*, as it is often called).

Signal tracing is essentially a matter of tracing, or listening for, a signal, starting at the receiver input and working stage by stage to the output. The stage where the signal is lost, or not heard, is where trouble may be suspected. A signal, of course, must be present at the receiver input.

For signal tracing, a suitable high-gain oscilloscope having adequate frequency response for the range of r-f, i-f, and a-f circuits encountered, may be used. In the absence of a reasonably strong station signal, a signal-generator output should be coupled to the antenna terminals. The signal is first obtained with the oscilloscope connected to the antenna, or r-f input, and its pattern adjusted. The oscilloscope connections are then moved to the grid of the first r-f stage, where the signal should be present. The connections are next moved to the plate circuit, where an increase in signal amplitude should be noted. The process is repeated, moving successively first to the grid and then to the plate of each stage. The oscilloscope frequency controls should, of course, be adjusted when the output of the mixer and the detector are reached. A blocking capacitor or special probe should be used to connect the oscilloscope to the receiver circuits. A gain should be noted at each amplifier stage as the probe is moved from grid to plate of the tube. Little or no gain, of course, should be expected at the mixer or detector stages.

An audio device, such as a *signal tracer*, is often used instead of an oscilloscope. Such a device is essentially an audio amplifier and speaker (or meter) for use in the audio section of the receiver, with a detector probe for use in the r-f and i-f sections. In either case, the point where signal discontinuity is noted is the point where a search for the specific trouble should begin.

The second method for finding a faulty stage in a radio receiver is *signal injection*. Signal injection is a method whereby a signal is actually applied in turn to each stage in the signal path. In the signal injection method, the indicating device is either the receiver loudspeaker or a meter (or oscilloscope) connected at the speaker terminals. A signal is then applied at the grid and plate of each stage, moving from the final (audio power amplifier) stage forward until signal discontinuity is observed. An audio signal, of course, must be injected at the audio stages, a modulated i-f signal (at the proper i-f frequency) at the i-f stages, and a suitable, modulated r-f frequency (at the frequency indicated by the receiver dial), at the r-f and antenna circuits.

For either signal tracing or signal injection, the direction of search may be reversed. However, it is usually preferable to work from the known to the unknown in any troubleshooting procedure. It is often quicker, especially in the cases where no output can be heard at the speaker, to first ascertain if the audio section is working. Therefore, an audio test signal applied at the output of the audio amplifier should produce some sound at the speaker. A click should be heard when even a low d-c voltage is applied to the speaker terminals. If not, the speaker itself may be at fault. Any audio signal, such as from a phonograph or audio oscillator, applied to the audio amplifier input, should result in a substantial output. If not, the audio amplifier or power supply may be at fault.

Trouble Shooting the Non-Functioning Receiver

When a receiver is "dead", or totally inoperative, there are many possibilities as to the location of the fault. Not to be overlooked are the more obvious troubles, such as broken, defective, or unplugged cables or cords (including power and antenna connections), blown fuses, switches in improper position, and defective or improperly positioned tubes or batteries. Visual inspection should be made to determine whether or not the tube filaments are lit. If not, the trouble may be in the power supply or the filament circuit. In series-connected tube-filament circuits, if any one tube filament is burnt out, the circuit is open. A listening test may reveal a fault such as open filter capacitors, which cause a loud hum to be present at the speaker or output regardless of volume control setting. A check of the B-plus voltage usually reveals whether or not the power supply is functioning properly. Further analysis by means of a step-by-step procedure should be made, if these initial steps have not revealed the trouble.

There are several basic methods of troubleshooting a defective radio receiver. The availability of equipment is perhaps the primary factor governing choice of the method, although the method used may be dictated by personal choice. In any case, a logical approach requires following a step-by-step procedure.

Step-by-Step Procedure

Four easy-to-follow steps, which can be applied to trouble shooting any electronic equipment, are the following:

1. Establish the *symptoms*.
2. *Localize* the fault to a major function.
3. *Isolate* the trouble to a unit or circuit.
4. *Locate* the specific trouble within the unit or circuit.

The first step in finding a fault in a radio receiver, as in any electronic equipment, is to establish the symptoms of the trouble. Once these are established, an analysis of the trouble or fault may be made. Often this takes but a few moments, or it may take considerable time. The time consumed in a proper analysis is usually repaid in time and effort saved in the steps that follow.

By proper analysis, the fault may be *localized* to a major function, such as tuning, detection, amplification, control, or power.

The next step is to *isolate* the trouble or fault to a unit, sub-unit, circuit, or stage responsible for the fault. Careful observation of the performance of a receiver when power is first applied often helps to localize the fault. Often a stage-by-stage signal-tracing procedure will pinpoint a defective stage, when the trouble is in the signal path. A voltage check at any major junction of the B-plus leads will indicate power supply troubles or shorted components if this voltage is abnormally low.

Location of the specific trouble within a unit, circuit, or stage may be made in a number of ways. Tube faults can be eliminated by tube testing or substitution. Plug-in units or components may be checked by direct substitution, when such parts known to be good are available. Burned or charred resistors can often be spotted by visual observation or by smell. The same holds true for oil- or wax-filled components, such as capacitors, chokes, and transformers. When overheated, the oil or wax in these components expands and usually leaks out, or perhaps causes the case to buckle, or even explode. Overheated components can be located quickly by touch. Thus the senses of sight, smell, touch, and hearing can be used to locate many defective components. Voltage and resistance measurements may be made and compared with the proper values in the manufacturer's data.

11-5 SPECIAL RECEIVER CIRCUITS

So far, only the basic receiver circuits have been considered. Present-day producers manufacture a variety of receiver models, some of which offer simplicity of design, construction, and, consequently, reduced cost. Still others, more complex in nature, offer simplicity of operation, better control, or provide for inclusion of the receiver in a multiple-unit system. Further variations include receivers designed for auto, marine or aircraft installation. Portable operation demands reduction in weight and structural size and the inclusion of batteries as a power source. Some of these variations are straightforward and require no special consideration, but others require the use of special circuitry which may be troublesome, even to a skilled electronic technician. A few of the many special circuit applications which affect the actual receiver circuitry will be presented here.

Tuning Indicators

Highly selective m o d e r n superheterodyne receivers are difficult to tune to the center (carrier) frequency of t h e incoming signal accurately. Mistuning causes sideband cutting and consequent distortion. Because the a-v-c circuit tends to maintain the loudness level of the receiver output, even for considerable mistuning,

it is difficult to judge by ear alone when the receiver is tuned properly. A visual indicating device, which readily indicates the proper tuning of a received signal, is easily incorporated in the receiver circuitry. Two types of such indicating devices are used. These are the meter-type indicator and the *electron-ray,* or *magic eye,* indicator.

Meter Indicators

The simplest type of tuning indicator is an ordinary d-c milliammeter connected in series with the plates of the a-v-c controlled i-f or r-f tubes, or both. When the receiver tuning is off frequency, the grid bias on the r-f and i-f tubes is low, and consequently the plate current is high. As the receiver is tuned more closely, the a-v-c circuit applies increasing negative bias to the tubes, and the plate current decreases. The correct tuning point is indicated by minimum plate current registered by the meter. Since the pointer deflection decreases as the correct tuning point is approached, meter-type tuning indicators are often mounted in an upside-down position. Scale calibration points may be provided to indicate relative signal strength, a meter so calibrated is often called an *S* meter. In some receivers, the tuning meter reads the unbalanced current of a bridge circuit connected across the a-v-c line. A forward meter indication is obtained in this case, and the meter can be mounted in the conventional position.

Electron-Ray Indicator

Electron-ray, or *magic eye,* indicators are used frequently as visual tuning aids in modern receivers, especially of the home-broadcast type. The tube consists of a double-electrode system, or two sections combining a miniature cathode ray tube and an ordinary triode, which functions as a d-c amplifier, in the same envelope.

A cutaway view of the tube is shown in part A of figure 11-12. In addition to the triode, there are two special electrodes, namely, the target and the deflector, or ray-control electrode. The fluorescent target is connected to the plate supply voltage of the receiver. Operating at a high positive voltage, it attracts electrons from the cathode of the tube. When electrons strike the target, they cause the coating on the target to fluoresce and give off a faint green light. The tube is so positioned that the target can be readily seen by the operator of the receiver. The ray-control electrode is mounted between the cathode and the target. It is a thin vertical vane which shades

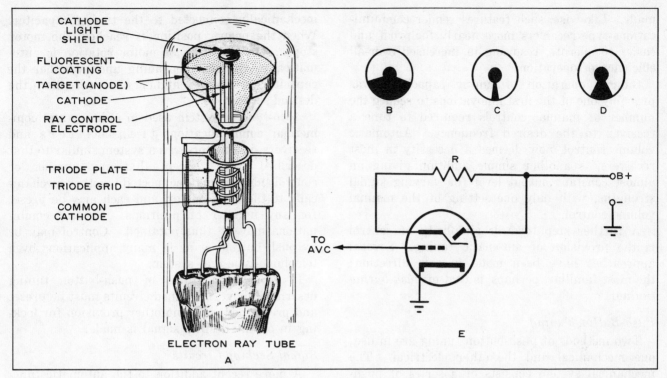

Figure 11-12. Electron-Ray Tube Tuning Indicator

part of the target. When the ray-control electrode is less positive than the target, electrons flowing to the target are repelled by the field of the ray-control electrode and do not reach the portion of the target behind the electrode. Since these portions of the target do not glow, the ray-control electrode casts a shadow on the target. The width of the shadow depends upon the relative voltages of the target and the ray-control electrode. When the ray-control electrode is much more negative than the target, the shadow appears widest, as in part B of the figure. When they approach the same value, the shadow appears as in part C. Some intermediate values of relative voltage make the shadow appear as in D. The dark spot in the center of the ring of light is caused by the cathode light-shield, which is purposely added to make the deflection more noticeable.

The circuit connections of the electron-ray tube are shown in part E of the figure. The grid of the triode section is connected to the a-v-c voltage. When no signal is received, the a-v-c voltage is zero; therefore, the voltage on the triode grid is also zero. Consequently, there is high plate current through the tube, producing a large voltage drop across plate load resistor R. This voltage drop subtracts from the voltage on the plate, and consequently from that on the ray-control electrode, which is internally connected to the

plate. The voltage on the ray-control electrode, therefore, is much less than that on the target, which is connected to the high plate-supply voltage. For this condition, the shadow angle is a maximum.

When the receiver has been properly tuned to the carrier-frequency of a radio station, the a-v-c voltage is a maximum, and therefore the triode control-grid voltage is highly negative. Consequently, the plate current is low, and the voltage drop across R is small. The ray-control electrode has nearly the same voltage as the target, and therefore the shadow angle is a minimum. The greater the strength of the signal, the larger is the a-v-c voltage, and the smaller the minimum shadow. The electron-ray tuning indicator, therefore, indicates both correct tuning and relative signal strength.

Automatic Tuning Circuits

Automatic operation of any of the control functions of a receiver add to the simplicity of operating it. Unfortunately, the additional components, wiring, and service increase the cost of receivers containing such features. Still, these features are desirable, and the cost, unless excessive, is usually justified by the added convenience. This is usually the case with the home-type receiver, where it is desirable to reduce the number of controls or critical adjustments to be made. Likewise, such features render communications-type receivers more nearly foolproof and easier to operate, resulting in increased over-all efficiency of operation.

Ganged operation of tuning capacitors was probably one of the first innovations to reduce the number of manual controls required to tune a receiver to the desired frequency. Automatic volume control, now deemed a necessity in most receivers, is another simple addition giving an almost constant output level for varying signal strengths, with only one setting of the manual volume control.

A further step towards simplicity of control is the provision of automatic tuning. Several approaches have been made in this direction; the most familiar, perhaps, is that of *push-button tuning*.

Push-Button Tuning

Two methods of push-button tuning are in use; one mechanical and the other electrical. The mechanical system consists of a series of push-buttons, any of which, when depressed, moves a bar, or control arm, that is mechanically linked to the ganged tuning capacitor, or, in permeability-tuned receivers, to the tuning slugs of the r-f amplifier, mixer, and oscillator tank circuits. Permeability tuning is advantageous with the mechanically-tuned system, since slight variations in position of the slugs result in considerably less tracking error than do variations in capacitor setting.

The depth of travel of each push button, which is controlled by an individual adjustable stop arrangement, determines the resulting position of the tuning component. Each button is adjusted to a different station frequency.

Several electrical systems have been commonly used to perform this same function. One method employs a separate tuned circuit for each station frequency, the corresponding push button simply performing the necessary switching function for insertion of the proper pretuned tank circuit into the signal circuit. Separate sets of tank circuits, of course, are necessary for each r-f stage, the mixer, and the oscillator.

Still another method employs a motor to rotate the variable-tuning capacitors. When a push button is depressed, the motor operating voltage is applied to a special indexing switch, the positions of which are adjusted to correspond to the proper capacitor settings for the desired signal frequencies. The indexing-switch r o t o r is

mechanically connected to the tuning capacitor. When the proper position is reached, the motor stops. The direction of motor rotation is automatically reversed, depending upon whether the capacitor setting is higher or lower than the desired setting.

Auto-tune, a system used in military and commercial communications t r a n s m i t t e r s and receivers, is a motor-driven system similar to that described above, except that any number of control shafts may be connected together mechanically to the drive motor, and each may be preset for any number of positions. Greater combinations may be thus obtained. Control may be by push button, or as in many applications by a telephone-type dial system.

In all of the forms of push-button tuning described above, the tuned circuits must be preset and prealigned, since no other provision for locking in on the desired signal is made.

Signal-Seeking Circuits

A more recent addition to the automatic functions of AM radio receivers is that of *automatic station selection*. One common method, especially in automobile receivers, is the use of a *signal-seeking* circuit, so called because a motor-driven tuning mechanism, when activated, tunes the receiver until a signal of a predetermined amplitude is found, at which time the mechanism stops. When the system is again activated, by push-button control, the tuning mechanism is operated until the next signal of a given amplitude is found, when the mechanism again stops. Hence, the next station is selected by the automatic circuit, rather than selected by the operator.

The system operates from the receiver a-v-c circuit. In order to provide quick stopping (to prevent overshoot), a spring-operated system is usually used. The s p r i n g operated drive mechanism is mechanically damped for proper tuning speed by the use of a revolving vane. The spring drive operates the mechanism from one end (usually the low end) of the tuning dial toward the opposite end. When a signal is intercepted, the resulting a-v-c voltage is applied to a control tube, which in turn actuates a solenoid-operated pawl. The pawl, or lever, engages with the rotating vane to quickly stop the mechanical system. The level of a-v-c voltage required to operate the solenoid is determined by the setting of a sensitivity potentiometer, which affects the bias on the control tube. When the push-button control is operated, the voltage at the solenoid

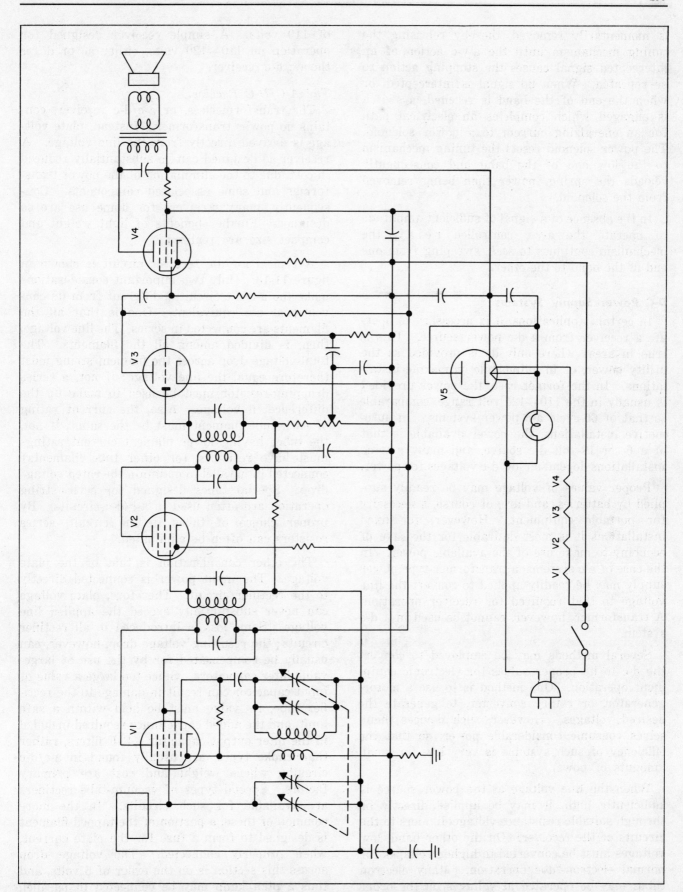

Figure 11-13. Typical AC/DC Receiver

is momentarily removed, thereby releasing the tuning mechanism until the a-v-c action of an intercepted signal causes the stopping action to be repeated. When no signal is intercepted, or when the end of the band is reached, a switch is engaged which completes an electrical path for an energizing current to a power solenoid. The power solenoid resets the tuning mechanism to the low end of the band and consequently reloads the spring, power then being removed from the solenoid.

In the absence of a signal of sufficient amplitude to operate the a-v-c controlled r e l a y, the mechanism continues to *seek,* sweeping from one end of the band to the other.

D-C Power Supply Systems

In certain applications, it is necessary to operate a receiver from a d-c power source. This is true in areas where only dc is provided as the utility power, or in automobile or marine installations. In the former case, the power provided is usually in the 110—120 volt range, comparable to that of 60-cycle a-c power systems. In automotive installations, the power available is that of a 6- or 12-volt d-c source, and many marine installations depend on low d-c voltages for power.

Proper values of voltage may be readily supplied by batteries, and are, of course, a necessity for portable equipment. However, for fixed installations it is most desirable for the sake of economy to make use of the available power. In the case of a-c systems, a transformer-type power supply may be readily applied to convert the line voltage to that required for receiver operation. A transformer, however, cannot be used in a d-c system.

Several methods may be employed to convert the d-c to its proper values for electronic equipment operation. One method is to use a motor-generator, or rotary converter, to generate the desired voltages. However, such devices themselves consume considerable power, so that the efficiency of such systems is very low for small amounts of power.

When the line voltage at the power source is sufficiently high, it may be applied directly or through suitable resistance voltage-dividers to the circuits of the receiver. On the other hand, low voltages must be converted to higher voltages for normal electron-tube operation. Many electron tubes may be operated at voltages on the order

of 110 volts. A simple receiver designed for operation on 110—120 volts, either ac or dc, is the a-c/d-c receiver.

The A-C/D-C Receiver

The transformerless, or a-c/d-c receiver, contains no power transformer. Instead, plate voltage is derived directly from the line voltage. A receiver so designed can be substantially reduced in cost, due to the elimination of the power transformer and some associated components. Consequently, many receivers for home use are so designed. Further benefits of light weight and compact size are realized.

A typical a-c/d-c receiver circuit is shown in figure 11-13. Only two important considerations make the a-c/d-c circuitry different from its conventional a-c equivalent. One is that all the filaments are connected in series. The line voltage, then, is divided among all the filaments. The total voltage drop across the filament string must therefore equal the line voltage; if not, a series dropping-resistor must be used to make up the difference in voltage. Also, the current rating of each tube filament must be the same; if not, the tubes having lower filament current ratings must have resistors (or other tube filaments) connected in parallel to maintain the rated voltage drop. Special tubes designed for series-string operation are often used in a-c/d-c circuits. By proper choice of tubes in the circuit, series resistors can often be eliminated.

The other consideration is that of the plate voltage. The input power is connected directly to the rectifier circuit. Therefore, plate voltage can never substantially exceed the applied line voltage. Some loss is introduced in all rectifier circuits; the resulting voltage drop, however, can usually be compensated for by the use of large-value filter capacitors. Since too large a value of input capacitor can result in damage to the rectifier tube, its value must be held within a safe limit, and the added capacitance required included in the filter output capacitor. R-F filters, rather than choke types, are usually found in a-c/d-c circuits, where weight and cost are primary factors. Special types of vacuum-tube rectifiers are available for such circuits. In the more common of these, a portion of the tapped filament is designed to form a fuse for the plate current, when properly connected. The voltage drop across this section is on the order of 6 volts, and thus a pilot lamp may be connected in parallel.

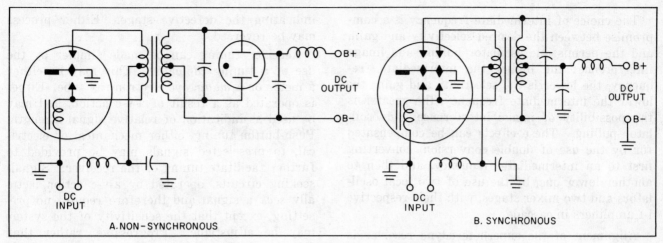

Figure 11-14. Vibrator Power Supply Systems

Vibrator-Type Power Supplies

When a low value of d-c voltage is used as the primary power source for a radio receiver, sufficient plate voltage cannot normally be supplied directly. However, recent developments in tube design have provided some tube types that may be operated on plate voltages as low as 12 volts. Such tubes may, in proper circuitry, be operated directly from 12 volt electrical power systems. Dynamotors, of course, can be used to raise the voltage to the proper level for vacuum tube operation, with some loss in efficiency. In most automobile radio receivers, a vibrator-type power supply is used. Two such systems are illustrated in figure 11-14. In the circuit shown in part A a vacuum-tube rectifier is used. Often the tube may be of the gas-filled cold-cathode type, so that filament drain on the system can be minimized. Another method, which eliminates the need of a rectifier tube, is that which uses a synchronous vibrator, as in part B of the figure. The non-synchronous vibrator interrupts the d-c voltage applied to the primary of the power transformer. The output, taken from the secondary of the transformer, is a stepped-up, a-c voltage, which is then rectified. The synchronous vibrator similarly converts the source d-c into a-c but also simultaneously rectifies it. Both rectified outputs must be filtered for use as the receiver d-c supply.

Radio-Phonograph Combinations

In order to make the home-type radio receiver more versatile, it may include provisions for the attachment of a record player, or phonograph. Since the receiver includes a complete audio amplifier, all that is needed is an input jack connected to the grid of the first audio-amplifier tube. In still other systems, the record player is combined with the receiver into a radio-phono combination. Suitable switching is provided so that either the record player or the radio tuner is connected to the audio amplifier.

A radio tuner (AM and/or FM), consisting of a complete radio receiver except the audio amplifier (and often the power supply), may be used with any audio system. Provision for the use of such units gives the system versatility.

11-6 SUMMARY

The superheterodyne receiver differs essentially from the t-r-f receiver in that it changes the frequency of the received signal to a lower, fixed value, called the *intermediate frequency*. The tuned circuits for the fixed intermediate frequency may then be designed to operate with maximum selectivity, sensitivity, and stability.

The conversion of the received signal into a lower i-f frequency is based on the *heterodyne* principle. When a modulated radio signal is heterodyned with a locally generated signal, the envelope of the resulting beat frequency, or i-f, contains the modulation of the original radio signal. The bandpass of the i-f amplifier section must be such that this modulation, and its sidebands, are not impaired.

Frequency conversion is effected by vacuum-tube oscillator and mixer circuits. The plate current of the mixer tube contains the input-signal frequency, the oscillator frequency, and their sum and difference frequencies. Only the difference frequency is selected by the tuned plate circuit of the mixer stage for transfer to the input of the i-f amplifier. Separate mixer and oscillator tubes may be employed, or a pentagrid converter, comprising both oscillator and mixer in a single stage, may be used.

The choice of intermediate frequency is a compromise between the desired selectivity and gain, and the permissible oscillator pulling and image interference: the higher the intermediate frequency, the lower is the selectivity and gain; the lower the intermediate frequency, the greater is the possibility of image interference and oscillator pulling. These effects can be compensated for by the use of double conversion, converting first to an intermediate frequency, and then to another lower one, by the use of two local oscillators and two mixer stages, with their respective i-f amplifiers in cascade.

Alignment of the superheterodyne receiver is accomplished by first aligning th i-f stages, then the oscillator, and lastly the r-f and antenna circuits. R-F and oscillator trimmers are adjusted at the high end of the band, and the oscillator padder is adjusted at the low end. Repeating the alignment process for each section corrects for interaction between adjustments. Rocking-in assures correct oscillator padder setting.

Trouble shooting a receiver is made simpler by *signal tracing* or *signal injection*. *Signal tracing* is performed by aural or visual means by searching for and detecting a received signal from the antenna, stage by stage through the receiver, until the signal is lost, indicating the stage where the trouble probably lies. *Signal injection* is performed by applying a signal of the proper frequency range at the output of the receiver, and moving the point of signal injection back, stage by stage to the antenna, until the signal is lost, indicating the defective stage. Either process may be reversed.

Receiver tuning can be made simpler by the use of a tuning indicator. This may be either a meter or a *magic eye* electron-ray tube. Either is operated as a result of a-v-c action, and may be used as indication of relative signal strength. Push-button tuning, either mechanical or electrical, to preselected signals may be provided to further facilitate tuning of the receiver. Signal-seeking circuits, operated by a-v-c action, actually *seek* a signal and therefore require no presetting, except that the sensitivity of the system may be adjustable. Progressive, rather than selective, tuning, consequently, is the result.

A variation of receiver circuitry, permitting use with either a-c or d-c power systems is the transformerless, or a-c/d-c receiver. Proper choice of tubes must be made to satisfy the series-string filament circuit and lower plate-voltage limitations.

Vibrator-type power supplies are normally used in automobile radio receivers, although dynamotors can be used for mobile installations with reduced efficiency.

The audio circuit of any receiver may be utilized as an audio amplifier for phonograph or other audio use, if proper provisions are made in the receiver. A radio tuner, consisting of only the r-f, i-f, and detector circuits, may be used with any audio amplifier. Thus, this versatility of the receiver renders its adaptability into any sound system or combination practical.

REVIEW QUESTIONS

1. State t h r e e disadvantages of the t-r-f receiver which are overcome by the superheterodyne receiver.
2. What steps are involved in the reception of a signal by a superheterodyne radio receiver?
3. Describe the process of frequency conversion.
4. What is the *beat* frequency?
5. What frequencies are present in the plate current of a mixer tube?
6. What factors influence the choice of the intermediate frequency?
7. What is the difference between a mixer and a converter?
8. What tuned circuits must be aligned first, when aligning a superheterodyne receiver?
9. At which end of the band is the oscillator padder adjusted?

10. How is the tracking of the r-f amplifier and oscillator made to agree at the low end of the band?
11. Why should each step in the alignment of a superheterodyne radio receiver be repeated at least once after subsequent adjustments have been made?
12. How may the defective stage of a malfunctioning receiver be quickly located?
13. How does *signal injection* differ from *signal tracking*?
14. Name two methods of push-button tuning.
15. What are the major differences between an a-c/d-c receiver and a conventional a-c receiver?

CHAPTER TWELVE

Frequency-Modulation Transmitter Principles

12-1 Introduction

In the study of AM transmitters, the transmitted signal was found to be a fixed radio-frequency carrier wave which was varied in amplitude, or the amount of power it contained, by a modulating signal. Two methods of deriving the amplitude variation were encountered — the low-level and high-level methods. With the latter method, it was found that quite a high level of audio power is required to vary the amplitude of the carrier.

In contrast, the FM system involves the use of a comparatively low level of audio modulating power to change the frequency — not the amplitude — of the transmitted signal. Therefore, the *frequency* of the FM transmitted signal will vary at the audio modulating rate while the amplitude remains fixed. A comparison of the AM and FM transmitted signals is shown in figure 12-1.

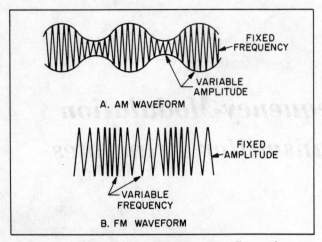

Figure 12-1.   AM and FM Waveform Comparison

12-2 AM AND FM TRANSMITTER BLOCK DIAGRAM COMPARISON

Block diagrams of an AM transmitter and an FM transmitter are shown in figure 12-2. The AM transmitter, in part A of the figure, uses the high-level type of amplitude modulation. The FM transmitter, part B of the figure, is of the reactance-modulator type, in which the master-oscillator frequency is directly varied.

The reactance-modulator type of FM transmitter is one of three basic types of FM transmitters. All three types are classified by, and differ only in, the means of obtaining the master-oscillator frequency variation. Since the oscillator, buffer, multiplier, and amplifier circuitry of the AM and FM transmitters are functionally identical, a study of the primary differences in the FM modulator circuits will serve to indicate the means of obtaining the FM transmitter waveform. Like the AM transmitter, the FM transmitter uses a frequency multiplier; however, the frequency multiplication takes place after the signal is modulated. In the AM transmitter the frequency multiplication must take place before the signal is modulated, in order to retain the original modulation.

12-3 MODULATION PRINCIPLES

Regardless of the method used to produce a frequency-modulated r-f waveform (this will be studied in detail later in this chapter), certain fundamental requirements must be met. Of these requirements, the most important are those imposed by the Federal Communications Commission, which has control of all radio transmission in the United States.

The assignment of a maximum power of 50 kilowatts, a 10-kilocycle bandwidth, and a definite frequency in the commercial broadcast band of 540 to 1600 kilocycles to each amplitude-modulated station was achieved by the FCC. FM broadcasting is governed by regulations similar to these, applicable to the band of 88 to 108 megacycles. Since the FM carrier frequency is actually changed by the modulating signal, a limit is set by the FCC concerning the maximum amount of change to either side. This limit is ±75 kilocycles. Assuming that the center frequency assigned to an FM station is 100 megacycles, the limits of carrier frequency swing, or *deviation* are up to 100.075 megacycles and down to 99.925 megacycles. Thus, the maximum total r-f carrier swing of any one FM station is 150 kilocycles. This wide band allocation, shown in figure 12-3, also has a separation area between adjacent channels of 25 kilocycles on each end, called the *guard bands*. These guard band areas are allowed for the prevention of adjacent channel interference, although two stations in the same locality are rarely assigned adjacent channel allocations.

The total frequency deviation of 150 kilocycles allowed by the FCC is called "100 percent" modulation. In the true sense of the word, 100 percent FM modulation would drive the rf from its resting, or unmodulated, value downward to zero cycles, and upward to twice the carrier frequency. This theoretical value is not practical; however, the FCC limits are generally considered as 100% modulation.

FM Sidebands

It was previously found that amplitude modulation of an r-f waveform produces upper and lower sidebands. Likewise, when an r-f signal is frequency-modulated, sidebands also will be produced, the frequency separation of the sidebands being dependent on the frequency of the modulating signal. Assume, for example, that the FM carrier is modulated by a 100-cycle signal; the sidebands will appear in even multiples of 100 cycles above and below the carrier frequency. Likewise, if the carrier is modulated by a 5000-cycle signal, the sidebands will appear in even multiples of 5000 cycles above and below the carrier frequency. There will be multiple sidebands, unlike the single pair of sidebands resulting from AM modulation of a carrier with a tone.

The number of significant sidebands depends on the amount of deviation produced and the modulating frequency. Calculation of the factor called *modulation index* is the first step in deter-

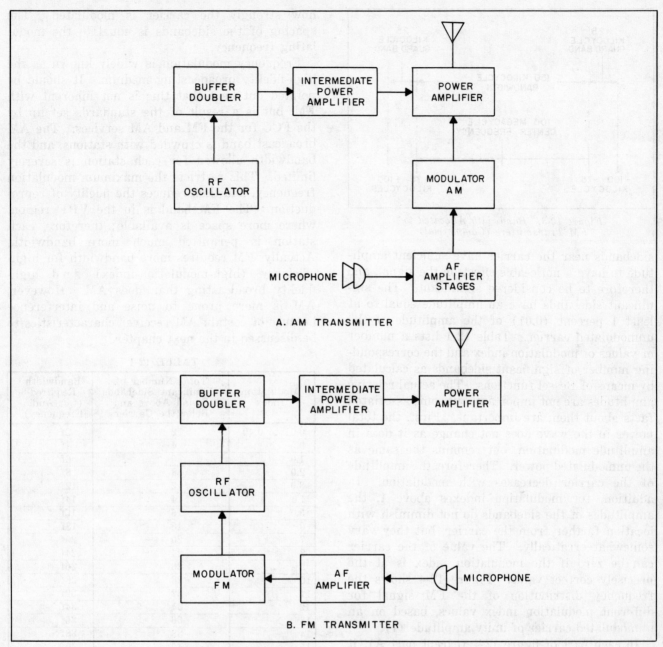

Figure 12-2. Comparison of AM and FM Transmitters

mining the number of sidebands. The modulation index can be determined by use of the formula below.

$$\text{Modulation Index} = \frac{\text{carrier deviation}}{\text{modulating frequency}} \quad (12\text{-}1)$$

As mentioned earlier, the maximum deviation in the FM broadcast band is limited by law to 75 kc. Thus the maximum modulation index for the highest audio frequency normally used, 15 kc, is:

$$\text{Modulation Index} = \frac{75,000}{15,000} = 5$$

The maximum legal deviation at 100 cycles results in a somewhat higher index:

$$\text{Modulation Index} = \frac{75,000}{100} = 750$$

The modulation index will be greater for low-frequency modulation than for high-frequency modulation producing the same deviation.

Application of the modulation index to a set of equations known as the *Bessel functions* allows calculation of the relative amplitude of an extremely large number of sidebands. Only those

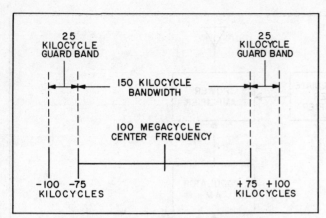

Figure 12-3. Bandwidth Allocated to FM Transmitters (Commercial)

sidebands near the carrier have sufficient amplitude to have a noticeable effect on the signal, and therefore to be considered significant. The significant sidebands have an amplitude equal to at least 1 percent (0.01) of the amplitude of the unmodulated carrier. Table 12-1 lists a number of values of modulation index and the corresponding number of significant sidebands as calculated by means of Bessel functions. The actual relative amplitudes are not important, but some associated facts about them are important. First, the total power in the wave does not change as it does in amplitude modulation, but remains the same as the unmodulated power. Therefore, the amplitude of the carrier decreases with modulation. In addition, for modulation indexes above 1, the amplitudes of the sidebands do not diminish with location farther from the carrier, but they vary somewhat erratically. The value of the carrier can be zero if the modulation index is at the precisely correct value. Figure 12-4 shows the frequency distribution of the FM signal for different modulation index values, based on an unmodulated carrier of unity amplitude (1).

In each part of figure 12-4 (except part A), it may be seen that there are significant sidebands farther from the carrier than the maximum carrier deviation to either side of the unmodulated carrier frequency. If the deviation is 75 kc, this means that there will be sidebands outside the assigned channel, in the guard band. This has been allowed for in the frequency allocations, so that negligible interference results. The FCC allows further margin for this phenomenon by avoiding adjacent channel assignments to stations in the same locality.

From this it can be concluded that the number of significant sidebands and their relative amplitudes are determined by the modulation index, or

how strongly the carrier is modulated. The spacing of the sidebands is equal to the modulating frequency.

Frequency modulation is widely known as the high-fidelity broadcasting medium. It should be pointed out here that this is not inherent with FM, but is a result of the standards set up by the FCC for the FM and AM services. The AM broadcast band is crowded with stations, and the bandwidth allowed for each station is severely limited. This restricts the maximum modulation frequency, and thus reduces the fidelity of reproduction. The FM band is in the VHF region, where more space is available; therefore, each station is permitted much more bandwidth. Actually, FM requires more bandwidth for high-efficiency (high-modulation-index) and high-fidelity broadcasting than does AM. However, AM is more prone to noise and interference because of certain AM receiver characteristics to be discussed in the next chapter.

TABLE 12-1

Modulation Index	Total Number of Significant Sidebands Found Above and Below the Carrier	Bandwidth Required (f = Audio Frequency)
0.01 to 0.40	2	2f
0.5	4	4f
1.0	6	6f
2.0	8	8f
3.0	12	12f
4.0	14	14f
5.0	16	16f
6	18	18f
7	20	20f
8	24	24f
9	26	26f
10	28	28f
11	32	32f
12	34	34f
13	36	36f
14	38	38f
15	40	40f

12-4 MODULATOR TYPES

In order to show how an audio signal is used to frequency modulate an r-f carrier, the three methods of accomplishing the frequency changes are explained below.

Mechanical Modulator

The simplest method of producing frequency modulation is by mechanical control of either the inductive or capacitive oscillator tank circuit component. As previously explained, the resonant frequency at which any tank circuit will oscillate is dependent upon the values of L and

C in that circuit. Therefore, if a capacitance-type microphone, consisting of a fixed and a movable plate, is placed in parallel with the tank-circuit capacitance of an oscillator, the capacitances will add. This circuit is shown in figure 12-5. When no audio is present to vary the position of the capacitance-microphone plates, the center, or resonant, frequency of the circuit can be determined by using the tank circuit inductance and total capacitance, which includes the silent-state capacitance of the microphone.

When the capacitance microphone is spoken into, the movable plate, or diaphragm, moves toward and away from the fixed plate at an audio

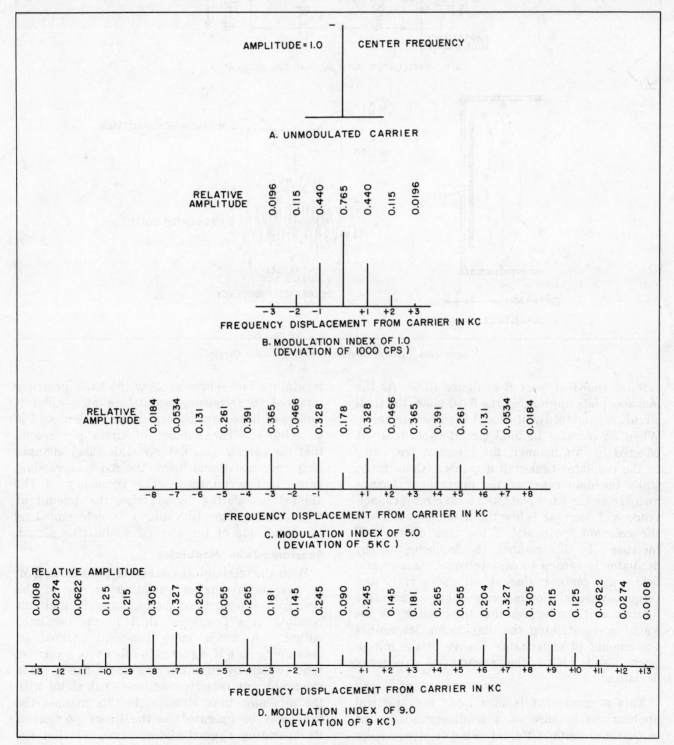

Figure 12-4. Sidebands of an FM Signal Modulated by 1000-cps Tone

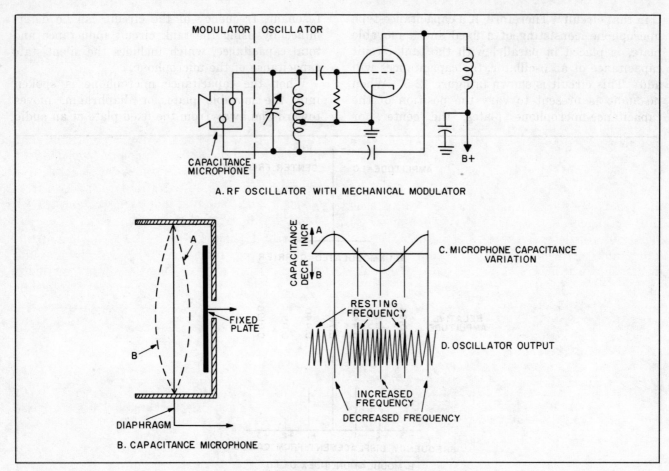

Figure 12-5. Simple Frequency Modulation Circuit

rate, as shown in part B of figure 12-5. As the movable plate approaches the fixed plate, the total circuit capacitance will exceed the average value. When an increase in total circuit capacitance is effected in this manner, the resonant frequency of the oscillator tank will decrease. Conversely, when the diaphragm of the microphone swings away from the fixed plate, the total circuit capacitance will decrease below the average value, and the resonant frequency of the tank circuit will increase. In this manner, the frequency of the oscillator is caused to deviate equally above and below the center value at an audio rate, and frequency modulation is accomplished. From this discussion it can be seen that the intensity of the sound wave striking the diaphragm determines the amount of capacitance change in the microphone, and t h u s the amount of frequency deviation.

This arrangement is unsuitable for practical applications because of a nonlinear change of capacitance with different a u d i o frequencies applied to the microphone. However, this funda-

mental method serves to show the basic principle involved in frequency-modulating an oscillator. The most important concept to be remembered is as follows: The number of times per second that the carrier (oscillator in this case) changes frequency above and below the fixed, or resting, value is determined by the frequency of the applied modulating signal; also, the amount of frequency change (deviation) is determined by the amplitude of the applied modulating signal.

Reactance-Tube Modulator

With the mechanical method of generating FM, it was shown that a variation in one of the reactive components of the oscillator tank circuit resulted in a frequency shift in the oscillator output.   A much more practical method of developing an FM signal is to substitute a vacuum tube (which, by circuit arrangement, can be made to appear as a reactive component) in shunt with the oscillator tank circuit. In this manner the tube may be operated on the linear portion of its operating characteristics curve, so that the audio modulating signal applied to its control grid will result in a linear change in effective reactance, and thus a linear oscillator frequency deviation.

The circuit arrangement that will cause a vacuum tube to appear as a reactive component is shown in figure 12-6. Part A of this figure is a schematic diagram of a standard reactance-tube modulator circuit. Part B is the same circuit, redrawn to show specifically which component of the R-C phase-shift network (enclosed in broken lines) appears across the grid-to-ground circuit of the reactance tube. This particular R-C phase-shift arrangement will cause the tube to appear as a variable inductance in parallel with the oscillator tank. Other phase-shift circuit arrangements, shown in figure 12-7, may be substituted; by use of one of these arrangements, the tube

can be made to appear either capacitive or inductive, as desired.

To show how the phase-shift circuit can cause a tube to appear, to the oscillator tank, as a variable reactive component, a brief review of capacitive and inductive reactance is necessary. Previously, it was shown that a resistor offers an opposition (in ohms) to the current, and that the opposition is a fixed amount regardless of frequency. Also, it was shown that capacitive reactance (in ohms) varies inversely with a frequency change, and that inductive reactance varies directly with frequency change.

It was also shown that as the frequency of the applied voltage is changed in a reactive circuit, the c i r c u i t appears more reactive or more resistive, depending upon the phase relationship

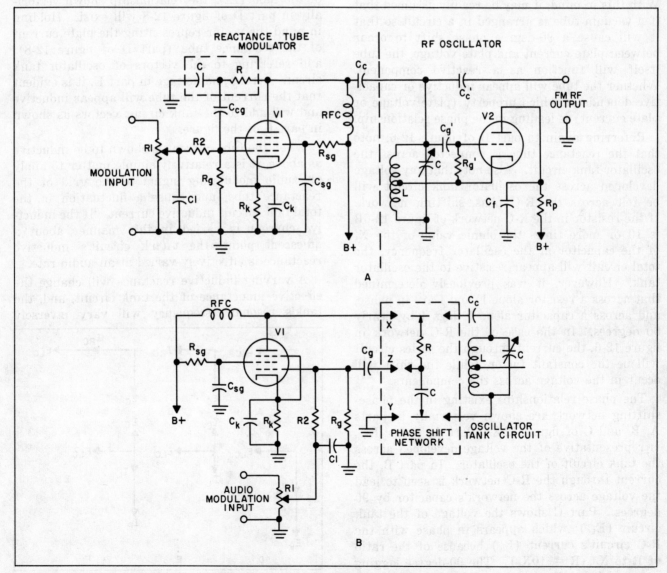

Figure 12-6. Reactance-Tube Modulator Circuit

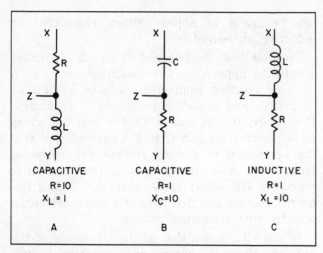

Figure 12-7. Reactance-Tube Phase-Shift Networks

between the voltage and current in the circuit. With this in mind, it may be readily assumed that if a vacuum tube is arranged in a circuit so that it will cause a 90-degree phase shift to occur between plate current and plate voltage, the tube itself will function as a reactive component. Whether the tube will appear inductive or capacitive depends on which property (plate voltage or plate current) is leading in the phase relationship.

Referring again to part B of figure 12-6, note that the reactance tube is connected across the oscillator tank circuit. Also note that any voltage developed across the oscillator tank circuit will be felt across the R-C phase-shifting network. If the resistor in the R-C network of figure 12-6B is 10 or more times the ohmic value of the X_C of the capacitor at the oscillator frequency, the total circuit will appear resistive to the oscillator tank. However, it was previously determined that across a resistor alone E and I are in phase, and across a capacitor alone E lags I by nearly 90 degrees. In the case of the R-C network in figure 12-6, the current through the series circuit will be the constant factor, while the shift will occur in the voltage across the components.

The phase relationships existing in the phase-shifting network are shown vectorially in parts A, B, and C of figure 12-8. Part A, vector E_{LC}, is representative of the voltage developed across the tank circuit of the oscillator. In part B, the current through the R-C network is seen to lead the voltage across the network's capacitor by 90 degrees. Part C shows the voltage of the tank circuit (E_{LC}), which appears in phase with the R-C circuit's current (I_{RC}) because of the ratio of R to X_C (R = $10X_C$). The 90-degree lagging vector, labeled E_g, is representative of the grid

voltage applied to the reactance tube because of the capacitor in the network. This vector is merely E_C in part B of figure 12-8, relabeled to show that it appears on the grid of the tube. The fact that this voltage is present on the grid of the tube may be substantiated by noting the location of the phase-shift network's capacitor, shown in part B of figure 12-6.

With the above phase relationships established, the relationships of current and voltage inside the vacuum tube may now be shown. First, it is a known fact that in any amplifier, tube grid voltage (E_g) controls plate current (I_p). In this manner, it is obvious that I_p and E_g will be in phase and lagging the r-f voltage on the plate, furnished by the oscillator tank circuit, by 90 degrees. Since E_{LC} is effectively the plate voltage of the tube (E_p), the relationship shown vectorially in part D of figure 12-8 will exist. Holding in mind the vector representing the plate current of the reactance tube (part D of figure 12-8), and referring to the vectors of oscillator tank circuit current and voltage in part E, it is evident that the current of the tube will appear inductive and will add to the tank circuit vectors as shown in part F of the figure.

When the tube current is shown to be inductive as above, it is a relatively simple matter to apply an audio modulating signal to the grid of the reactance tube, and cause a fluctuation in the total tank circuit inductive current. If the inductive current is varied in this manner about a quiescent point, the tank circuit's inductive reactance is effectively varied at an audio rate.

A varying inductive reactance will change the effective inductance of the tank circuit, and, the tank's resonant frequency will vary inversely

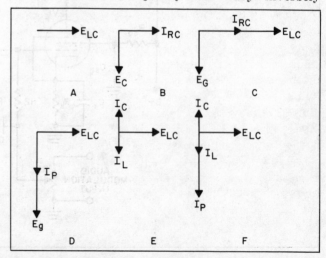

Figure 12-8. Vector Analysis for Reactance-Tube Circuit

with the inductance of the tank. Therefore, applying a positive-going audio signal to the reactance tube grid, will cause more current to flow and increase the inductive current of the oscillator tank circuit. This increase in inductive current appears in the tank circuit as a decrease in inductance, because inductive reactance and inductance vary directly. The decreased inductance causes the resonant frequency of the tank circuit to increase. Conversely, when the audio modulating signal on the reactance tube grid swings negative, less tube current will flow and the tank circuit inductive current will decrease. This decrease in inductive current serves as an increase in the value of tank circuit inductance; thus the resonant frequency of the tank circuit will decrease. In this manner, the audio modulating signal applied to the grid of the reactance tube changes the resonant frequency of the oscillator tank above and below a quiescent value, resulting in frequency modulation at an audio rate.

The phase shift in the voltage fed to the reactance tube from the oscillator tank circuit can be made to either lead or lag the current through the reactance tube, whichever is desired. This is accomplished by substituting the R-C phase-shift network with one of the three alternatives shown in figure 12-7.

By substituting an inductor for the capacitor in the R-C phase-shift network, as shown in part A of figure 12-7, the reactance-tube grid voltage will be shifted 90 degrees ahead of the tank circuit voltage. The plate current, with this arrangement, will also lead the tank circuit voltage at the plate of the tube, and the tube will appear capacitive rather than inductive.

If the positions of R and C, as shown in figure 12-6, were arranged as in B of figure 12-7, the capacitive reactance would be greater in ohmic value than the resistance of the circuit, causing the phase-shift circuit to be capacitive. The current through this capacitive circuit will lead the tank circuit voltage at the plate of the reactance tube. Since the current leads by 90 degrees, the voltage developed across R in the circuit, which is a result of this current, will lead by 90 degrees. The leading voltage developed at the grid of the reactance tube will cause the tube current to lead the plate voltage, and the tube will appear as a capacitive component to the oscillator tank circuit, thus, the application of an audio modulating signal will cause the total capacitance of the

oscillator tank to vary, and once again a frequency-modulated signal will result. In any case, the component placed between the plate and grid of the phase-shift network will be greater in ohmic value than that component connected from grid to ground. The choice of an inductive-appearing circuit or a capacitive-appearing circuit is simply one of design and cost considerations; the choice, however, determines whether the resultant frequency increases on the positive alternations or on the negative alternations of the modulating signal.

The amount of capacitance or inductance, represented by the reactance tube, injected into the oscillator tank circuit is determined by one of the following formulas.

For the inductive-appearing reactance tube:

$$L_i = \frac{CR}{g_m} \quad \text{(where an R-C phase-shift circuit is used)} \quad (12\text{-}2)$$

$$L_i = \frac{L}{g_m R} \quad \text{(where an L-R phase-shift circuit is used)} \quad (12\text{-}3)$$

For the capacitive-appearing reactance tube:

$$C_i = g_m RC \quad \text{(where an R-C phase-shift circuit is used)} \quad (12\text{-}4)$$

$$C_i = g_m \frac{L}{R} \quad \text{(where an L-R phase-shift circuit is used)} \quad (12\text{-}5)$$

In the above formulas:

C_i = injected capacitance, in farads
L_i = injected inductance, in henrys
g_m = mutual conductance of the tube, in mhos
C = phase-shift circuit capacitance, in farads
R = phase-shift circuit resistance, in ohms
L = phase-shift circuit inductance, in henrys

The factor of tube transconductance in the above formulas, as previously studied, was found to be measured in mhos, the reciprocal of resistance measured in ohms. The formula for determining transconductance is as follows:

$$g_m = \frac{\Delta I_p}{\Delta E_g} \bigg|\ E_p = \text{Constant} \quad (12\text{-}6)$$

where:

ΔI_p = change in plate current
ΔE_g = change in grid voltage
E_p = plate voltage

With this fact in mind, it is readily apparent that the control of plate current (I_p) in the tube by grid voltage (E_g) will cause the g_m of the tube to vary. Therefore, the only variable component in the injected-capacitance and injected-inductance formulas is that of tube transconductance.

From the standpoint of the tubes used for reactance tube applications, the pentode or power pentode types, which have a high g_m value, are most often used. Another advantage of using this type is that plate voltage is relatively independent of plate current because of the screen and suppressor grids. Thus, the reactance tube modulating circuit is considered, at present, to be the most popular method of obtaining a frequency-modulated signal at the oscillator stage of the transmitter. To obtain frequency modulation at a location in the transmitter other than the oscillator, a system referred to as *phase modulation* is used.

Phase Modulator

In the phase-modulation system of obtaining an FM signal, the phase modulator follows the master oscillator in an FM transmitter circuit chain. Phase modulation usually occurs immediately after the oscillator in an FM transmitter, thereby permitting the utilization of low power levels of the audio modulating signal. Also, by making it occur after the oscillator and before the multiplier stages, the small frequency change in the r-f signal due to phase modulation can make use of the multiplier stages to attain the maximum allowable frequency deviation in the same manner as the reactance-tube type of modulation.

A typical schematic diagram of the circuitry used in the phase-modulation system is shown in figure 12-9. A special consideration of this system is that the frequency deviation it creates is dependent upon the frequency of the modulating signal, as well as the amplitude of the modulating signal. The following discussion of the system explains the manner in which phase modulation, or the shifting of the phase of an r-f signal along its time base, results in frequency modulation.

Referring to figure 12-9, it can be seen that a crystal-controlled master oscillator is used. This permits the elimination of any frequency-controlling devices because of t h e inherent stability of the crystal-oscillator circuit. The output of the master oscillator may be fed into a buffer amplifier to prevent loading of the oscillator stage; however, the buffer amplifier is not shown in the illustration for reasons of simplicity.

The output of the crystal oscillator is shown fed through coupling capacitor C1 to the grids of V2 and V3, connected in parallel, in the balanced modulator circuit. As the signal passes to the grid of V2, it is shifted in phase 45 degrees by phase-shift network R3 L1. Also, the oscillator signal at the grid of tube V3 is shifted 45 degrees in the opposite direction by phase-shift network R2 C2.

The phase relationship between the oscillator signals at the grids of V2 and V3 is a total of 90 degrees (refer to figure 12-10). When no audio modulating signal is applied, the r-f signals at the grids of the tubes are equal in amplitude,

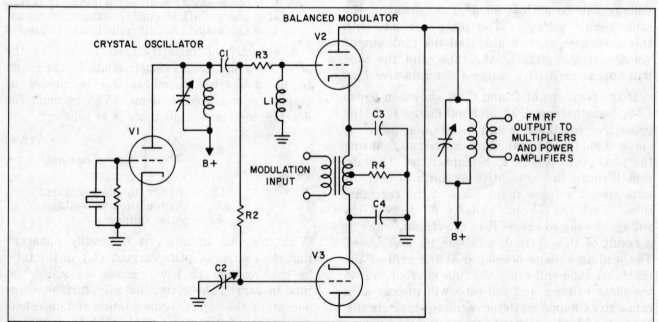

Figure 12-9. Phase-Modulator Circuitry

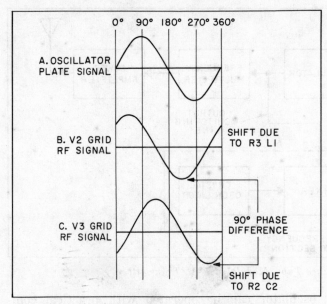

*Figure 12-10. R-F Waveforms in the Balanced Modulator
of the Phase-Modulating System*

and the vector sum of the 45-degree lagging and 45-degree leading voltages will be equal and in phase with the voltage of the oscillator. Therefore, the output of this circuit without a modulating signal will be the fixed frequency of the crystal oscillator circuit, even though there is the standard 180-degree phase inversion due to V2 and V3.

The modulating signal is applied to the cathodes of V2 and V3. Effectively, then, this provides a means of varying the individual currents through the modulator tubes. Since the modulating signal is applied across the transformer, the cathode of V2 will be driven positive by the modulating signal as the cathode of V3 is driven negative, and vice versa. (Note the transformer connections.)

Assume that the cathode of V2 is driven positive and that the cathode of V3 is simultaneously driven negative, by the modulating signal. The current flow through V2 will decrease, and the current through V3 will increase. The greater current flow through V3 results in a phase lag in the output of the balanced modulator. While the phase is being retarded, each cycle of rf will have a slightly longer period than normal, and the frequency will be shifted downward. When the maximum phase shift is reached, at the peak of the audio alternation, there is momentarily no change of phase, and the rf is that of the input. During the remainder of the alternation, the phase advances to the quiescent (or unmodulated) position, so that the cycles of rf are compressed in time. This

advancing phase causes the frequency to rise above the input frequency. In other words, the frequency shift will lead the phase shift of the r-f signal, and the frequency shift is proportional to the rate of phase change of the modulator output.

The shifting of the r-f signal by the audio modulating signal is shown in figure 12-11. In this figure, the modulating signal applied to the cathode of only one vacuum tube in the balanced modulator is considered (the rf is represented as a low frequency for ease of illustration). The cathode modulating signal is shown with relation to the r-f oscillator signal, and the resulting phase shift of the r-f waveform is shown.

The basic difference between phase modulation (indirect frequency modulation) and direct frequency modulation, as in the reactance tube circuit, is an issue here. Suppose that the phase changes are accomplished at a higher modulating frequency. The effective phase shift, to accomplish the same frequency change and rate of phase change in the shorter period of a higher-frequency modulating signal, will be smaller. Therefore, in a phase-modulated signal, the deviation of the r-f output is determined by the frequency of the modulating signal as well as its amplitude. The relationship, however, is a linear one, with deviation being proportional to the modulating frequency for a constant modulating signal amplitude. The function of providing a modulating signal to produce the needed modulating-amplitude to modulating-frequency

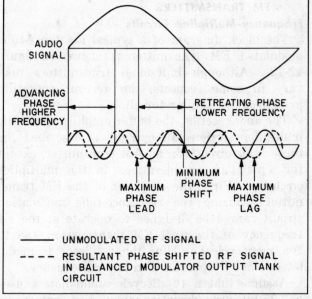

*Figure 12-11. Phase-Shifting an R-F Wave
at an Audio Rate*

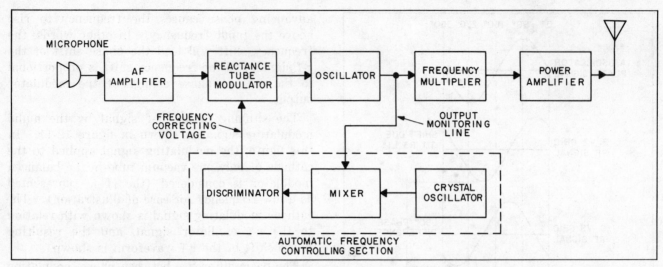

Figure 12-12. Block Diagram of a Reactance Tube Modulated F-M Transmitter

ratio is accomplished by the use of frequency discriminating circuits in the audio system. These circuits attenuate the high modulating frequencies in the audio portion of the circuitry to the same degree that these high frequencies are accentuated in the modulating process. This is done to make phase modulation of the rf produce the same over-all effect as frequency modulation.

Just as in the reactance-tube modulated FM transmitter, the phase-modulated device of the phase-modulated FM transmitter, is also followed by multiplier stages, to add to the deviation of the FM output waveform. This is a standard method of utilizing the full r-f bandwidth allotted by the FCC to FM transmitting stations.

12-5 SPECIAL CONSIDERATIONS OF FM TRANSMITTERS

Frequency-Multiplier Circuits

The block diagram of a typical reactance-tube modulated FM transmitter is shown in figure 12-12. Although individual transmitters may vary in some respects, the general operating principles are similar for all.

The audio section, the buffer amplifiers, and the multiplier sections all operate as described for these same circuits in an AM transmitter, except for s p e c i a l considerations in the multiplier circuitry. First, the oscillator of the FM transmitter utilizing the reactance-tube modulation circuit cannot be designed to operate at the r-f frequency of the final FM transmission (88 to 108 megacycles). Thus the oscillator is modulated, since it operates at a lower frequency.

Assume that a 10-kilocycle audio note causes a 3.75-kilocycle deviation about the center frequency of 5 megacycles, at which frequency the oscillator can be operated with practical component values in the tank circuit. The multiplying factor required to produce the assigned broadcast frequency of 100 megacycles and still not exceed the maximum deviation of ±75 kilocycles is 20. If the fundamental frequency and its 3.75-kilocycle deviation are doubled, the resultant is a center frequency of 10 megacycles with a deviation of 7.5 kilocycles. Proceeding through the multiplier stages until a factor of 20 is realized, the original 5-megacycle center frequency is increased to 100 megacycles, the desired broadcast frequency. Also, as the multiplication factor of 20 is applied to the center frequency, it will affect the deviation frequency. The original 3.75-kilocycle deviation, after a multiplication factor of 20, is equivalent to a 75-kilocycle deviation at the broadcast frequency. Thus, an allowable deviation is developed through the multipliers, and the amount of deviation in the oscillator stage must be considered throughout all stages of multiplication.

The reactance-tube modulated FM transmitter is similar to the low-level modulated AM transmitter, in that high-power audio and modulating circuits are not required. This characteristic results in a saving in bulk and weight of circuit components. Usually, one or two stages of voltage amplification produce a satisfactory modulation voltage. However, low-level modulated AM stages must be followed by linear amplifiers, and must modulate the output r-f frequency.

Frequency-Control Circuits

Another circuit of a special type my be required by the reactance-tube modulated FM transmitter. This circuit is an automatic frequency control (a-f-c) device to prevent the master oscillator circuit from drifting in frequency. The phase-modulated transmitter rarely requires a circuit of this type, since it employs a very stable crystal-controlled r-f oscillator circuit; however, the reactance-tube modulated type, using standard L and C components for the oscillator, may drift in frequency as a result of temperature changes and other conditions.

To prevent frequency drifting in this type of circuit, the circuit arrangement shown in the block diagram of figure 12-12 may be used. The transmitter shown uses a stable crystal oscillator to feed a mixer, along with a sample of the master-oscillator output. As long as there is no difference frequency in the output of the mixer circuit, no correction voltage will be developed by the discriminator. However, any difference in frequency developed in the mixer circuit will cause the discriminator to react and develop a correction voltage. The correction voltage developed by the discriminator circuit may be fed back to the react-ance-tube circuit as a positive or negative bias to compensate for any positive or negative drift in oscillator frequency. The action of the discriminator circuit is discussed in Chapter 13, in connection with FM receiver principles. The type of a-f-c circuit described here is one of the most popular in commercial FM transmitters today.

12-6 SUMMARY

FM transmitters may be divided into two categories — those having a reactance-tube modulation device and those having a phase-modulation device. Both types require much less audio power for modulation than the high-level AM transmitter. The audio power required to modulate either type of FM transmitter is more on the order of the audio power required to modulate the low-level AM transmitter.

The advantages of FM over AM are primarily due to the wide frequency band of the allotted channel. Assuming a well designed receiver, FM is superior in both sound reproduction and noise-limiting.

REVIEW QUESTIONS

1. What is the maximum deviation in carrier frequency allowed by the FCC?
2. What modulation index is the maximum permissible for 15-kc modulation? For 200-cycle modulation?
3. The deviation of oscillator frequency in the reactance-tube circuit depends upon what property of the modulating signal?
4. The frequency separation of the FM sidebands is dependent upon what property of the modulating signal?
5. The number of sidebands developed in the transmitted FM signal is dependent upon what property of the modulating signal?
6. Why is the amount of frequency deviation obtained in the modulating circuitry of an FM transmitter of great importance in the multiplier section of the transmitter?
7. When an FM signal is obtained by phase modulation, where does the modulation occur with respect to the master oscillator in the transmitter chain?
8. Why are a-f-c circuits required by some of the reactance-tube modulated FM transmitters?
9. What is the function of an a-f-c circuit?
10. Why are a-f-c circuits not required by the phase-modulated type of FM transmitter?
11. In the phase-modulated FM transmitter, is the frequency deviation linear with respect to a change in modulating frequency?
12. In the phase-modulated FM transmitter, does the deviation depend on the frequency of the modulating signal as well as the amplitude of the modulating signal?
13. What are *guard bands?*
14. 100-percent modulation occurs in an FM transmitter when what value of deviation is reached?
15. When calculating the frequency of the master oscillator of a reactance-tube modulated FM transmitter, what three values are involved?
16. Indirect frequency modulation is developed through what process?
17. Direct frequency modulation is developed through what process?
18. If a reactance-tube modulator circuit has a phase-shift network with a resistor f r o m plate to grid, and an inductor from grid to ground (an R-L network), what reactive property will be reflected into the oscillator tank circuit?
19. How many significant sidebands are created on each side of the FM carrier when a modulation index of 5 is attained?
20. Neglecting the current FCC regulations, does FM have any inherent advantage over AM as far as fidelity of reproduction is concerned?

CHAPTER THIRTEEN

Frequency-Modulation Receiver Principles

13-1 Introduction

The reception of an FM signal requires some circuitry in addition to that studied for the reception of an AM signal. The additional circuitry consists of a limiter, a special type of detector, and in some cases a squelch network. These circuit differences may be seen in the functional block diagrams of the AM and FM receivers in figure 13-1.

In many applications, the use of FM offers two important advantages over the use of AM — improved frequency response and better noise-limiting; however, full realization of these advantages requires the use of a well designed receiver. With such a receiver, the use of FM will result in higher fidelity of the audio modulation and quieter reception than is possible with AM.

13-2 COMPARISON OF AM AND FM RECEIVERS
R-F Amplifier

In the block diagrams of the AM and FM receivers, presented for comparison in figure 13-1, very little difference is indicated in the sections ahead of the detector circuits. However, the r-f amplifier, the mixer-oscillator (or converter), and the i-f amplifier circuits of the two receivers differ considerably in actual physical design.

The r-f amplifier of the FM receiver uses smaller values of inductances which possess low values of Q. Smaller inductance values are necessary to permit operation in the higher FM frequency range (88 to 108 megacycles), and low values of Q are required to broaden the tuning of the r-f amplifier so that it will pass all of the incoming signal. Of primary importance is the passage of the center FM frequency and all of its sidebands through the r-f and i-f stages.

Other factors to consider in analysis of the r-f amplifier are stage gain, vacuum-tube transconductance, and inherent noise. The stage gain of the r-f amplifier is usually on the order of 8 to 10, and the transconductance of the tube chosen

is of a high value to permit this amount of r-f gain. The noise generation in the r-f amplifier tube must be kept to a minimum, because any noise generated by the first stage in the receiver will be amplified by all following stages along with the received FM signal.

Another important factor to consider in analysis of the r-f voltage amplifier is the careful placement of leads and the use of minimum-length leads in construction. Excess lead length serves to increase the amount of stray capacitance and inductance in the circuit so that, under certain conditions and at some incoming frequency in the 88- to 108-megacycle range, the signal may be capacitively shorted to the chassis, or an undesirable howl may be generated by a resonant circuit formed by the stray inductance and capacitance.

Generally, an AM r-f amplifier circuit requires an incoming signal-to-noise ratio of 100:1 to receive and amplify the signal successfully, but because of the inherent noise-limiting capability of the FM receiver a well constructed FM r-f amplifier requires an incoming signal-to-noise

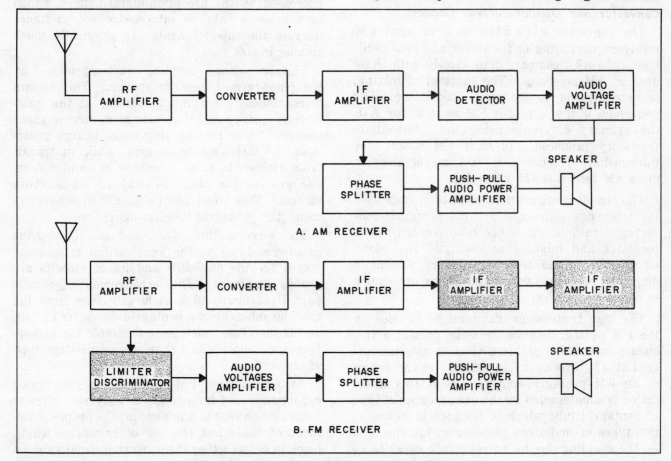

Figure 13-1. AM and FM Receiver Block Diagrams

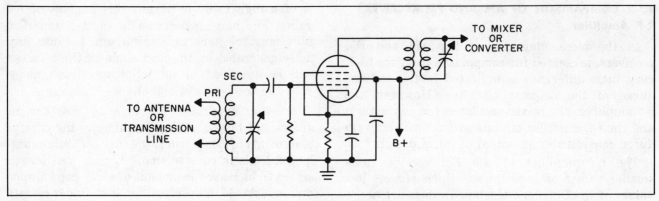

Figure 13-2.   A Typical FM R-F Amplifier

ratio of only 2:1 for reception and amplification. FM r-f amplifiers are usually capacitively tuned in the same manner as AM r-f amplifiers; however, both types may also be inductively or permeability tuned.   A typical capacitively tuned FM r-f amplifier is shown schematically in figure 13-2.   Most FM r-f amplifiers make use of triode tubes in a special circuit, called a *cascode* circuit; however, the pentode may also be employed as shown in the figure.

Converter and Oscillator-Mixer Circuits

The converter circuits used in most FM receivers, consisting of the mixer and local-oscillator networks, compare quite closely with those used in AM receivers.   The function of mixing, or heterodyning, to produce a fixed intermediate frequency is the same for FM as it is for AM, the primary difference being the intermediate frequency produced.   In most FM tuners, the intermediate frequency is 10.7 megacycles; in most AM sets, it is 455 kilocycles.

The circuit configurations most commonly used for frequency conversion are the pentagrid-converter circuit, in which one tube performs both oscillator and mixer functions, and the mixer circuit with a separate local oscillator.   Schematic diagrams of these two configurations are shown in figure 13-3.

The high frequencies that must be handled by the FM pentagrid-converter stage present a frequency-interaction problem which is not encountered at AM broadcast frequencies.   In the design of an FM pentagrid-converter stage this interaction is counteracted by the use of a special type of pentagrid tube which is designed to minimize two types of undesired coupling within the tube — the coupling due to interelectrode capacitance between the local oscillator grid and the incoming-signal grid, and the coupling due to the space-charge effect.

As the oscillator and incoming frequencies increase, the coupling due to inter-electrode capacitance, also increases because of the decrease in capacitive reactance between the two grids. This effect is overcome by careful tube design, or more frequently, by using separate tubes for the oscillator and mixer functions.   The coupling due to interelectrode capacitance may also be decreased by the use of miniature tubes, which have a lower value of interelectrode capacitance because the tube elements are physically much smaller in size.

The space-charge coupling effect is produced by the plate-current electron stream.   This stream is continuously varying in density at the oscillator frequency and thus acts as a varying space charge.   Since this varying space charge passes near the incoming-signal grid, while in transit from cathode to plate, a voltage is coupled from one grid to the other by way of the electron stream.   This effect occurs mainly in converters using the pentagrid-tube configuration.

To overcome this effect, and also to provide greater stability to the local oscillator, separate stages for the oscillator and mixer circuits are usually employed.   This arrangement, shown in part B of figure 13-3, is largely free from the troubles inherent in a pentagrid-converter circuit, and is therefore much more desirable for higher-frequency applications than the single-stage type of converter.

As in the case of FM r-f amplifiers, distributed capacitance and inductance in converter circuits must also be kept to a minimum; the proper placement of leads and the use of minimum length leads in constructing the converter circuitry must be carefully observed.

Stability of FM Local Oscillators

Oscillator circuits operating at frequencies of 88 to 108 (+ or − 10.7) megacycles are subject to frequency drift unless special means are used to prevent it. The presence or absence of drift in an oscillator is referred to as *instability* or *stability*, respectively. Frequency drift may be caused by changes in the ambient temperature of the circuit elements by variations in the humidity of the air circulating around the components, or by small variations in B+ due to loading of the power supply.

The effect of humidity, which may cause leakage (low-resistance paths) between windings of the tank coil or between plates of the air dielectric capacitor, may be overcome by placing the oscillator components near a high-temperature operating component to keep the components dry. An often used means of protecting coils from leakage caused by humidity is to coat the coil with a moistureproof substance.

To overcome the effect of changing values of capacitance and inductance, caused by changes in ambient temperature, materials having a low temperature coefficient are used in constructing these components. A low temperature coefficient material is one which changes electrical characteristics only a very small amount for a large increase in temperature. Primarily, the heat effects on an oscillator tank circuit are controlled by constructing the capacitance of the circuit with negative temperature coefficient materials. When this method is employed, an increase in temperature causes a slight increase in inductance and a corresponding decrease in capacitance; thus frequency drift is minimized.

Other specialized circuits, known as automatic frequency control circuits (afc), are used in the correction of oscillator drift. An a-f-c circuit makes use of a sensing circuit, called a *frequency discriminator,* and a reactance tube to keep the tank circuit tuned to the desired frequency. These circuits are discussed later.

Intermediate-Frequency Amplifier Section

The output of the frequency-converter stage, as previously mentioned, is usually 10.7 megacycles. This is the center frequency about which the FM intelligence varies after leaving the converter stage. Conversion of the relatively wide band of FM carrier frequencies to a fixed frequency, called the *intermediate frequency,* greatly simplifies the circuitry following the converter stage.

As stated previously, the i-f stages of an FM receiver are similar to those of an AM receiver.

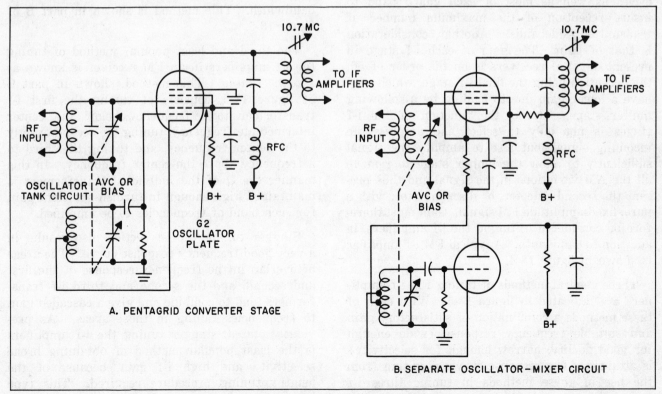

Figure 13-3. Two Converter Configurations Used in FM Receivers

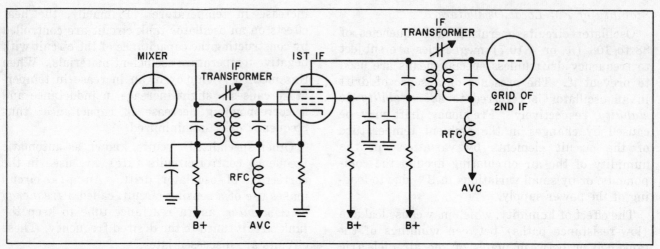

Figure 13-4. A Typical FM I-F Amplifier

The principal differences are due to the higher band of frequencies that must be selected and amplified by the i-f section of the FM receiver. Most of the i-f transformers and stages used in present day FM receivers are designed to pass a bandwidth of at least 150 kilocycles, the minimum bandwidth required. However, in the case of 100-percent modulation (75 kc deviation) of the transmitted FM signal, a slightly wider band would be desirable. This wider band should cover the total transmission band of 150 kilocycles as well as most of each guard band to insure reception of the maximum number of transmitted sidebands. Another consideration is that of gain. The gain of each i-f stage in present day FM receivers is on the order of 50, the exception being the final i-f stage, which may have a lower gain due to loading by a following limiter stage. Hence, the function of the i-f stages is not only to select and amplify the incoming signal, but also to amplify the signal sufficiently to allow the limiter stage to remove all the AM variations in the signal and thus present the second detector, or discriminator, with a pure, fixed-amplitude FM signal. Gain must therefore be considered in tuning the i-f amplifiers, in addition to bandwidth. A typical FM i-f amplifier is shown in figure 13-4.

Three general methods of tuning FM i-f amplifiers are indicated in figure 13-5. With each of these methods a combination of satisfactory gain and suitable frequency response (wide enough for good fidelity, narrow enough for selectivity) is attained. The response curves resulting from the use of these methods in tuning three i-f transformers are also shown in the figure.

The first method, shown in part A of figure 13-5, makes use of three single-tuned i-f transformers having a low Q to provide sufficient bandwidth. The low Q tends to decrease the gain derived from any one stage; however, the three tuned circuits in cascade produce a satisfactory over-all gain figure with good bandwidth.

The second method of tuning the i-f section utilizes a single-peaked first and third transformer, and a double-peaked (overcoupled) second transformer to furnish a satisfactory bandwidth. This method is shown in part B of figure 13-5.

The third and least popular method of tuning the i-f amplifiers in an FM receiver is known as *stagger tuning*. This method, shown in part C of figure 13-5, consists of tuning the first i-f transformer to a frequency below the center intermediate frequency, tuning the second exactly to the center frequency, and tuning the third to a frequency above the center frequency. In this manner the Q of the individual transformers is maintained high enough to furnish sufficient gain for each band of frequencies to be amplified.

Stagger tuning the i-f section also results in a very good frequency response curve. The areas of overlap in the frequency response of the first and second, and the second and third i-f transformers tend to combine and give a cascaded gain to frequencies falling in those areas. As previously stated, stagger tuning the i-f amplifiers is the least popular method of obtaining broad selectivity and high i-f gain, because of the lengthy tuning procedure required. This type of tuning is used more often in commercial tele-

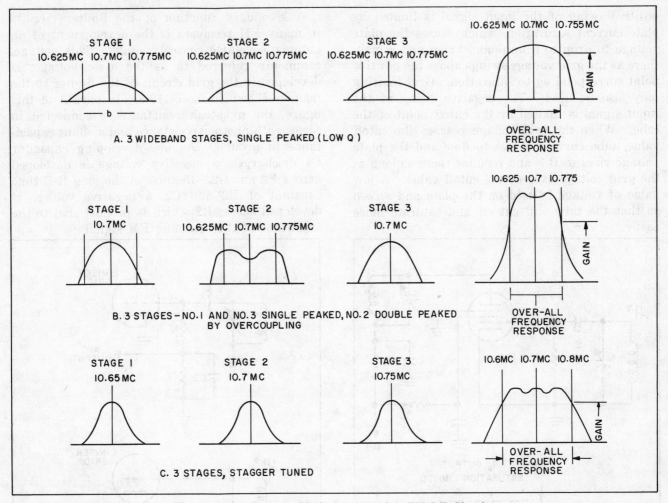

Figure 13-5. Common Methods of Tuning FM I-F Circuits

vision i-f systems, in which the bandwidth requirements are far greater than those in ordinary FM receivers.

FM Detection Circuits

At this point in the comparison of AM and FM receivers an outstanding difference in circuitry is encountered. Immediately following the final i-f stage in the i-f strip, the FM receiver employs either a limiter-discriminator combination or a ratio detector. These circuits are shown in block diagram form in figure 13-6. Also frequently used is the gated-beam discriminator, the block diagram of which resembles that of the ratio detector. The operation of these detector circuits is explained in the following paragraphs.

Limiter Operation

The limiter circuit is an amplifier stage which not only amplifies the signal, but also removes all amplitude variations from the i-f input and supplies the required fixed-amplitude signal to the discriminator stage.

Functionally, the limiter operates as an over-driven amplifier. The circuit uses a sharp cutoff tube to produce amplification and limiting. The

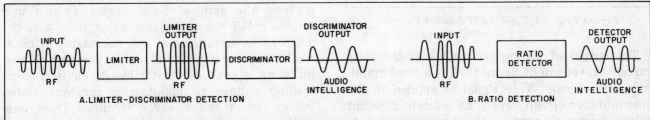

Figure 13-6. Primary Methods of FM Detection

positive swing of the input signal is limited by plate current saturation, which causes the plate voltage to drop to a minimum value and remain there as the grid voltage swings above the positive point corresponding to saturation. Grid limiting may also be used. The negative swing of the input signal is limited by the cutoff point of the tube. When the grid voltage reaches the cutoff value, tube current ceases to flow and the plate voltage rises to B+ and remains there as long as the grid voltage exceeds the cutoff value. A low value of voltage is used on the plate and screen so that the tube will cut off and saturate more easily.

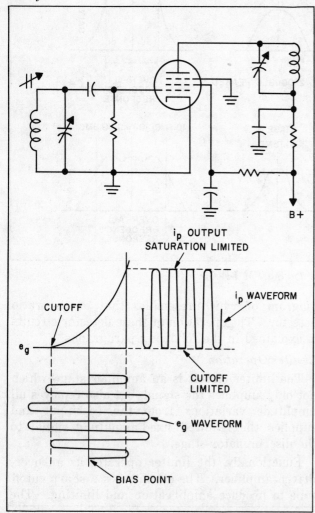

Figure 13-7.   A Typical FM Limiter Circuit

The output of the limiter, shown as the plate current waveform of figure 13-7, is a fixed amplitude FM signal. This signal is applied to the discriminator circuit, where an entirely different action occurs to remove the audio intelligence from the signal.

A secondary function of the limiter circuits in many FM receivers is the development of an automatic volume control voltage. This voltage, commonly referred to as the a-v-c voltage, is developed in the grid circuit of the limiter in the manner shown in figure 13-8. In part A of this figure, the grid-leak resistance is connected in series with another resistance and a shunt capacitance to ground. As bias-developing capacitor C1 discharges, a negative voltage is developed across R2 and C2. Because of the long R-C time constant of R2 and C2, a negative voltage is developed across R2 which is proportional to the amplitude of the incoming FM signal.

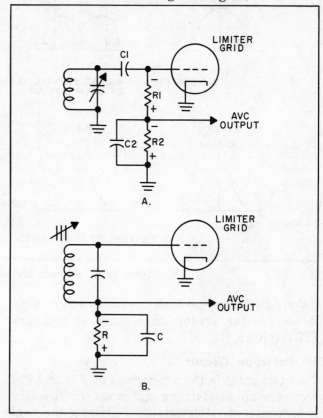

Figure 13-8.   Methods of Developing A-V-C Voltage in Limiter Circuit

The a-v-c voltage is applied to the grids of preceding stages, such as the i-f amplifiers, converter, and r-f amplifier. This negative voltage controls the gain of these stages (which use remote cutoff tubes) by increasing their bias on a strong incoming signal and decreasing it on a weak incoming signal. Thus, the strength of the incoming signal automatically develops a controlling voltage to maintain a constant audio volume when the receiver is tuned from one station to another or when its location is being changed, as in mobile applications.

disadvantage too many tuned circuits

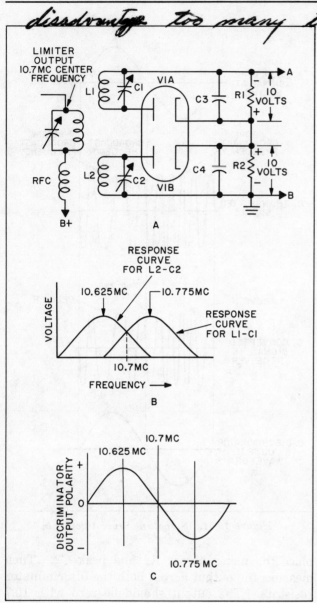

Figure 13-9. A Typical Double-Tuned (Crosby) FM Discriminator

circuit shown in part A of figure 13-9 consists of two separate tuned circuits, two diodes, and two parallel R-C networks connected in series. This discriminator is known as the *Crosby*, or *double-tuned*, discriminator. The voltages across R1 and R2 are equal at 10.7 megacycles.

The tank circuit composed of L1 and C1 is tuned to a resonant frequency of 10.775 mc and the tank circuit composed of L2 and C2 is tuned to a resonant frequency of 10.625 mc. The frequency response characteristics of the individual tuned circuits are illustrated in figure 13-9B. Observe that, at a frequency of 10.7 mc., the voltage developed across each tuned circuit is the same; thus each diode of the discriminator conducts the same amount. The voltage developed across R1 is equal to the voltage developed across R2 and the net voltage between points A and B of Figure 13-9A is zero. The voltage developed between points A and B for frequencies within the passband of the discriminator is illustrated in Figure 13-9C. At 10.7 mc, the center frequency of the discriminator, the output of the discriminator is zero. At 10.625 mc the output of the discriminator is at its maximum positive value which corresponds to maximum response from L2-C2. At 10.775 mc the output of the discriminator is at its maximum negative value; this corresponds to maximum response from L1-C1.

Figure 13-10A illustrates the way in which an output voltage from the discriminator is developed for an i-f signal greater than 10.7 mc, for example, 10.72 mc. The voltages developed across R1 and R2 are 9.7 and 11.3 volts respectively, thus the output voltage between points A and B is 1.6 volts. Figure 13-10B illustrates the way in which an output voltage from the discriminator is developed for an i-f signal less than 10.7 mc, for example, 10.68 mc. The voltage developed across R2 and R1 are 9.7 and 11.3 volts respectively, thus the output voltage between points A and B is 1.6 volts. The polarity of the output signal developed in figure 13-10B is opposite to that which is developed in figure 13-10A.

Figure 13-11 illustrates signals at several points in an FM system. Figure 13-11A illustrates the modulating signal at the station and Figure 13-11B illustrates the variation which the modulating signal causes in the transmitted frequency. Figure 13-11C illustrates the i-f signal and figure 13-11D the discriminator output.

A second method of developing an a-v-c voltage is shown in part B of figure 13-8. This method, in effect, consists of tapping off the automatic bias developed by the limiter input and using it as the a-v-c voltage. The voltage is fed back to the same circuitry and will perform the same function as the voltage developed by the network shown in part A of the figure; however, the a-v-c signal developed by the circuit in part A may be somewhat more stable with a fixed-strength input signal.

Frequency Discriminator Circuit

When used in conjunction with a limiter circuit, the discriminator removes the audio intelligence from the incoming FM signal. The discriminator

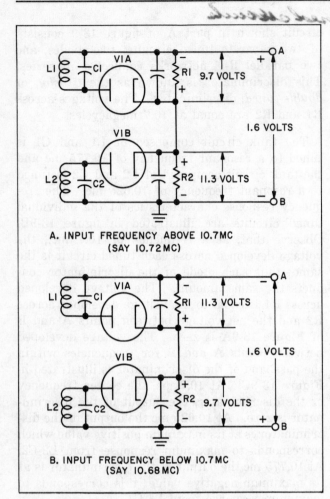

Figure 13-10. *Discriminator Output for I-F Signals Greater Than and Less Than the Intermediate Center Frequency*

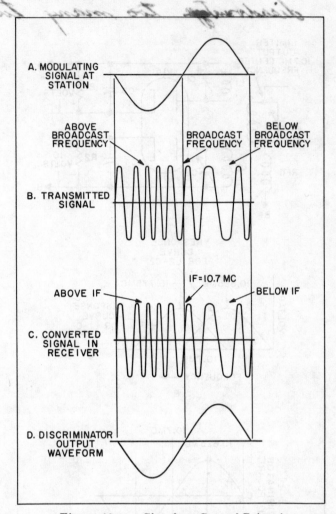

Figure 13-11. *Signals at Several Points in a FM System*

Frequency Discriminator Alignment

Alignment of the double-tuned, or Crosby, discriminator may be accomplished with the aid of an r-f signal generator and a vacuum-tube voltmeter. The output of the r-f signal generator, adjusted to the intermediate frequency of 10.7 megacycles, is applied to the grid of the last i-f stage. Amplification of the signal by this i-f stage is required, in some cases, to furnish sufficient drive for the limiter. If the output of the r-f signal generator is strong enough without amplification to drive the limiter stage, the signal may be applied directly to the grid of the limiter.

With the 10.7-megacycle signal applied, connect the vacuum-tube voltmeter across either of the discriminator load resistors, and tune the capacitor in the primary (limiter plate tank) for peak d-c voltage. Change the input frequency to 10.775 mc, place the vacuum-tube voltmeter across R1 (observe polarity), and adjust C1 for maximum output. Change the input to 10.625 mc,

place the meter across R2 and peak C2. Then measure the output across both the discriminator resistors. The output should be zero with 10.7 megacycles applied.

After aligning as above, vary the applied frequency in equal steps above and below the center frequency, while observing the voltmeter indication. The output of the discriminator should vary equally positive and negative, for equal shifts to either side of 10.7 mc.

The output of a discriminator, after proper alignment, can be plotted graphically as in figure 13-12. The linearity of the output curve shows that equal positive and negative output voltages are developed at 10 and 20 kilocycles above and below the center frequency of 10.7 megacycles. A check of discriminator linearity should be made, over a minimum bandwidth of plus and minus 75 kilocycles, to the peaks of the discriminator response curve.

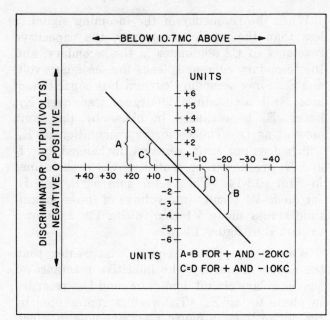

Figure 13-12. Voltages Obtained From a Properly Aligned FM Discriminator

Two other double-tuned discriminators may be encountered, particularly in military equipment. These are the Travis discriminator and the Weiss discriminator. In the Travis discriminator the diodes are moved to the opposite ends of the capacitors, and C1 and C2 are connected at the center. The same changes are made in the Weiss discriminator, and in addition, the input is coupled directly to the junction of C1 and C2. In this case, L1 and L2 are replaced by a single inductor, and the input circuit assumes a delta configuration. Double-tuned discriminators are seldom used in modern commercial equipment because of the critical, complex alignment procedures required.

Phase Discriminator

Many of the FM receivers in use today make use of another type of discriminator known as the *Foster-Seeley*. This type requires fewer tank circuit components than the double-tuned type, and is somewhat easier to align. However, the operation of the Foster-Seeley is slightly more complex than the double-tuned discriminator.

Figure 13-13 illustrates the Foster-Seely discriminator circuit. Owing to the fact that the secondary of the transformer is loosely coupled to the primary, a large portion of the total secondary inductance is not linked by the primary flux and this inductance in series with C2 forms a series resonant circuit. The secondary circuit is resonant at 10.7 mc.

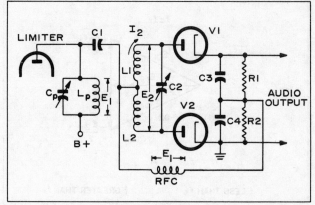

Figure 13-13. Foster-Seeley Phase Discriminator

With all factors considered, the secondary circuit shown in figure 13-13 appears resistive at the intermediate frequency of 10.7 megacycles. When the incoming frequency decreases below 10.7 megacycles, the circuit appears capacitive and I leads E in the secondary. When the incoming frequency increases above 10.7 megacycles, the secondary circuit appears inductive and E leads I. At the intermediate frequency of 10.7 megacycles, capacitors C1, C3, and C4 of the discriminator offer minimum reactance. These conditions lead to the phase relationships shown in figure 13-14.

To understand these relationships, assume that the voltage across the primary, E_1, has zero phase

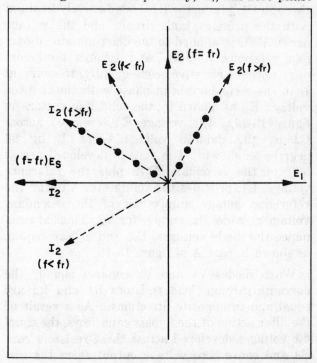

Figure 13-14. Foster-Seeley Discriminator Phase Relationships

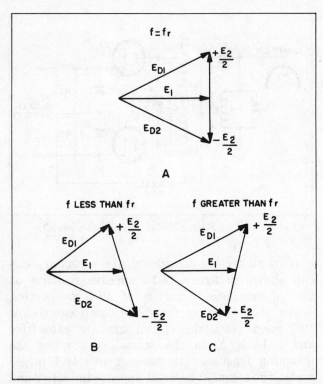

Figure 13-15.   Change of Discriminator Diode Voltages with Change in Applied Frequency

as shown. By transformer action, this voltage causes a voltage to be induced in the secondary, E_s, which is 180 degrees out of phase with E_1. A voltage in phase with E_1 is also developed across inductor RFC by capacitive coupling through C1. Inductor RFC is effectively in shunt with the primary tank circuit, and the voltage across RFC is applied to the discriminator diodes as a reference voltage. At resonance the secondary appears resistive; consequently, the current I_2 in the secondary is in phase with the induced voltage E_s, as shown by the solid line vectors in figure 13-14. The voltage E_2 developed across C2 by the induced voltage lags I_2 by 90 degrees as shown. The voltage developed across half of the secondary $E_2/2$ plus the reference voltage, E1, provides the voltage for V1, and the reference voltage minus half of the secondary voltage provides the voltage for V2. Thus, at resonance the diode voltages, E_{D1} and E_{D2} are equal, as shown in part A of figure 13-15.

When diodes V1 and V2 conduct equally the currents through load resistors R1 and R2 are equal and in opposite directions. As a result of the filter action of the bypass capacitors, the equal d-c voltages developed across these resistors cancel and cause zero voltage output from the discriminator with the resonant frequency applied.

When the frequency of the incoming signal is less than the carrier frequency, the capacitive reactance of C2 dominates in the secondary, and the secondary current I_2 leads the secondary voltage E_s. Since secondary current I_2 is capacitive, it must still maintain a 90-degree lead over E_2; hence, E_2 is advanced in phase by the same amount as I_2. The vector representation of E_1, which does not shift, remains unchanged, but I_2 and E_2 are now represented by the dashed lines in figure 13-14. The vector sum of E_1 and E_2 for diode V1 results in a voltage of lower magnitude across diode V1 than diode V2, as shown in part B of figure 13-15.

When the applied frequency is greater than the center frequency, the inductive reactance of the secondary circuit dominates, and I_2 is retarded in phase to lag E_s. The vectors represented by the dotted lines in figure 13-14 are now in effect. Since voltage E_1 still does not change, the vector sum of E_1 and E_2 across diode V1 results in a greater magnitude of voltage than across V2, as shown in part C of figure 13-15.

Under the conditions explained above, when the frequency is greater than the center frequency, diode V1 conducts more heavily than V2, and more current passes through R1 than R2; therefore, a positive output voltage is developed.

When the applied frequency is less than the center frequency, diode V2 conducts more heavily than V1, and more current passes through R2 than R1; therefore, a negative output voltage is developed. The d-c output voltage changes in proportion to the applied frequency variation; thus, within the range of the carrier frequency swing a d-c output voltage varying at an audio rate is produced and the FM input is detected.

The discriminator detector has one disadvantage in that low-power AM signals, too weak to cause the limiter to function, will allow E_1, the voltage across the r-f choke, to fluctuate. When this voltage fluctuates at the AM rate, the undesired AM signal is effectively passed by the discriminator, amplified by the following stages, and heard in the output of the receiver. This disadvantage is not encountered in the ratio detector.

Ratio Detector

Several differences exist between the ratio detector circuit, shown in figure 13-16, and the Foster-Seeley discriminator. The major differ-

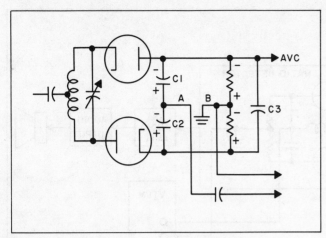

Figure 13-16. Ratio Detector

ence is the connection of the diodes. With the diodes connected in this manner, they conduct simultaneously on alternate half cycles of the applied signal, rather than separately on different half cycles as in the Foster-Seeley circuit.

R1 and R2 are shunted by the equivalent capacitors, of C1 and C2 in series, and C3 in parallel. C3 and the two resistors form a circuit for developing an AVC voltage for maintaining the voltage across C1 and C2 constant when amplitude fluctuations in the audio frequency range occur. Thus, the limiter stage can be eliminated by the use of the ratio detector circuit.

To understand the operation of this circuit, assume that the average instantaneous voltage appearing across the a-v-c network is 10 volts, which is determined by the amplitude of the applied FM signal. This 10 volts, which is impressed across capacitors C1 and C2 in series, is the maximum value to which these equal-value capacitors can charge. Thus, at the center frequency of the incoming signal, 5 volts is present across each capacitor, and across each resistor (R1 = R2) ; thus the voltage between points A and B is zero.

With the same amplitude FM input signal and a 10-volt average d-c voltage remaining on the a-v-c circuit capacitor, a deviation of the input frequency below the center frequency causes a higher instantaneous voltage to be developed across diode V2 than V1, just as in the Foster-Seeley discriminator. For this condition diode V2 conducts more heavily and causes an unbalance in the voltage developed across C1 and C2. This charges C2 more negatively, causing the output to become negative. For example, the voltage

across C1 might become two volts and the voltage across C2 eight volts. The sum is still ten volts, but the voltage between points A and B is now three volts and point A is negative with respect to point B.

A deviation of the input frequency above the center frequency, with a 10-volt average d-c voltage maintained on the a-v-c capacitor, causes a greater instantaneous voltage to be developed across diode V1 than V2. When diode V1 conducts more heavily than V2, an unbalance in the voltages developed across C1 and C2 occurs. Thus, the junction swings positive as electrons are removed, charging C1 and reducing the charge on C2. Assuming that the variations of the incoming signal above and below the center frequency are equal, a negative 2 volts now appears across C2, while the remaining 8 volts appears across C1. Therefore, the output voltage of point A will swing positive with respect to point B.

The ratio detector is so called because the rectified voltages are split into two parts in such a way that their ratio is proportional to the ratio of the instantaneous i-f volages applied to the detector diodes.

The long R-C time constant a-v-c circuit is used to perform the function of the limiter stage. If the station to which the receiver is tuned has some amplitude modulation in its output, the instantaneous changes in amplitude, which are undesired but passed by a discriminator without a limiter, are absorbed by the large R-C time constant of the a-v-c network. The change in a-v-c voltage with AM applied is negligible, and the undesired amplitude variations are effectively filtered out.

Whenever a stronger station is tuned in on the FM receiver, the allowable ratio of voltages developed across C1 and C2 remains the same. The stronger station develops a higher a-v-c voltage, which is fed back to decrease the gain of the preceding stages. The positive and negative swings of voltage out of the ratio detector circuit are then directly proportional to the variation of the incoming station frequency above and below the center intermediate frequency, and are not appreciably affected by amplitude variations.

Ratio Detector Alignment

To align the ratio detector accurately, it is always best to work from the detector toward the "front end," or r-f stage, of the receiver.

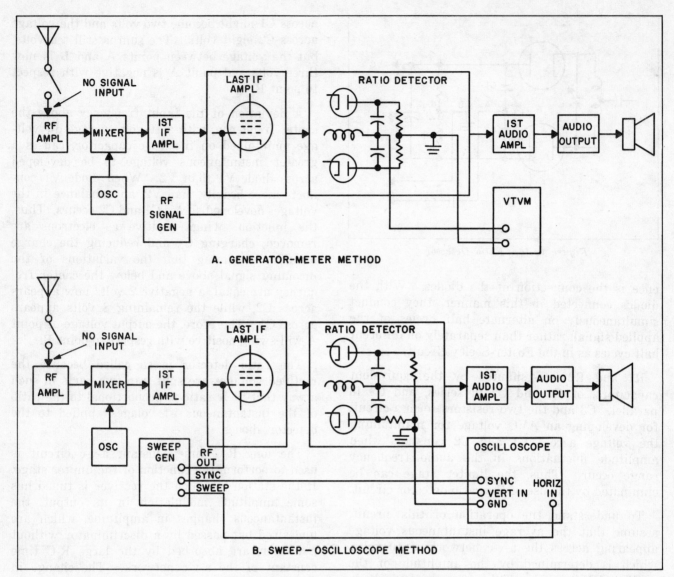

Figure 13-17. Ratio Detector Alignment

More than one method of aligning the ratio detector may be employed. One method makes use of an r-f signal generator, and a zero-center-scale vacuum-tube voltmeter. This method provides a meter indication of proper alignment, and the detector may be aligned before or after alignment of the FM i-f section. Another method of aligning the ratio detector utilizes an FM sweep generator and an oscilloscope. This method provides a visual oscilloscope presentation of the complete response curve of the ratio detector, and is one of the quickest, most accurate methods available.

In the first method mentioned above, connections are made as is illustrated in figure 13-17A. The r-f signal generator is then connected to the grid of the final i-f stage and adjusted to the desired center frequency. After these two steps are completed, t h e vacuum-tube voltmeter is placed across one of the resistors, and the primary of the circuit is tuned for maximum indication. The vacuum-tube voltmeter is then placed across each resistor, in turn, and the secondary of the transformer tuned for equal voltage drops across the two resistors. As a check of the alignment, the frequency of the r-f signal generator is varied in equal steps above and below the center frequency while the meter indication is observed. Equal variations above and below the original meter indication should occur for each pair of equal frequency changes above and below the center frequency. If not, a slight readjustment of the secondary may be necessary to improve the linearity of the output. The response curve should be linear over a 200-kilocycle bandwidth, with the crossover point for equal voltages across C1 and C2 occurring at the center frequency of 10.7 megacycles. As an additional check of the ratio detector alignment, a graph of the response curve may be plotted. The resulting graph should be similar to that in figure 13-12 for the discriminator circuit, except centered on half the a-v-c output voltage.

The second method of aligning a ratio detector, referred to as the *visual method,* requires equipment somewhat more complex in nature than that used in the first, but offers the advantage of requiring less time for the alignment. An FM sweep generator and an oscilloscope are used in place of the r-f signal generator and the vacuum-tube voltmeter, respectively. The connections are illustrated in figure 13-17B.

An FM sweep generator is a generator that furnishes an FM modulated signal extending equal amounts above and below a desired center frequency. The maximum deviation from the center frequency may be set anywhere from 30 kilocycles to 700 kilocycles. In the visual method, the FM sweep generator is set for approximately 200 kilocycles deviation, and the output is applied to the grid of the final i-f stage. The vertical input of the oscilloscope is connected to the junction of the ratio detector output capacitors, and the horizontal sweep voltage is obtained from the modulating signal of the generator or an internal sine-wave sweep. With these connections, the oscilloscope should display an S-shaped response curve as shown in figure 13-18. In this

figure the vertical transitions of the S curve represent the increasing and decreasing amplitude of the output audio signal and the horizontal transitions from zero represent the frequency deviation caused by the modulating signal.

The vertical amplitude of the S-shaped response curve is adjusted for maximum on the oscilloscope by tuning the primary of the ratio detector circuit. The linearity of the response curve is adjusted by tuning the secondary circuit of the ratio detector.

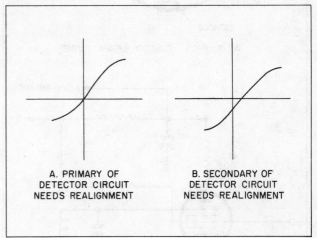

Figure 13-19. Distorted and NonLinear Response Curves of Improperly Aligned Ratio Detector

If the circuit is not properly balanced, an indication of the unbalance may be heard in the output of the speaker. Also, curves such as those in figure 13-19 may result. The curves shown in the figure may be corrected by performing the adjustments listed by them. The over-all response of the ratio detector circuit should be linear for a minimum of 150 kilocycles from the negative peak of the response curve to the positive peak, when checked along the horizontal axis. (This figure of 150 kc applies to FM broadcast band receivers, operating from 88 to 108 mc.)

Gated-Beam Discriminator

The gated-beam discriminator is a circuit which utilizes a specially designed gated-beam tube. The circuits used with it combine both limiter and discriminator functions, and in many cases provide sufficient output to eliminate the need for a first audio amplifier. This discriminator is popular where cost or size must be kept to a minimum. The quality of audio provided ranges from good to barely acceptable, depending on the particular design. Currently available gated-beam tubes produce too much distortion for high-fidelity applications.

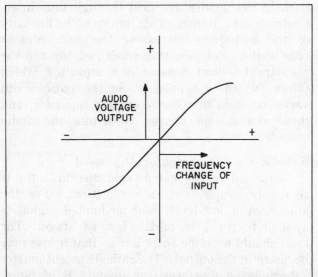

Figure 13-18. S-Type Response Curve of Properly Aligned Ratio Detector (Obtained by Use of FM Signal Generator)

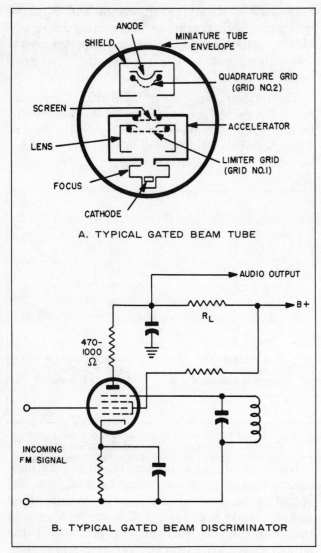

A. TYPICAL GATED BEAM TUBE

B. TYPICAL GATED BEAM DISCRIMINATOR

*Figure 13-20. Gated-Beam Tube and
Discriminator Circuit*

Part A of figure 13-20 is a schematic of the inner structure of the tube. Electrons emitted by the cathode are formed into a narrow beam by the focus and accelerator elements before they reach the first grid, called the limiter grid. This grid has extremely sharp cutoff characteristics in that it cuts off and saturates at very slightly different potentials. This is a result of the focused beam, and the fact that any space charge attempting to build up near the cathode (a condition which would ease the sharp cutoff) is drawn away by the accelerator. This limiter grid acts almost as a switching element.

Once past the limiter grid, the electron beam is focused again by a lens system, consisting of the same accelerator and the screen grid. The beam then passes through a pair of narrow slits,

one at the screen grid and the other at the entrance to the shield box. Here, the quadrature grid, with cutoff characteristics similar to those of the limiter grid, is encountered. When both of these switching grids permit conduction, the electrons finally reach the plate or anode.

In the practical circuit in part B of figure 13-20, the tube is shown with four grids. The two connected together are the screen and the accelerator element, which are o f t e n shown simply as a screen grid in schematic diagrams. The incoming signal from the i-f amplifier is applied to the limiter grid, which is biased for a small value of tube current with no signal. The limiter grid is driven to saturation and cutoff, even on weak signals, to provide effective limiting, and to produce pulses of tube current.

When the electrons reach the quadrature grid, the tuned circuit connected to this element produces a quadrature grid voltage which lags the current pulses in phase. At resonance, this shift is just 90 degrees, so that the quadrature grid will be cut off for about half the time the limiter grid conducts. When the incoming signal is below resonance, the tuned circuit produces less lag and a longer output pulse. When the signal is above resonance, the tuned circuit produces more lag and a narrower output pulse. Thus the width of the pulse reaching the plate is made to vary as the incoming f r e q u e n c y changes with modulation.

A small resistor in the plate circuit develops a small pulse voltage at the plate, which is fed back to the quadrature grid through tube interelectrode capacitance. This improves the linearity of the output by increasing the discriminator bandwidth. Between this small resistor and the regular plate-load resistor is a capacitor, which filters out the r-f pulses. As the pulse width varies, so does the charge on this capacitor, and these changes in charge constitute the audio output.

Gated-Beam Discriminator Alignment

Alignment of the gated-beam discriminator is relatively simple, but rather critical. For the alignment a low-level, tone-modulated signal is applied to the grid of the last i-f stage. The level should be sufficiently low so that a hiss may be heard in the output. The cathode potentiometer (shown as a fixed resistor in part B of figure 13-20) is adjusted for minimum hiss, while the input level is decreased as necessary to retain a small amount of hiss. Next, the quadrature tuned circuit is tuned for maximum output. Finally, if the limiter grid circuit employs tuning, this circuit is adjusted for maximum output.

In current equipment, most FM receivers use either the ratio detector or the Foster-Seeley discriminator. Television receiver sound systems usually use the gated-beam discriminator or the ratio detector. The double-tuned circuits discussed earlier and the Bradley and locked-in oscillator types are primarily found in older equipment or special purpose devices such as automatic-frequency-control circuits (in military gear, radar, etc).

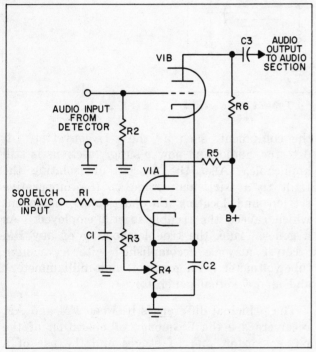

Figure 13-21. A Typical Squelch Circuit

Squelch Circuit

Another circuit used in some FM receivers is the squelch circuit, which is sometimes referred to as a *muting circuit* or a *squelch audio amplifier*. This circuit is shown in its basic form in figure 13-21. Tube V1B in this circuit serves as a straight audio amplifier which is controlled by tube V1A and the a-v-c voltage or squelch voltage developed in the limiter-discriminator circuit.

When an incoming signal is present, an a-v-c voltage or squelch voltage of a negative polarity is developed and applied to the control grid of tube V1A, to keep V1A cut off. Since the a-v-c voltage is usually insufficient to cut the tube off, a separate squelch rectifier is frequently used.

The cathodes of both V1A and V1B are connected to the bias-developing network R4 and C2; however, with V1A cut off, only the current drawn by tube V1B develops bias voltage, and the amplifier functions normally.

An FM receiver without this circuit will emit a hiss or other undesirable noise from the speaker when an incoming signal is not being received. An FM receiver using the squelch circuit will not emit this undesirable noise for, when the incoming signal is absent, no squelch voltage is developed; therefore, tube V1A will conduct heavily and develop sufficient bias voltage across resistor R4 to cut off tube V1B. With V1A conducting and V1B cut off, the audio section of the receiver is effectively disabled and no noise is emitted by the speaker. Usually, FM receivers which employ the ratio detector do not require a squelch circuit, because the output noise level of the ratio detector with no incoming signal is quite low.

Squelch Voltage Adjustment

The setting of the squelch voltage, or the selection of the a-v-c level at which silencing or squelching occurs, depends somewhat on the relative strength of the received FM signal. As previously studied, a strong or nearby station will develop a large negative a-v-c voltage, and a weak or distant station will develop a small negative a-v-c voltage. The same applies to the squelch signal. Therefore, when a strong signal is being received, the static bias of tube V1A need not be as great as when a weaker signal is being received. For the reception of weak FM signals, the static bias of V1A must be increased to prevent the squelch tube from conducting and blanking out the signals.

For the reception of strong signals, bias potentiometer R4 in the cathode of squelch tube V1A is set for a high resistance between the bottom of R3 and ground. This setting effectively causes less bias between the cathode and grid of V1A, by tapping off a higher positive voltage across R4 for application to the grid. Thus, the squelch voltage, which is large for a strong signal will hold the squelch tube only slightly below cutoff so that silencing will occur immediately whenever the signal is lost.

For the reception of weak signals, R4 is set for a small or minimum resistance between the bottom of R3 and ground. This setting places the grid closer to ground potential, and since the cathode remains at a positive value, the bias

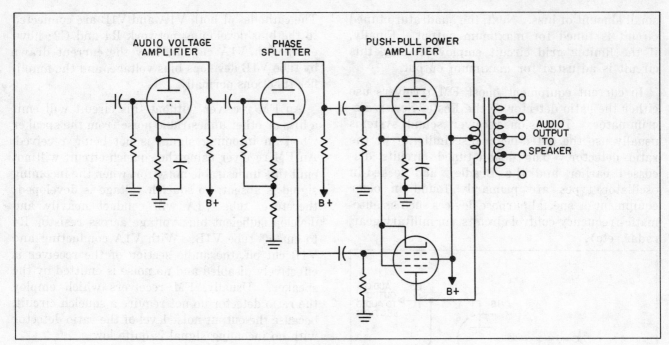

Figure 13-22. Audio Section of a Typical FM Receiver

on V1A is increased to allow the low squelch voltage developed in the limiter-discriminator stage to hold the tube below cutoff. Thus, the weak signal is passed and silencing will still occur immediately whenever the signal is lost. Squelch adjustment, therefore, is dependent upon the strength of the signal received and on the individual desires of the person operating the receiver.

FM Receiver Audio Section

The audio section of the FM receiver compares closely to the audio section of a standard AM receiver. The voltage amplifier, phase splitter (if used), and power amplifier sections are identical in parts arrangement to those found in the AM type. However, there are some slight differences in the quality and values of components used in the FM receiver audio amplifier due to the higher fidelity of the received sound, which results from the wider FM bandwidth.

A typical audio amplifier, phase splitter, and power amplifier circuit arrangement is shown, schematically, in figure 13-22. These circuits function exactly as those of the same type studied previously.

The trouble-shooting procedures used for repair of the audio section of an FM receiver are identical to those used for repair of the audio section of an AM receiver. The standard procedure of localizing the trouble of a particular section of

the equipment, such as the r-f, converter, i-f, detector, audio, and power supply sections is still applicable. Also, the process of isolating the fault to a particular stage of the inoperative section and locating the particular component which caused the trouble is still employed. As a general rule, the trouble-shooting of any FM receiver may be accomplished with a vacuum-tube voltmeter (or a good volt-ohm-milliammeter) and an r-f signal generator.

The principal differences between FM and AM receivers are the frequency of operation of the r-f, converter, and i-f stages and the use of a limiter-discriminator or ratio detector circuit in the FM receiver to change the received FM signal into a fairly high-quality audio output signal.

13-3 SUMMARY

The comparison of AM and FM receivers has shown that the audio sections and the majority of the radio frequency sections of the two types are very similar. The main differences are the component values, due to the difference in operating frequency, and the means of removing the intelligence from the incoming signal.

In the FM receiver, detection is accomplished by use of a limiter-discriminator, a phase discriminator, a ratio detector, or a gated-beam discriminator. The last is the simplest and most efficient. It has been shown that these circuits are quite different in operation from the AM diode type detector circuit.

The FM receiver employs some specialized circuits and devices not required by the AM type. Among these are temperature compensating components and an automatic-frequency-controlling device which maintains the frequency of the local oscillator 10.7 megacycles away from the incoming station frequency. Another specialized circuit is the squelch or silencing network. The squelch circuit, used with the limiter-discriminator and the phase discriminator types of FM detectors, cuts off the audio section of the receiver whenever the station signal is lost. Thus it eliminates any hiss or other undesirable noise that may be present in the absence of a transmitted signal. Some AM communication receivers also use squelch circuits.

The over-all construction of the FM receiver and the transmission of a high-quality signal are the main factors which cause FM to provide higher quality sound than AM.

REVIEW QUESTIONS

1. What are the fundamental differences between AM and FM receivers?

2. How may FM local oscillators be prevented from drifting in frequency?

3. What is the primary advantage of the ratio detector over the limiter-discriminator?

4. What two methods may be employed to align the ratio detector?

5. What is the total r-f bandwidth that the FM r-f amplifier must be capable of receiving?

6. What effect does a negative temperature coefficient capacitor have on the frequency of an oscillator tank circuit when the ambient temperature is increasing?

7. What are several causes of oscillator frequency drift?

8. What is the intermediate frequency of a typical FM receiver?

9. If the local oscillator of an FM receiver is tuned above the frequency of the incoming signal, what frequency range must the local-oscillator tank circuit have to cover the FM band?

10. What is the function of the squelch circuit of an FM receiver?

11. Is the squelch circuit necessary in an FM receiver which uses the ratio detector?

12. What is the total broadcast bandwidth of an FM station including the guard bands?

13. What three methods may be used to align the i-f amplifiers of an FM receiver?

14. Which of the three methods of aligning FM i-f amplifiers is the most difficult or requires the most complex equipment to accomplish?

15. What signal-to-noise ratio is required for an FM receiver to function properly?

16. What characteristic of the transmitted wave is the greatest distance-limiting factor in the transmission and reception of FM?

17. Explain how an S-shaped discriminator alignment curve can be obtained in an FM receiver.

18. What property determines the peak-to-peak amplitude of the S-shaped alignment curve?

19. What property determines the horizontal width of the S-shaped alignment curve?

20. Briefly explain the process of aligning the limiter-discriminator circuitry using an r-f signal generator and a vacuum-tube voltmeter.

21. What is the primary advantage of the gated-beam discriminator?

22. In what type of equipment is the gated-beam discriminator most often used?

CHAPTER FOURTEEN

Transistor Applications To Basic Circuits

14-1 *Introduction*

As a circuit element the transistor, like its vacuum-tube counterpart, is a biased, active, electronic device. A biased device is one requiring d-c operating potentials that fix its standby, or quiescent point. This static electrical condition is depicted by static characteristic graphs (collector and emitter families). By active device is meant a device whose internal action produces an enlarged signal in the output, when a signal is applied to its input. This dynamic condition causes the device to appear as though it contains an internal power source. The amplifier circuit current, voltage, and power gains depend upon the transistor orientation. Because the transistor is a current-operated device, its basic performance criterion is power gain. The transistor's *h-parameter* equivalent circuit, introduced in transistor fundamentals, shows a certain bidirectionality between its input and output circuits, namely, forward current transfer (or gain) and reverse voltage transfer (or feedback). Because of this output-input circuit interdependence, the transistor's h parameters, or d-c characteristics, vary with the circuit configuration, and with the circuit source and load impedances. The superimposition of the circuit load lines upon a transistor's input and output static characteristics graphs furnishes a representation of the transistor's operation as an electrical circuit functional element. However, this method is used only in large-signal amplifier analysis, due to the difficulty of graph interpretation. For small-signal amplifier analysis, various equivalent circuits based upon *black box* measurements, are used, although the graphical method is valuable for fixing the operating point, and in some other respects.

No single transistor equivalent circuit is of universal utility, however, the h-parameter equivalent circuit is most widely used; and will therefore, be employed in the following small signal analysis of transistor amplifiers. The term small signal analysis implies that the parameters remain constant over the operating range of the amplifier.

14-2 TRANSISTOR AMPLIFIER CLASSIFICATION

Transistor amplifier classification is the same as for vacuum-tube amplifiers, however, owing to the transistor's essential power-amplifying nature, the broadest division of service, is into low-level and high-level types. Coupling methods for transistor circuits are similar to those which are employed in vacuum tube circuits, that is, R-C, direct, transformer, and impedance methods. The same performance fidelity-qualities, namely, frequency response, transient and phase-shift response, harmonic and intermodulation distortion, and signal-to-noise ratio are pertinent, as for vacuum-tube amplifiers.

14-3 TRANSISTOR AUDIO AMPLIFIERS

Since the transistor is current-operated and its circuit impedances are relatively low, transistor-amplifier circuits require input power, so that amplification performance is best stated in terms of power gain. The common-emitter circuit configuration has a voltage gain which is quite large in value, but less than that of a common-base circuit, and a value of c u r r e n t gain which approaches that of the common-collector circuit. Therefore, f r o m a power-gain viewpoint, the common-emitter circuit is superior in practically all applications to the other configurations and consequently the most used. Accordingly, the following analysis, as well as the rest of the dis-

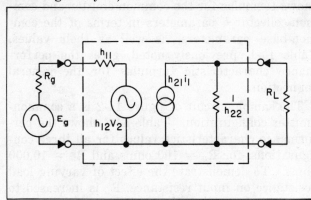

Figure 14-1. Transistor h-Parameter Equivalent Circuit (and Associated Circuitry)

cussion in this chapter, concern the common-emitter connection, although the same analysis procedures are applicable to the other two transistor-circuit arrangements.

The pertinent transistor-amplifier circuit-performance characteristics are its input and output impedances, and current, voltage, and power gains. The formulas for these characteristics, which are derived by simultaneous solution of the

input and output equations of the general h-parameter equivalent circuit with source and load impedances attached (as shown in figure 14-1), are given in table 14-1.

TABLE 14-1.

Performance Characteristics			
Name	Symbol	Definition	(h parameters)
input resistance	$R_i =$	$\dfrac{v_1}{i_1} =$	$\dfrac{h_{11} + \Delta h\, R_L}{1 + h_{22} R_L}$
output resistance	$R_o =$	$\dfrac{v_2}{i_2} =$	$\dfrac{h_{11} + R_G}{\Delta h + h_{22} R_G}$
current gain	$A_i =$	$\dfrac{-i_2}{i_1} =$	$\dfrac{-h_{21}}{1 + h_{22} R_L}$
voltage gain	$A_v =$	$\dfrac{v_2}{v_1} =$	$\dfrac{-h_{21} R_L}{h_{11} + \Delta h\, R_L}$
actual power gain	$A_p =$	$\dfrac{i_2 v_2}{i_1 v_1} =$	$A_i\, A_v$

$\Delta h = h_{11}\, h_{22} - h_{12}\, h_{21}$

NOTE: The fact that i_2 is preceded by a negative sign merely means, that the actual output current is opposite to the normal *black box* convention.

The general formulas are also applicable to all connections, provided their respective h-parameter values are substituted. Typical values of the h parameter, for all three connections, are given in Table 14-2.

TABLE 14-2.

General parameter		Configuration		
Name	Symbol	CB	CE	CC
input impedance (ohms)	h_{11}	h_{ib} 40	$h_{ie} \cong \dfrac{h_{11}}{1 + h_{21}}$ 2000	$h_{ic} \cong \dfrac{h_{11}}{1 + h_{21}}$ 2000
reverse voltage transfer ratio	h_{12}	h_{rb} 4×10^{-4}	$h_{re} \cong \dfrac{\Delta h - h_{12}}{1 + h_{21}}$ 16×10^{-4}	$h_{rc} \cong 1$
forward current ratio	h_{21}	h_{fb} $-.98$	$h_{fe} \cong \dfrac{h_{21}}{1 + h_{21}}$ 49	$h_{fc} \cong \dfrac{1}{1 + h_{21}}$ -50
output admittance (mhos)	h_{22}	h_{ob} 1×10^{-6}	$h_{oe} \cong \dfrac{h_{22}}{1 + h_{21}}$ 5×10^{-5}	$h_{oc} \cong \dfrac{h_{22}}{1 + h_{21}}$ 5×10^{-5}
determinant Δh		4.32×10^{-4}	216×10^{-4}	50.1

NOTE: Letter subscripts designate, in order, the parameter name and configuration initial. The general parameters (h_{11}, etc.), with configuration initial as third subscript, are also used. For assumed general configuration, h_i, or simply h_{11}, etc., may be used.

The input resistance, R_i, is that exhibited at the input terminals with a load impedance connected, while the output resistance, R_o, is that looking back from the output terminals with the source resistance attached but with the source disabled. The current and voltage gains, A_i and A_v, are the load current-input current and load voltage-input voltage ratios, respectively. But, as already stated, since a transistor is a current-operated device and as such requires input power, it is essentially a power amplifier. Therefore, power gain is the basic performance criterion: it specifies, for a certain amount of input power, the greater amount of output power available for conversion ultimately into other energy forms to do useful work. The *actual* power gain (A_p) is, then, the ratio of a-c output power dissipated in the load resistance to a-c input power.

$$A_p = \frac{P_{out}}{P_{in}} = \frac{I_o^2 R_L}{I_i^2 R_i} = A_i^2 \frac{R_L}{R_i} \quad (14\text{-}1)$$

Of course, maximum power is available at the input only when R_i, the transistor circuit input resistance matches R_G, the internal resistance of the source. The ratio of the power delivered to the load to this maximum available power from the generator is termed the *transducer gain*. This ratio is a measure of the efficiency of power source utilization, and serves as a basis of comparison for the performance of amplifiers with fixed loads and driven f r o m identical sources, specifying which circuit produces the higher output power. The transducer gain formula shows that it is a function of both R_G and R_L.

$$G_t = \frac{4 \ I_o^2 R_L R_G}{I_i^2 (R_G + R_L)} \quad (14\text{-}2)$$

If the terminations (R_G and R_L) match, respectively, the transistor circuit input and output resistances (R_i and R_o), *maximum available gain* (MAG), the optimum condition, results. The value of the MAG depends solely upon the transistor parameters. Moreover, the MAG can be regarded as a *figure of merit* (or standard) for comparison of various transistors, or of the several connections of a given transistor. The aim of small-signal and driver-stage amplifiers is maximum power gain. Such cascaded transistor-amplifier performance, as already indicated, is optimum only when maximum available power gain, requiring stage-to-stage impedance-matching, is realized. The situation is complicated by

the fact that R_L affects the transistor circuit's input impedance while R_G influences its output impedance, as seen from their formulas.

Single-Stage Class A Performance Analysis

Figure 14-2 is an example of a single-stage, single-battery bias, class A common-emitter, transistor audio-frequency amplifier. Table 14-2, already introduced, presents typical values of parameters for the common-base connection, using design-center characteristics for −5v collector voltage and 1 ma emitter current. The chart also

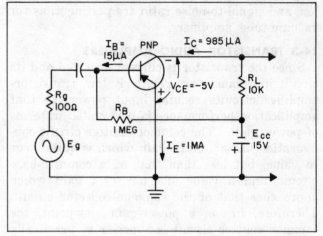

Figure 14-2. Class-A Common-Emitter Audio-Frequency Amplifier with Single-Battery Bias

shows formulas for the common-emitter and common-collector *h* parameters in terms of the common-base parameters, as well as their values. Table 14-1, previously noted, gives the performance characteristic formulas for the general connection.

The sample circuit of figure 14-2 is a common-emitter configuration. Table 14-3 shows the performance characteristics values for all three configurations, for $R_G = 100$ ohms and $R_L = 10,000$ ohms. To demonstrate the effect of varying load resistance on input resistance, R_L is increased to 100 K, which causes R_i for the common-emitter to decrease from 1477 to 693 ohms, as shown by evaluation of the formula, (from table 14-1) and graphically illustrated by figure 14-3.

$$R_i = \frac{h_{11} + \Delta h \ R_L}{1 + h_{22} \ R_L} =$$

$$\frac{2000 + (216 \times 10^{-4}) \ (10 \times 10^4)}{1 + (5 \times 10^{-5}) \ (1 \times 10^5)}$$

$$= 693 \text{ ohms}$$

Similarly, increasing R_G to 1000 ohms makes R_o decrease from 78,900 to 41,900 ohms, as substitution of the proper values in the formula, (from table 14-1) and figure 14-4 reveal.

$$R_o = \frac{h_{11} + R_G}{\Delta h + h_{22} R_G} =$$

$$\frac{2000 + 1000}{(216 \times 10^{-4}) + (5 \times 10^{-5})(100 \times 10^{1})}$$

$$= 41,900 \text{ ohms}$$

Changing R_L, as seen from evaluation of the respective formulas (from table 14-1) and the corresponding current amplification and power gain versus load resistance graphs (figures 14-5 and 14-6, respectively), causes the current gain to decrease from 33 to 8 but the actual power gain to increase from 7326 (38.6 db) to 9264 (39.6 db) because of the increased value of voltage gain (see table 14-3).

TABLE 14-3.
PERFORMANCE CHARACTERISTICS FOR
TRANSISTOR AMPLIFIER CIRCUIT OF
FIGURE 14-2

Performance Characteristic	Configuration		
	CB	CE	CC
R_i (ohms)	44 [76]	1477 [693]	335,000 [835,000]
R_o (ohms)	263,000 [730,000]	78,900 [41,900]	42 [60]
A_i	.973 [.89]	−33 [−8]	33 [8]
A_v	221 [2211]	−222 [−1158]	.994 [.997]
A_p	215 [1968]	7326 [9264]	32.8 [7.99]

NOTE: Bracketed values are those resulting from change of R_G or R_L.

Notice that changing R_G increases the transducer gain, since 1000 ohms more closely matches the 2000-ohm R_i than the original 100 ohms. However, the MAG stays the same since it depends only on the transistor h parameters.

Cascade Audio Amplifiers

Audio-amplifier design specifications call for delivery of a required amount of power to a specified load impedance from a specified source, so that the design problem consists essentially in selection of a series of amplifier stages to match, as nearly as possible, this signal source to the final useful load impedance. A cascaded amplifier may consist of low-level and/or high-level stages.

If, for example, the circuit of figure 14-2 were RC-coupled into an identical stage, there would result quite a mismatch between the 78,900-ohm

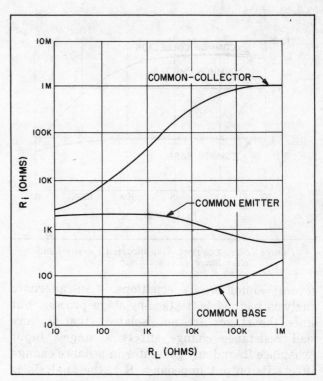

Figure 14-3. Input Resistance Versus Load Resistance (Logarithmic Scale)

output resistance of the first stage and the 1477-ohm input resistance of the second. Such a cascade arrangement can be analyzed as a whole by writing input mesh and output nodal equations involving the transistor equivalent circuits, but this complex-network method would result in

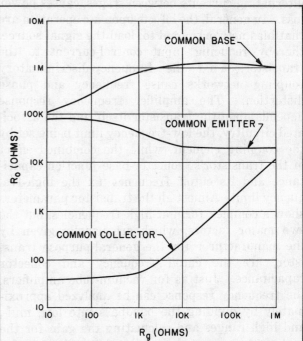

Figure 14-4. Output Resistance Versus Generator Resistance (Logarithmic Scale)

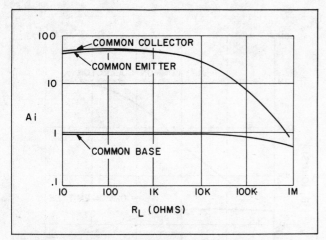

*Figure 14-5. Current Amplification Versus Load
Resistance (Logarithmic Scale)*

several simultaneous equations. An alternate
analysis method is a stage-by-stage process, but
since the stages are not isolated (that is, any
load resistance change affects a stage's input
resistance R_i and any generator impedance change
affects its output impedance R_o), the analysis is
complicated. Consequently, to compute the final
output impedance, it is necessary to start at the
first (input) stage and work forward, and, conversely, to get the over-all input impedance,
to start at the final (output) stage and go backward. The interstage coupling, which performs
the dual function of blocking the unlike output
and input direct (bias) currents and of passing
alternating currents between stages, causes power
loss. In general, the effects upon a-c operation are
that bias networks tend to load the signal source,
thereby reducing input control-current to the
transistor, and the frequency-discriminatory
coupling networks cause frequency and phase
distortion. The amplifier frequency response
depends upon the transistor itself and the associated circuitry, the low-frequency limit being set by
the coupling element, while the combined effect
of the transistor's collector-base junction capacitance and its cutoff frequency fix the high-frequency limit. Almost all the transistor parameters
show a complex form at high frequencies, but the
two major factors, which are usually given by
the manufacturer for the general-purpose transistor, are the cutoff frequency and collector
capacitance. Just as for vacuum-tube amplifiers,
the frequency response can be analyzed approximately by dividing the bandpass into low, mid-,
and high ranges and calculating the gain for the
mid-band range, and then the change in gain for
the low and high ranges. Low-frequency attenu-

ation (gain reduction) is due to capacitance in
series with the input, the half-power point occurring where its reactance equals the transistor's
input resistance. The high-frequency response
can be approximated by calculation of the effects
of its two major limitations, namely, collector
capacitance and variation of h_{21}, separately
treated. An important point here is that in the
common-emitter arrangement the output capacitance is $1/1 + h_{21b}$ times greater, and the cutoff
frequency $1 + h_{21b}$ times smaller, than for the
common-base circuit arrangement, thereby
lowering the high-frequency limit. Because of
the complexity of analysis, the best way to
determine transistor-amplifier frequency response
is by an experimental plot of voltage gain versus
frequency.

RC-Coupled Audio Amplifier

As already stated, the problem of cascading
consists in effecting the closest possible match
for maximum power gain. Of the various configuration cascaded combinations, both matched
and unmatched, in order to get the over-all optimum power gain, the common-emitter chain
yields either maximum or so close thereto, that
any detailed analysis for such optimization is not
worthwhile. Such an iterative, or repeating
amplifier, stage (one driven by and feeding into
a similar stage) is gainful only for a common-
emitter chain. For applications requiring
special impedance terminations at either end,
the common-base (low input, high output) and
common-collector (high input, low output) are
suitable.

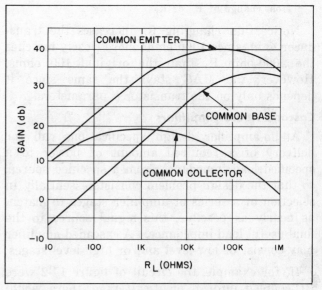

*Figure 14-6. Power Gain Versus Load Resistance
(Semi-Logarithmic Scale)*

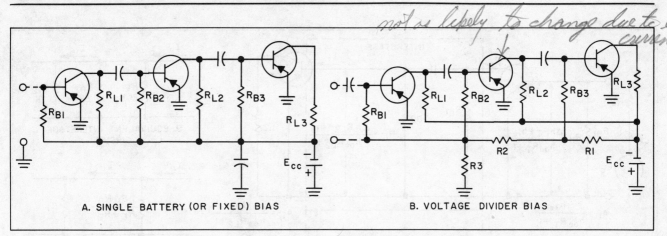

not as likely to change due to extra current flow

Figure 14-7. Common Cascade Biasing Arrangements

Common cascade biasing arrangements consist of returning the base-biasing r e s i s t o r and collector-load resistor of each stage to the proper supply-battery terminal, with a bypass capacitor across the battery to minimize a-c feedback through its low internal resistance, as illustrated in part A of figure 14-7. Another arrangement, in part B of the figure, returns the base-biasing resistors to voltage-divider taps. Since all base-biasing resistor values are high to prevent shunting the a-c signal, the sum of the signal currents in all the external base resistances is much less than the voltage-divider bleeder current, so that the input direct current of each stage is easily calculated by dividing the voltage at the tap point by the R_B of that stage. These input direct currents, in conjunction with each stage loadline, locate the respective operating points.

In order to demonstrate the stage-by-stage analysis m e t h o d, a generalized RC-coupled common-emitter amplifier cascaded pair is presented in parts A, B, and C of figure 14-8, and the method of calculating the mid-band power gain indicated. Working backwards, inspection of part A of the figure shows the formulas for getting the power gain of the second stage. Notice that it depends upon the load resistance, as well as the circuit current gain and input resistance, both of which in turn depend upon the transistor parameters and c i r c u i t load resistance. Examine next the dashed-in interstage coupling circuit, which is shown detached in part B of the figure, with arbitrarily assigned resistance values and with the coupling capacitor omitted (since it is assumed a virtual short over the mid-band frequency range). Part C of the figure combines R_{L1} and R_{B2} and drops the secondary subscripts for convenience. I_o is the output current from the first stage, part of which passes

through t h e collector-load a n d base-biasing equivalent resistance, the rest entering the input resistance, R_i, of the second stage as input current. The interstage current gain, obtained by utilizing the current division theorem, is

$$A_i = \frac{I_i}{I_o} = \frac{\dfrac{R_L\ R_B}{R_L\ +\ R_B}}{\dfrac{R_L\ R_B}{R_L\ +\ R_B}\ +\ R_i} = .8$$

The mid-band interstage-coupling power loss is then given by

$$A_p = A_i{}^2\ \frac{R_i}{R_T} = .8$$

where R_i serves as the interstage load resistance and R_T is the parallel combination of the three interstage resistances. The power gain of the first stage is readily found by substituting in the appropriate formulas (shown in part A of the figure). Notice that its load impedance is the parallel combination, R_T, of its own collector load resistance and the base-biasing and input resistances of the next stage. All power values can be converted to decibels by db $=$ 10 $\log_{10}A_p$, and the power loss of the interstage network is subtracted from the sum of the two amplifier gains in order to get the over-all mid-band db power gain.

Untuned Transformer-Coupled Audio Amplifier

For audio-frequency, small-signal operation, the higher power gain of the common-emitter configuration, a l o n g with the transformer's impedance-matching flexibility, rules out the less gainful other configurations. The impedance-matching advantage of the transformer either to form an image stage (one matched at both input and output) or to match special input and output impedances, for maximum available over-

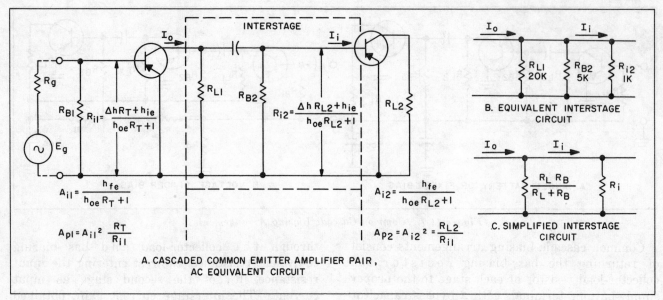

Figure 14-8. R-C-Coupled Transistor Cascaded Amplifier

all gain, is offset by the poor frequency response of the miniaturized versions. For a specified over-all power gain, transformer coupling requires fewer stages than R-C coupling. However, this advantage decreases appreciably if higher-value alpha transistors are used, since the higher the alpha, the closer the input and output resistances of a transistor.

Transformers can be used to eliminate the problem of signal-shunting by base-biasing resistors merely by connecting them in series with the base lead.

Manual Gain (Volume-Level) Control

A manual gain control is a necessary accessory to most audio amplifiers in order to allow initial adjustment and/or readjustment for the exact signal amplitude required to compensate for various changes, including ambient noise level, component performance variation w i t h age, temperature, or replacement, or to suit the hearing convenience of the user. The ideal gain-control function is to adjust amplifier gain from zero to maximum without otherwise affecting the amplifier performance. Therefore, it must be inserted so as not to change the amplifier d-c (biasing or load) resistances, since this would disturb the d-c operating point and alter the operating characteristics. If the gain control is located too early in an amplifier chain, the over-all signal-to-noise factor may suffer, since the noise power generated in following stages may become comparable to the signal level at those stages; or, if placed too late, it cannot prevent

overloading in a prior stage, should signal levels become excessive or cross-modulation products due to non-linearity occur. Satisfactory input-circuit gain-control arrangements are shown in parts A and B of figure 14-9. In part A of the figure, the potentiometer arm varies the signal amplitude fed to the transistor amplifier without however varying the static or d-c, base and collector currents. For negligible signal-shunting, or input loading effect, in full volume position, the potentiometer resistance should be at least ten times the input-transformer secondary winding resistance. The input gain-control arrangement of part B of the figure, with the volume control tied directly to the emitter rather than ground, keeps it from shunting the emitter bias network consisting of R_3 and R_4, and thus deteriorating the low-frequency response. The coupling capacitors, C_1 and C_2, which isolate the control from the biasing circuits, have large values due to the low circuit impedances involved. A satisfactory output-circuit gain control, illustrated in part C, consists merely of a potentiometer as collector load impedance (whose resistance sets the d-c operating point), with a series isolating capacitor in its arm feeding proportional signal-amplitude level to the input of next stage.

14-4 TUNED OR FREQUENCY-SELECTIVE (R-F AND I-F) AMPLIFIERS
Narrow-Band Tuned Amplifiers

A narrow-band amplifier (single or cascade) is one whose bandwidth is only a small fraction of the mean signal frequency, which is well below

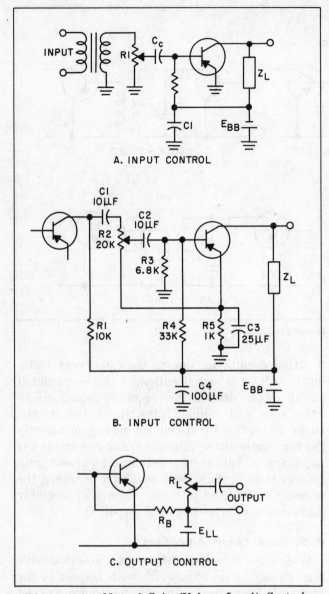

Figure 14-9. Manual Gain (Volume-Level) Controls

The most suitable transistor configuration, from the power-transfer efficiency standpoint, is the common-base or common-emitter. With respect to the tuning, the close coupling between the input and output circuits makes the resonant frequency particularly sensitive to variations in input and output load impedances. When the interstage network is tuned to resonance, the load impedance on the preceding stage is practically resistive. At radio frequencies, with a resistive load, the input impedance is inductive for a common-base and capacitive for a common-emitter, but both their output impedances are capacitive. These output capacitances, modified by the impedance ratio, add to the resonant circuit capacitance. The inductive component of the common-base input impedance, modified by the transistor impedance ratio, appears in parallel with and therefore decreases, the resonant circuit L. Similarly, the common-emitter input-impedance capacitive component adds to the capacitance of the resonant circuit. The combined result is an increase of capacitance and no change of L, whereas for the common-base the L decreases. Consequently, to make alignment of the resonant circuit less sensitive to variation of input and output impedances, the L/C ratio should be relatively small, so that the input and output capacitances are only a small fraction of the total capacitance, and the resonant circuit L is not affected too much by the input-impedance reactive components. In general, the load impedance has a greater effect on the input impedance than the generator impedance has on the output impedance, hence the best procedure for i-f strip alignment is to start at the last stage and work toward the first. Tuned-transformer coupling serves the dual purpose of operating-frequency selection and impedance matching along with low ohmic losses for efficient power transfer.

The parallel-resonant circuit is used, then, as the frequency-selective element in various coupling arrangements. One method, in part A of figure 14-10, is the direct connection of the input of the next amplifier stage into the tuned circuit in series with the inductor or capacitor (for inductor or capacitor feed, respectively), forming a parallel-resonant load impedance on the first stage. The complex load impedance includes the first stage output and second stage input impedances, maximum power transfer being attained when the input resistive component equals the sum of the resistive components of the output and the interstage (which decreases the

the transistor cutoff frequency. The coupling network must give the r e q u i r e d bandpass characteristic and good power transfer from driver to driven stages.

The interstage-coupling network that best fulfills the requirements of selectivity, low loss, and reduced sensitivity to variation of output and input impedances is a parallel-tuned circuit with a relatively low L/C ratio but high effective Q (in order to reduce power loss). The effective Q of the tuned amplifier is the ratio of the mean, or resonant frequency (f_o), to the bandwidth (Δf) at the half-power points of the response curve. Most r-f and i-f amplifiers of broadcast and communications receivers have an effective Q greater than 10.

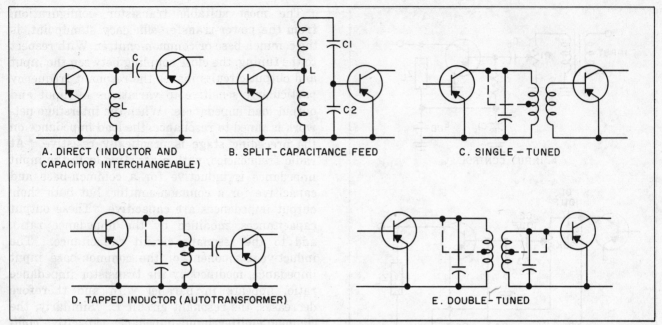

Figure 14-10. Parallel-Resonant Coupling

available power). In another coupling method, in part B of the figure, the second stage input is connected to the junction of two capacitors, which are elements in the output tank, proportioned to match impedances. In this *split-capacitance feed,* the output electrode is normally connected to a tap on the inductor. Both output and input impedances are stepped up to satisfy the narrow-band requirement. The resonant frequency is determined by L, C1, and C2, and the reactive components of the output and input impedances. The impedances seen by the output and input are functions of Q and the input and output impedances, respectively. The third, and most common method, is inductive or transformer coupling, including several variations, as shown in parts C, D, and E, of the figure: In part C, the *single-tuned,* the tuned primary offers high output impedance while the secondary L is usually low for impedance-matching; in D, the *inductor, tapped* or *autotransformer,* variation, there is a coupling capacitor in the input lead to block the higher collector bias from the second stage and to reduce the input-circuit loading of the tank circuit; in part E, the *double-tuned,* is used as shown, heavy-lined, or with tapped primary and tapped-coil (as dashed in) or split-capacitance secondary (see part B). The purpose of tapping primary and/or secondary inductances is to increase the effective Q, in order to improve the power-transfer efficiency. Parallel-tuned coupling of point-contact transistors demands special care

to avoid oscillation, due to their inherent instability w h e n short-circuited. A series-resonant circuit can be used as the frequency-selective load impedance and coupled directly or inductively. However, in the direct-coupled arrangement, only the common-emitter junction transistor meets the necessary condition of short-circuit current gain greater than 1, while, with inductive coupling, the impedance reflected into the primary appreciably decreases the series-resonant circuit Q.

Wide-Band Tuned Amplifiers

Wide-band tuned amplifiers are those that have a relatively broad bandwidth with respect to the resonant frequency. In this category are i-f amplifiers with an effective Q of 10 or less, such as are used in television and radar receivers. The pass-band of a multistage amplifier using single-tuned coupling circuits, all resonant to the same frequency, becomes narrower with increasing number of stages. In the double-tuned coupling circuit, if the coefficient of coupling is loose or critical, the over-all bandwidth becomes less as the number of stages is increased. If it is over-coupled, the mid-band *valley* increases with added stages. *Stagger-tuning* of successive stages, that is, detuning each stage slightly about the desired center frequency, is a practical method of getting a relatively flat, wide-band response curve, just as for vacuum-tube amplifiers. The resonant circuit can be single or double-tuned. The resonant frequency of each stage is affected by the immediately preceding and following stages. Because of the coupling between input and output circuits i n h e r e n t in a transistor amplifier, changing the impedance of one element in one stage affects every other stage. Fortunately, however, the effect of reflected impedance is not cumulative. Since the individual stages are stagger-tuned (to different frequencies), the over-all power gain is less than for the same number of narrow-band stages, but the bandwidth is broadened.

R-F Amplifiers

Transistor r-f amplifiers, like their vacuum-tube correspondents, are used to improve the gain, over-all signal-to-noise r a t i o, or selectivity characteristic of a multistage circuit. The design is basically the same as that of an i-f amplifier, the chief problem being selection of a transistor with a high enough cutoff frequency.

To avoid the critical tuning problem, each stage of an i-f or r-f cascade may be neutralized, which allows adjustment of each resonant coupling circuit without introducing any detuning on, or by, the other stages. The means of effecting neutralization are similar to those used in vacuum-tube circuits. A common method is the use of a feedback capacitor placed to provide the required amount of degeneration.

14-5 TRANSISTOR OSCILLATORS

Just as for vacuum-tube sinusoidal oscillators, the basic requirements of a transistor harmonic oscillator circuit are a non-linear power-gain device, an external or internal positive feedback path that is frequency-selective (by means of an LC resonant combination, RC phase-shifting network, or piezo-electric crystal), and an external d-c energy source. The purpose of the power-amplification element is to convert the external d-c energy into a-c energy in order to replace that dissipated in the external-circuit e l e m e n t s, including the load resistance, by returning part or all of the a-c output power, of the right amplitude and proper phase, via the feedback path to the input. To limit the output-oscillation amplitude a nonlinear element is necessary. However, this nonlinearity causes a slight oscillation-frequency shift and also distorts the waveform, although a nonsinusoidal waveshape is sometimes desirable, as for harmonic generators, or frequency multipliers. Transistors can replace the vacuum-tube as a nonlinear power-gain element in many of the standard oscillator circuits. The

fact that they are bilateral and have an appreciable internal phase shift within the frequency range of usable power gain complicates the design of high-frequency oscillators capable of producing a stable output-oscillation frequency and amplitude with a good sinusoidal waveform. Transistor oscillator frequency-instability causes include the following: collector-capacitance change due to changes of collector or emitter potentials, change in equivalent shunt resistance of the tank circuit under a varying coupled load, and, most serious of all, variation of practically all transistor parameters with operating-point shift caused by the effect of temperature change on collector back current (I_{CO} or I_{CEO}). Frequency-stabilization techniques consist of maintaining a constant supply voltage, minimizing the effect of changed internal capacitances by connection of the transistor to points on the tuned circuit of as low impedance as possible, and rendering of fixed-frequency oscillators independent of transistor parameters by insertion of proper compensating reactances as stabilizing elements. This latter remedy is, naturally, unsuitable for variable-frequency oscillators because of t h e frequency dependence of such stabilizing elements. With respect to amplitude stabilization, a single-transistor sinusoidal oscillator may be treated as an unstable power amplifier, with the oscillations assumed as starting in the transistor's linear operating region, that is, with the emitter-base diode conducting and collector-base diode non-conducting (or forward-biased and reverse-biased, respectively). As the oscillation amplitude rises, a nonlinearity in the characteristics of the transistor may cause the power gain to drop enough to level off the amplitude. In other words, so long as the signal amplitude is small, the transistor's operation is quite linear, the instantaneous excursions of the operating point being restricted to a range over which the circuit as a whole exhibits a dynamic negative resistance or an impedance with a negative real part, and thus the active element (t h e transistor) continuously supplies power to the passive elements, sustaining this regenerative oscillatory action through a feedback circuit with the required amplitude and phase characteristics. This represents an equilibrium state where the transistor exactly replenishes the circuit power losses, or the resonant circuit reaches a precise underdamped condition as determined by the circuit Q. Otherwise, as the amplitude keeps increasing in the linear

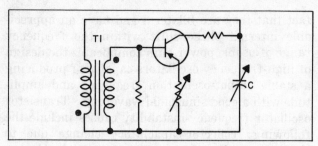

Figure 14-11. Typical Transistor Feedback Audio Oscillator, A-C Equivalent Circuit

region, the expanding signal will eventually cause clipping by overdriving the amplifier and reversing polarity of either the collector-base diode, which makes it conduct and effectively short-circuit the resonant circuit, or of the emitter-base diode, cutting it off and causing a voltage surge across the inductances. Both effects lead to a relatively poor waveform, and can be compensated for by inserting resistances in series with the collector or in shunt with the emitter-base winding, as shown by the a-c equivalent circuit of a typical junction transistor feedback oscillator in figure 14-11. The insertion of a variable emitter resistor allows amplitude control.

Typical Junction Transistor Oscillators

Figure 14-12 s h o w s an *Armstrong*-type or *tickler-coil*, junction transistor audio-frequency oscillator. Transformer T, with step-down ratio to match impedances and windings poled for positive feedback, inductively couples output to input. The variable capacitor tunes the collector winding, although the input-circuit winding may be tuned. The base coupling capacitor, which keeps the secondary winding from d-c shorting the transistor input, must be large enough to prevent tuning the transformer base winding. Instead of the capacitance-coupled high-impedance output shown, the output may also be taken from a third winding,

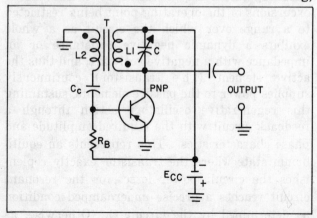

Figure 14-12. Armstrong-Type Transistor Audio Oscillator

proportioned for proper impedance match to the load service. Close adjustment of emitter current by a series emitter resistor or the base resistor R_B is necessary for a good sine wave. If either V_{BE} or R_B is too low, peak-clipping may occur, and in extreme cases the circuit may pulse. A common-base arrangement would be the same except that emitter and collector voltages would require separate batteries or would be taken from taps on a center-grounded voltage-divider shunting t h e supply.

Figure 14-13 illustrates junction transistor versions of the Hartley radio-frequency oscillator. In both parts of the figure the circuits are self-

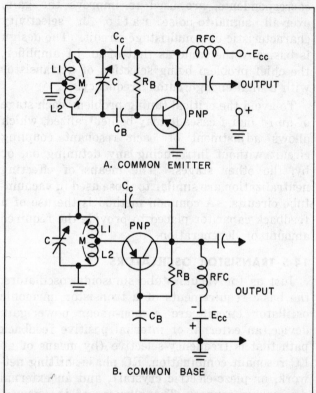

Figure 14-13. Common-Emitter and Common-Base Hartley R-F Oscillators

biased by R_B and the battery supply decoupled by radio-frequency choke. C_C and C_B block the bias currents completely from the tank in the common-emitter arrangement, making it shunt-fed; in the common-base connection, however, the bias current passes through the lower part of the winding, making it series-fed. Feedback is through the autotransformer action of the tank coil common to both input and output circuits. Insertion of input in the case of the common-base circuit partially within the parallel L-C circuit (part A of figure 14-14) capitalizes on the current amplification of the circulating tank current. Connection of the base input, as shown in part B of the figure, to the opposite end (from the output) of the parallel L-C tank circuit with respect to the common-emitter tap gives the necessary phase inversion for positive feedback. Note that in either case the electrical operation is the same.

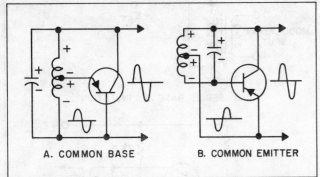

<figure>*Figure 14-14.* *Common-Base and Common-Emitter Hartley Oscillator, A-C Equivalent Circuits*</figure>

The circuit of figure 14-15 is the same as that of part A of figure 14-13 except for the biasing arrangement, the d-c operating point being established by the base-bias currents in R1, R2, and R_E and collector supply voltage E_{CC}. Passage of the collector bias current through L1 makes the circuit series-fed. Part of the a-c output voltage across L2 is fed back via C_C. The output frequency is always lower than the isolated resonant-tank frequency because of the change in the effective value of inductance caused by the coil tap.

Part A of figure 14-16 is a diagram of a *Colpitts*-type junction transistor radio-frequency oscillator. Capacitor-divider coupling, with the capacitance ratio adjusted for proper feedback amplitude, requires close tracking for accurate tuning, but it enables the use of a transformer without center-tap, one winding serving for the frequency-determining tank L, and the other for output coupling. Substitution of a series-resonant

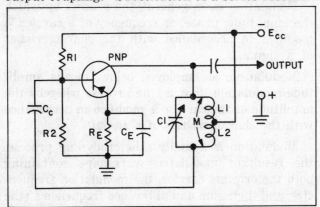

<figure>*Figure 14-15.* *Common-Emitter Hartley R-F Oscillator with Different Bias Arrangement*</figure>

circuit, as shown in part B of the figure, converts the Colpitts to a *Clapp*-type oscillator, allowing C1 and C2 to be very large and fixed, although C2 must not be so large as to deprive the emitter of the required feedback current. The resonant-circuit capacitor, C, can be small and variable (or adjustable). The oscillation frequency is slightly above the series LC product (the small net inductance of the series L-C combination resonating with the large parallel capacitance C_T), with the advantage that the over-all tank impedance, which is small due to the large C_T, reduces the effect of the transistor's output capacitance on the resonant frequency, thus allowing the circuit to be made tunable by varying only one small capacitor.

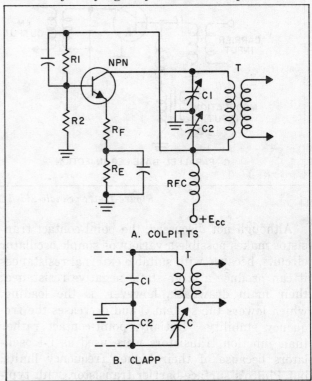

<figure>*Figure 14-16.* *Colpitts and Clapp Type R-F Oscillators*</figure>

From the foregoing analysis, a transistor sinusoidal oscillator consists essentially of an unstable power amplifier and a frequency-selective instability-control circuit. The parallel-resonant circuit is shunted by the transistor's output impedance, the transformed input impedance and the oscillator load impedance, inductively or capacitively coupled to the tank circuit. The major difference between the vacuum-tube oscillators and their transistor versions lies in the loading effect of the transistor input resistance, which shunts the tank coil. The circuit Q pertains to the loaded tank circuit and must be high for good frequency stability.

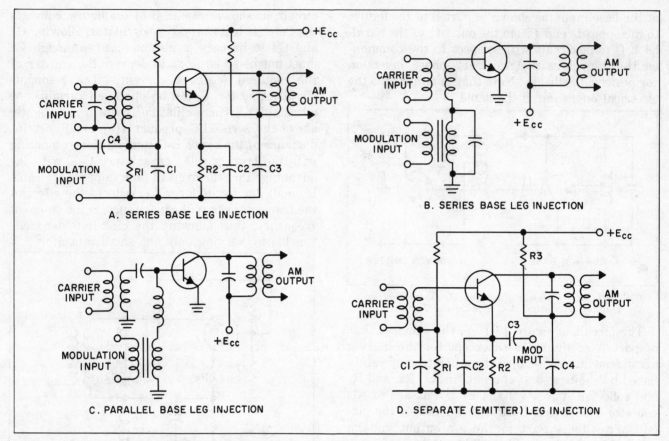

Figure 14-17. Single-Sided Modulators, Base-Emitter Injection

Although not discussed, the point-contact transistor makes possible a variety of simple oscillator circuits, because with suitable external resistances it can produce a large static negative resistance; their main drawback, however, is the loading, which lowers the system Q and decreases the frequency stability. Initially, point-contact rather than junction transistors were used as r-f oscillators because of their higher frequency limits, but Philco's surface-barrier transistor, with typical alpha-cutoff frequencies above 50 Mcps and the subsequent extension of the frequency response of other junction transistors, has made their use preferable.

14-6 TRANSMISSION AND RECEPTION

The basic processes of modulation and detection are alike in that an electronic device is operated in such a way that its output frequency spectrum differs from the input, but is controlled by it. Both processes require the use of a nonlinear element, that is, one w h o s e current-voltage characteristic exhibits a gradual curvature, or offers a nonlinear impedance when a voltage composed of one or more frequencies is applied, thus resulting in the production of new frequencies.

Unwanted currents can be excluded by filters, and the desired frequency selected by tuned circuits. Semiconductor devices, like vacuum tubes, exhibit various nonlinear characteristics that are utilized to get the desired output-input relationship. The amount of nonlinearity they exhibit is frequency-dependent to a very marked extent. A semiconductor diode or a transistor's emitter-base junction can serve as the nonlinear element.

Transistor Modulators

Modulation is, in general, the process by which the amplitude, phase, or frequency of a carrier is modified in accordance with the characteristics of a signal.

Modulation, as employed below, means amplitude modulation, that is, the process whereby the amplitude of the carrier is modified in accordance with the characteristics of a signal.

Modulation is actually a heterodyning process, the resultant modulated waveshape containing both the original carrier, the modulation frequencies, and their sum and difference frequencies (the sidebands). Since the carrier component undergoes no change, evidently the modulated wave contains more power than before and the intelligence resides in the sidebands. Each separate sideband component has an amplitude relative to the carrier of m/2 (or relative power of $m^2/4$), and the carrier power is wasted. Since the carrier supports no intelligence, suppressed-carrier modulation is possible. A single-sideband system, eliminating also one sideband, cuts the required transmission spectrum in half, while still retaining the intelligence. A vestigial-sideband system, utilizing the carrier and one sideband, has a narrow spectrum but lower transmission efficiency.

Nonlinear (Square-Law) Modulation

Nonlinear base-emitter modulation includes *base-leg injection,* both in series and parallel with the carrier input, and *separate-leg,* or *emitter-leg,* injection. In figure 14-17, parts A and B, both modulation and carrier voltages are fed into the base of a common-emitter stage. C1, of the capacitive-fed circuit, should be sufficiently large so that its reactance is low enough at the carrier frequency to bypass the base-biasing resistor R1,

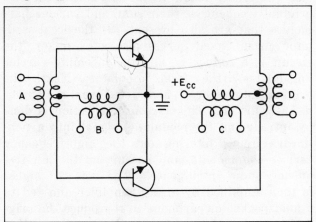

Figure 14-18. Generalized Balanced Modulator

but not so large as to shunt the upper modulation frequencies. Capacitors C2, C3, and C4 must be very large so as to offer low reactance to the lowest modulation frequency. In part B of the figure, the modulation input-transformer secondary capacitor keeps the low-impedance winding from shunting the transistor input. Part C of the figure shows parallel base-leg injection. Emitterleg, or separate-leg, injection is depicted in part D. C2 is small since it is an r-f bypass only. C1, C3, and C4 must be large enough to offer low reactance to the lowest modulation frequency.

Removal of C3 and replacement of R3 by an audio-modulation input transformer in part D of figure 14-17, alters the circuit for collector-injection. Other necessary modifications include mak-

ing C2 large enough to offer little reactance to the modulating signal and C4, which serves as r-f bypass only, small.

Balanced Modulators

Figure 14-18 represents a generalized *balanced modulator* using a matched transistor pair. Injecting the carrier at A and the modulation at B gives an output at D from which the even harmonics of the carrier frequency are absent. This circuit is suitable for adaptation as a frequency tripler, since the wider harmonic separation facilitates their s u p p r e s s i o n (especially the normally stronger lower ones), while allowing a low enough circuit Q to pass the sidebands. Switching inputs A and B eliminates the carrier at output D, thus making this arrangement suitable for suppressed-carrier modulation. Besides, the absence of even harmonics lowers the distortion for a given modulation amplitude. Insertion of the carrier at A and the modulation at B, yields an output at C which contains no odd harmonics of the carrier frequency, making this scheme useful for frequency doubling or quadrupling. Several other arrangements are also possible. Any mismatch of the NPN pair would naturally mean unbalanced operation, with consequent harmonic distortion. A complementary NPN-PNP pair can also be used for the various arrangements, but balancing may be critical.

Large-Signal or Linear Collector Modulation

If the r-f signal is larger than the emitter bias, partial rectification results. For base or emitter modulation, distortion in the modulated output may increase appreciably due to the resulting bias-point shift. However, collector-circuit modulation permits satisfactory operation even under this larger r-f signal condition. Figure 14-19 depicts a practical circuit. C1 is small, since it is an r-f bypass. There is no quiescent emitter

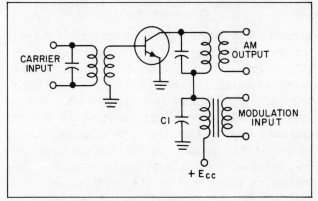

Figure 14-19. Large-Signal or "Linear" Collector Modulator

bias. When the input carrier amplitude is large enough, the emitter-base diode rectifies, producing a d-c emitter circuit bias with consequent d-c collector current which, as collector voltage increases, increases slightly, being linear up to several hundred microamperes for initially small collector currents. A disadvantage of collector modulation is the greater modulating power required.

Amplitude-Modulated Oscillator

If slight frequency-modulation effects are tolerable, the oscillator itself can be modulated with greater economy of parts and supply power. Figure 14-20 represents such an amplitude-modulated oscillator in generalized form, showing possible modulating-signal injection points A, B, and C. C1 is a feedback capacitor, C2 is the tank-circuit capacitor, and C3 and C4 are bypass capacitors. For example, if the modulation is fed into the emitter circuit at A, C3 is an r-f bypass, while C4 is large enough to bypass both r-f and the lowest modulation frequency. Amplitude modulation is effected by changing the emitter-bias current. The emitter-base diode is forward-biased, so that it is conducting and V_{EB} is thus

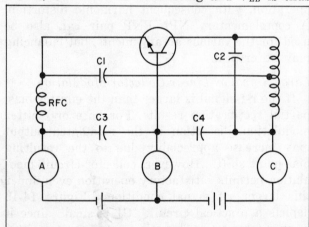

Figure 14-20. Amplitude-Modulated Oscillator, Generalized Form

normally low, being dependent upon the d-c emitter current. If the sum of the instantaneous modulation-signal voltage and the r-f feedback voltage is great enough, the emitter diode is blocked during part of the negative alternations. Consequently, there is a slight emitter-bias current increase due to the diode rectification action. Since C4, the bypass capacitance, is large, the collector bias voltage is virtually constant. Distortion is introduced in the modulated output, just as in the amplitude-modulated amplifier where the r-f signal is large, but it can be re-

duced by decreasing the feedback factor. Selection of the bias point depends upon the frequency and stability requirements of the oscillator. However, impairment of the frequency stability makes the amplitude-modulated oscillator useful only when frequency stability is not essential.

Transistor Detectors

Detection is the process of abstracting the intelligence from the high-frequency carrier. The superheterodyne radio receiver, almost universally preferred because of its best all-around selectivity, sensitivity, and stability qualities, uses a double-detection system. The incoming intelligence-bearing carrier signal, after possibly first being amplified by an r-f amplifier, is then *heterodyned*, that is, mixed with a lower or higher local oscillator sine-wave frequency in a nonlinear circuit, where a new, constant-difference, lower (*intermediate*) frequency, also containing the original modulation sidebands, is generated. Fixed-tuned i-f amplifiers select this new i-f carrier (difference frequency) from among the two original frequencies, their sum, and various harmonics that are also present. If the local-oscillator circuit itself serves also as a mixer, the circuit is a *converter*, and the incoming carrier "modulates" the local oscillator. Next, the original intelligence is abstracted from the amplified i-f carrier. This (*second*) detection is done by introducing the modulated signal into a nonlinear circuit, filtering out the high-frequency carrier components, and passing on the low-frequency audio intelligence. The detected signal is then amplified by an a-f amplifier and fed to a loudspeaker or earphone to reproduce the original sound. Notice that both these reception processes (heterodyning and detection) involve, like modulation, the generation of new frequencies.

Mixers and Converters

First detection, or *mixing*, is the process whereby a band of frequencies centered about one frequency is transformed to another related band that is centered about some other frequency. As already stated, nonlinear electronic properties are essential for the production of new frequencies in combining two different frequencies. Part A of figure 14-21, shows separate mixer and local oscillator. Both r-f and local-oscillator voltages are fed into the base. The latter can also be coupled into the emitter or collector circuits. A tank circuit, resonant to the i-f and connected into the collector circuit, forms the load impedance.

difference between vacuum tube cut off and transistor cut off is vacuum tube takes more bias to cutoff transistor takes less to cut off

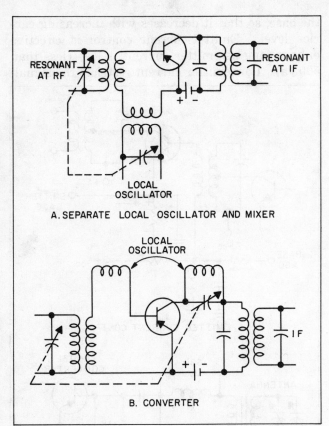

Figure 14-21. Transistor Frequency Converters

If the same transistor serves both mixer and local-oscillator functions, the local oscillation is generated by inductive feedback between collector and base, as seen in part B of the figure, or between collector and emitter. In both cases, the r-f is fed into the base and the i-f taken across the collector tank circuit. Although the frequency conversion results from the nonlinear characteristic of the mixer, this nonlinearity affects only the local oscillator. The r-f and i-f voltages are normally of such small amplitude, relatively, that the relationship between them and their corresponding currents is virtually linear. The local oscillator must meet several specific requirements, namely: adequate power for efficient converter operation, since the oscillator feeds a transistor whose input impedance is quite low and presents an appreciable load; fairly uniform oscillation amplitude over the frequency range, so that the converter output is essentially independent of signal frequency; and amplitude stability with battery-voltage and ambient-temperature changes.

Second Detectors

Second detection is effected by rectifying the modulating carrier and filtering out the i-f, thus giving a fairly faithful reproduction of the audio

modulation at the transmitter. Although semiconductor diodes and transistors both perform square-law amplitude-modulation detection at small-signal levels, transistor detection affords several advantages, namely: the change-over from square-law to linear detection occurs at a slightly lower power level; there is appreciable power gain resulting from the accompanying amplification, so that, like the vacuum-tube plate detector, it serves also as a first audio amplifier; and, consequently this power is conveniently available for automatic gain control of the transistor r-f and/or i-f amplifiers. Part A of figure 14-22 shows the more common low-impedance-source diode detector, while part B illustrates a common-emitter transistor-triode detector. If the incoming modulated-carrier amplitude is large, the diode or transistor emitter-base junction acts as a rectifier, yielding a series of modulated half-wave sinusoids. For good rectification efficiency, the operating point must be on the nonlinear portion of the dynamic diode characteristic curve. The transistor must have a high cutoff frequency relative to the carrier frequency; otherwise, due to hole storage effects, its emitter-base diode does not exhibit a sharp knee, and consequently, has a poor forward-to-reverse resistance ratio. In both circuits, the bypass capacitor tends to filter out the higher-frequency components and to hold

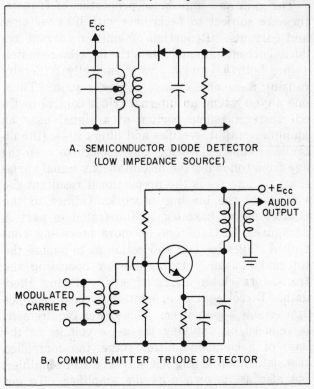

Figure 14-22. Transistor Detectors

a charge corresponding to the momentary modulation amplitude. The R-C time constant, including loading effects, should be long to effectively filter out the higher-frequency components, but at the same time short enough that the fastest rates of change in the modulation envelope are faithfully reproduced. The bias network is selected to bias the transistor detector close to cutoff, so that rectification occurs when r-f or i-f is applied to the input. Detection is nonlinear if the incoming signals are very small, but distortion may be high. For linear detection, the i-f amplifier must be at a relatively high voltage and impedance level. For reasonable efficiency, an audio transformer with i-f bypass capacitor should be used to transform the audio stage's higher output level. To keep the peak incoming signal from causing high-current saturation or clipping, the supply voltage should be large and/or the load resistance small. R-C coupling can also be used.

Automatic Gain Control

An automatic-gain-control system electrically readjusts the overall signal gain of a radio receiver, so as to maintain a constant audio-output power level by compensating for carrier-wave field strength variations due either to differences of distance or transmitted power of various stations or to propagation conditions (fading signals).

The gain and impedance properties of transistors are subject to variations with bias voltages and currents. Reduction of emitter current reduces current gain and alters the impedance match (since both h_{ob} and h_{ib} vary radically), thereby causing a sizeable change in power gain. Thus, one a-g-c system, an internal triode control method, abstracts some portion of a signal near an amplifier output, rectifies and filters it — (the filter time constants being long enough to keep the agc from following the instantaneous signal variation) — and feeds the proportional resultant d-c voltage to the biasing networks (either to the emitter leg or base leg, as illustrated in part A of figure 14-23) of one or more preceding controlled stages in such a direction as to oppose the internal emitter current, thereby operating the transistors closer to cutoff and reducing their gain. Direct control of emitter current requires appreciable a-g-c power. This power requirement is reduced by applying the a-g-c voltage to the base of a common-emitter stage, the controlled transistor then acting not only as an i-f amplifier, but also as its own a-g-c d-c amplifier. To get a-g-c action, the a-g-c voltage must be applied to

the base, so that it decreases with increasing carrier level. Emitter-current control is effective only so long as emitter current is low (less than 500 μa). Low emitter current restricts the signal-

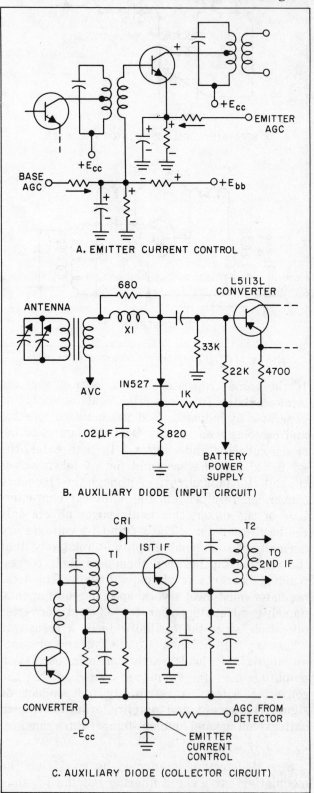

Figure 14-23. Automatic Gain Control Circuits

handling capability of the stage, if input clipping, and consequent distortion of the modulation envelope, is to be avoided.

Because of collector leakage current, I_{co} or I_{CEO}, which keeps a transistor from being cutoff, its gain is controllable only up to a point. Also, to prevent i-f amplifier overloading on large signal strength, a diode, serving as *auxiliary a-g-c* function, is often used as a variable, interstage, external-control shunt. Such an overload diode may be incorporated into the converter (as shown in part B of figure 14-23) or i-f amplifier input, connected in parallel with, but in opposite polarity to, the transistor's emitter-base diode, and normally biased to cutoff. As a higher signal-strength level produces a greater a-g-c voltage, the increase in voltage on the crystal diode lowers its incremental impedance, permitting greater conduction. Thus, the diode's shunting effect tends to keep the signal current applied within the operational design level of the controlled transistor and so maintain its input impedance constant.

The diode may also be connected into the first i-f amplifier circuit, as illustrated in part C of figure 14-23, so that large signal peaks cause the diode to conduct, thereby loading the primary and lowering the stage gain.

The sensitivity of an a-g-c system is sometimes referred to in terms of *stiffness ratio*, that is, the ratio in decibels of change in the input signal to the ensuing change at the output.

14-7 TRANSISTOR SUPERHETERODYNE AM RADIO RECEIVER

To exploit fully the unique characteristic of transistors and to minimize their disadvantages, transistorization of electronic equipment requires new design approaches and techniques. In addition to the transistor's portability advantages of small size, light weight, and immunity from mechanical shock, it is extremely economical in power consumption, and has other peculiar electrical properties. For example, a transistor's impedance-matching property enables direct feeding of a voice coil by an audio amplifier, thus eliminating the usual output transformer with its attendant size, weight, and cost. Disadvantages include present-day limitations of frequency response, power-handling capabilities, and ambient-temperature range, and also power drain from the signal source. The transistorization of portable AM broadcast receivers, realized all of the transistor's advantages, while satisfactorily overcoming its

limitations. Although a transistor superheterodyne radio receiver block diagram would be the same as that of a vacuum-tube receiver, the underlying design of the individual blocks and their relationship are somewhat different. Starting at the second detector which can be considered the functional center of a superheterodyne receiver, certain design differences are to be noted. Transistor detection is often preferable to diode detection for several reasons, but mainly because it affords linear detection at lower power levels. While it is true that more transistors than tubes may be required for comparable performance (since their gain is l o w e r) greater gain per transistor s t a g e can be achieved at audio frequencies. This is the reason that as much of the system gain as possible is derived from the audio section. Consequently, in the r-f section between the antenna and the second detector, there is need for just enough selective gain to amplify the weakest signal the receiver is intended to handle until it is of sufficient amplitude to be detected linearly. The design of the audio stages is straightforward, their number being determined by the desired output level and signal level available at the second detector. Often a low-noise preamplifier follows the detector, feeding either the output stage, or perhaps, a driver supplying a push-pull stage. Problems encountered in the forward section of the receiver include bandwidth variation due to variation of transistor impedances, and also the tendency of the i-f amplifiers to oscillate at 455 kc due to sufficiently strong internal feedback in many currently available transistor types, unless they are properly neutralized. Since transistors are particularly advantageous for portable receivers, they are battery-operated. The voltage requirements for all low-level (signal) stages seldom exceed 3 volts, while for reasonable output power from high-level (power) stages, 6 volts may be regarded as a desirable minimum. When size and cost are pertinent, a reflex circuit, that passes the audio back through the i-f stages to reduce the number of audio stages, may be incorporated.

Figure 14-24 is the schematic diagram of a simple, laboratory-assembled, but nonetheless typical, all-transistor superheterodyne AM radio receiver. This 6-transistor receiver contains 5 stages — converter, i-f amplifier, and detector-audio amplifier, that use high-frequency Philco surface-barrier types, and audio-driver and push-pull output stages, which use junction types be-

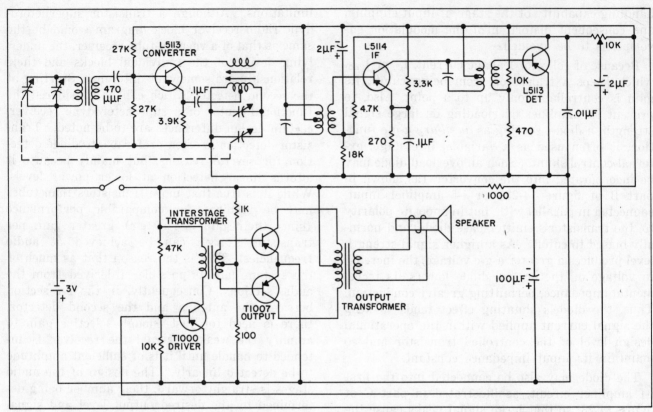

Figure 14-24. Simple Transistor Superheterodyne Radio Receiver, Schematic Diagram

cause of the greater power demand of the audio section. The first stage converts the r-f signals to 455 kc i-f signals. This stage is followed by a single i-f amplifier stage which increases the i-f signal level and provides an output for the transistor detector stage. The audio output of the transistor-triode detector is taken off the 10K volume-control potentiometer that serves as collector load resistance, while the automatic d-c gain-control current is fed back via the 4.7K resistor. The .01 μf detector output-circuit capacitor is the r-f bypass, and the 2 μf capacitor shunting the a-g-c feedback resistor is an a-f bypass.

Figures 14-25 and 14-26 are the schematic diagram and composite panel view, respectively, of a typical commercial all-transistor radio receiver. This Philco Portable Radio Transistor Model T-7 is a compact, lightweight unit, housed in a 7 x 4-1/2 x 2 inch plastic case. The receiver uses a printed-circuit panel that serves as the chassis. Of the seven transistors, four high-frequency surface-barrier types are used in the converter, 1st and 2nd i-f amplifier stages, and 2nd detector, and the other three, comprising the 1st audio-amplifier and class B push-pull output stages, are alloy-junction type because of power requirements.

All are common-emitter stages. The power supply consists of two 1-1/2-volt D batteries in series with the chassis-connected negative terminal for a 3-volt maximum.

The incoming signal on the magnecore antenna is coupled to the base of the autodyne converter stage whose output is a 455 kc i-f signal. The 1N527 crystal diode, connected into the base (input) circuit as a shunt-impedance device, operates in conjunction with the a-g-c circuit to limit the amount of signal fed to the converter base. An increase of signal strength produces a greater a-g-c voltage, which is fed through the antenna secondary and the antenna-isolating choke X1 to the crystal. The voltage increase at the crystal anode lowers its impedance, allowing greater conduction and thus bypassing more of the incoming signal to ground, so that the amount of signal fed to the converter base is kept within the transistor's operational design level. The 455 kc output signal from the converter is transformer-coupled to the 1st i-f amplifier base, to which a-g-c voltage is also applied through the i-f transformer secondary. The a-g-c voltage effectively raises or lowers the bias voltage applied to the base, thus compensating for signal-level variations. Capacitors C7 and C8 are i-f amplifier neutraliz-

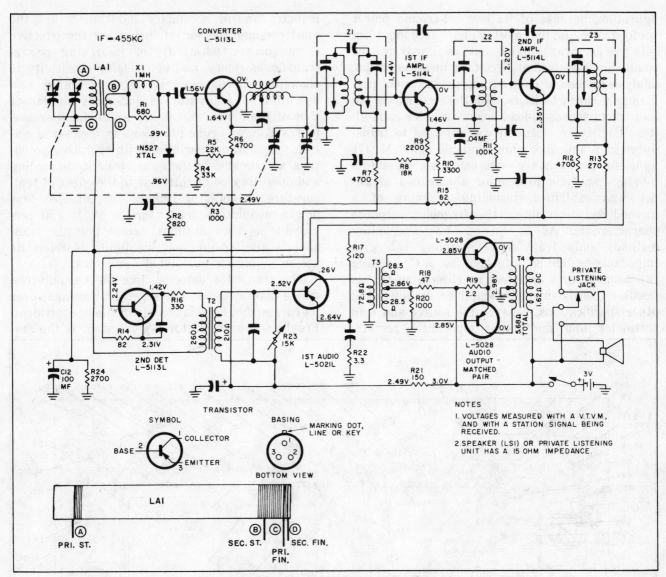

Figure 14-25. Philco Transistor Portable Radio Model T-7, Schematic Diagram

ing capacitors. In the 2nd detector stage, the i-f signal fed to the base is amplified and detected, and then fed through an audio-coupling transformer to the 1st audio-amplifier stage. The 2700-ohm load resistor and 100 μf filter capacitor parallel combination produces the a-g-c voltage by filtering out the detected audio frequencies. The 15,000-ohm potentiometer across the audio-transformer secondary, shunted by a hi-cut tone-compensation capacitor, is the manual volume control. The matched pair transistors in the push-pull audio-output stage are base-fed through the center-tapped audio-transformer secondary, for the necessary signal phasing. Emitter-bias voltage for the first audio transistor is derived from the battery power supply through the speaker output transformer, the resistive voltage-

divider arrangement forming a feedback circuit for tonal compensation. The speaker is a special 2-1/2 inch diameter type, with a voice coil impedance of 15 ohms. Insertion of the earpiece attachment plug into the private listening jack disables the speaker.

14-8 SUMMARY

The transistor amplifier, it has been seen, is a biased, active, electronic device whose basic performance criterion is its power gain. Although its function and classification (according to frequency range and interstage coupling) are the same as for vacuum-tube amplifiers, the fact that it is a current-operated device and has input-output circuit interdependence makes its operation analysis more complex. The common-emitter configuration, because of its best all-around power performance, is the most widely used, and for this reason was singled out to illustrate the small-signal equivalent-circuit, or linear equation, analysis method of determining the pertinent performance characteristics, with the emphasis being laid on its source-to-load power-transfer capability. Particular attention was directed to transducer gain and maximum available gain (MAG) as useful performance criteria. Also, the stage-by-stage analysis process of a cascaded amplifier was explained, including outlining of a method for determining the frequency-response characteristic. As to interstage coupling methods, only transformer coupling can give impedance-matching, although for R-C coupling the usual aim is to effect as close a match as feasible, consistent with amplifier stability and other specifications, between the source and load transistor input and output impedances, respect-

primary and/or secondary inductances are the most common method of increasing the effective Q for proper selectivity, of improving power-transfer efficiency, and of reducing sensitivity to changing impedances. While the circuitry and operation of transistor oscillators is similar to that of their vacuum-tube forerunners, they are, however, more prone to instability because of collector capacitance variation with operating potentials, and because of their susceptibility to loading and operating-point shift due to the effect of temperature on collector leakage current. As low-power modulators, transistors prove just as serviceable as vacuum-tubes, except that the transistor's greater inherent instability restricts its use in amplitude-modulated oscillators.

The transistor detector, like the vacuum-tube triode plate detector, has several advantages over its corresponding semiconductor diode equivalent. Peculiar to a transistor a-g-c system is the fre-

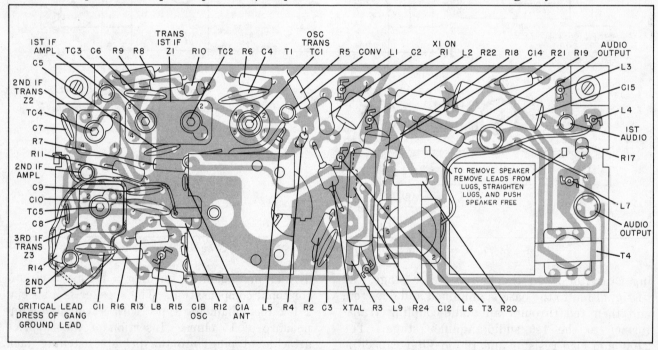

Figure 14-26.   Philco Transistor Portable Radio Model T-7, Composite Panel View

ively, for greater power transfer. Insertion of a manual gain control requires special care, so as not to shift the operating point of the transistor because of the dependence of its impedance and gain characteristics thereupon. The tuned interstage of transistor r-f amplifiers likewise demands special attention in order to meet the requirements of selectivity, low power-transfer loss, and reduced sensitivity to variation of output and input impedances while tuning. Tapped

quent necessity for auxiliary external agc, because of its limited gain controllability and to prevent i-f amplifier overloading. The transistor superheterodyne radio receiver, at once suggestive of portability, has the same block diagram as the tube version, but inspection discloses, in addition to some of the circuit differences mentioned, placement of the major amplification function in the audio section. Besides, economy of cost and size often make the reflex circuit practicable.

Although transistor benefits include long life and reliability, as compared with vacuum-tube equipment where over 90% of failures is due to tubes, certain testing precautions and servicing techniques (see transistor fundamentals) must be observed for transistor and printed circuits. One particular trouble-shooting practice, often used in tube radio servicing, that must be avoided, is perhaps worth mentioning. Because transistors are very sensitive to improper bias voltages, the technique of shorting various points to ground and listening for a click must be avoided, since short circuits are likely to damage transistors.

REVIEW QUESTIONS

1. Upon what assumptions is the transistor *h-parameter* equivalent circuit, or small-signal, analysis method based?

2. Why is power gain used as a basic performance criterion of a transistor amplifier?

3. How is the common-emitter configuration superior to the other two transistor amplifier circuit arrangements?

4. What are the pertinent performance characteristics of a transistor amplifier circuit?

5. Find the db equivalent of the actual power gain values of Table 14-3 and locate each on figure 14-6.

6. How are input and output impedances of a transistor amplifier circuit defined?

7. What is the actual power gain of a transistor amplifier circuit?

8. Define *transducer gain* and state the usefulness of this criterion for transistors.

9. Define *maximum available gain* and explain the usefulness of this criterion as a transistor *figure of merit*.

10. What is the dual function of interstage coupling and what are its effects on a-c operation?

11. What are the two major high-frequency limiting factors of a transistor amplifier?

12. What is the most important condition relating to placement of a transistor amplifier manual gain control?

13. What is the purpose of tapping primary and/or secondary inductances of tuned r-f transistor amplifiers?

14. Explain why a nonlinear element is necessary to limit the output amplitude of a sinusoidal oscillator and how this is done by a transistor.

15. What is the most serious cause of transistor sinusoidal oscillator instability?

16. What are the frequency-stabilization techniques used?

17. What is the major difference between vacuum-tube oscillators and their transistorized versions?

18. What are the essential requirements for a transistor local oscillator?

19. What are the advantages of transistor over semiconductor-diode detection?

20. What characteristics of a transistor make it adaptable to an a-g-c system?

21. Why is an auxiliary external a-g-c system often used with transistors?

22. Explain why as much of the system gain as possible is designed into the audio section of a transistor superheterodyne radio receiver, rather than into the r-f section as in vacuum-tube receivers.

23. What is a *reflex receiver*?

24. List the most desirable performance characteristics and features of a transistor superheterodyne radio receiver.

25. How well does Philco's Transistor Portable Radio Model T-7 (figure 14-24) fit this list?

CHAPTER FIFTEEN

*Single-Sideband
Communications
Principles*

15-1 Introduction

The concept of single-sideband (SSB) transmission and reception is not new in electronics; however, the development of operational systems is relatively recent. As the term implies, single-sideband transmission is a method of transmitting intelligence whereby the r-f carrier and one sideband of an amplitude-modulated double-sideband wave are suppressed, and only one of the intelligence-bearing sidebands is transmitted.

As studied previously, the components of a standard amplitude-modulated signal consist of the carrier and two side frequencies (double sidebands) spaced above and below the carrier by an amount equal to the frequency of the modulating signal. Amplitude-modulated signals used in standard broadcast require a 10-kc bandpass (for a 5-kc maximum modulating frequency), while amplitude-modulated communications signals, both commercial and military, require a 6-kc bandpass (for a 3-kc maximum modulating frequency). The side frequencies which are produced by this mode of transmission are actually mirror images of each other, where either is capable of being demodulated to obtain the transmitted intelligence. As can be seen, standard amplitude modulation is actually wasteful of the frequency spectrum, since it requires at least twice the bandwidth of the original modulating signal. To transmit a given form of intelligence (voice, teletype, video, etc), single-sideband systems use only one-half the bandwidth required for AM double-sideband systems. One of the important advantages of SSB systems, therefore, is the conservation of the frequency spectrum.

The main factor which has limited the applications of single-sideband transmission up to this time has been the lack of precise frequency control of the transmitters and receivers used in this mode of communications. With the development of n e w manufacturing techniques which allow closer-tolerance circuit components, single-sideband communications is no longer limited to wide carrier-telephone systems and low-frequency (below 3 mc) radiotelephone-telegraph, but has extended its coverage to such an extent that it is generally accepted as standard for long-range point-to-point communication systems (30 mc and below).

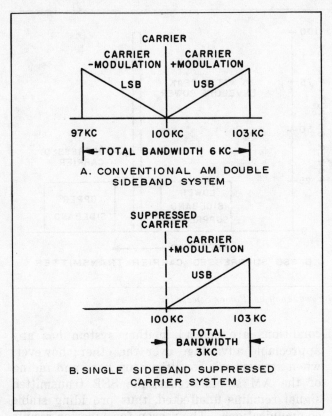

Figure 15-1. Comparison of AM DSB and SSB Frequency Spectrum Utilization

15-2 SINGLE-SIDEBAND CONSIDERATIONS

A graphical representation of the comparison of standard double-sideband (DSB) and single-sideband (SSB) frequency spectrum coverages is presented in figure 15-1. Assuming a carrier frequency of 100 kc, and modulating information (voice) from 100 to 3000 cps, the total bandwidth of the AM double-sideband system is 6000 cycles, or twice the highest modulation frequency. With the same carrier and modulating signals, the bandwidth of the SSB system is only 3000 cycles. Since the carrier does not contain any of the modulating intelligence, it is suppressed in the transmitter prior to signal transmission. With the single-sideband method of transmission, it is possible to increase the number of channels to twice that of conventional amplitude-modulated systems. Either two separate transmitters or one dual-channel transmitter could be employed to make use of this additional channel. Figure 15-2 shows a simplified block diagram of an SSB dual-channel system. Note that two entirely unrelated modulation signals are placed in the same frequency area normally taken up by the signal of a conventional AM system.

Power Output and Signal-to-Noise Ratio

Single-sideband transmission as compared to conventional AM transmission has decided advantages with respect to transmitter power and system signal-to-noise ratio. To provide the same coverage as an AM transmitter, an SSB transmitter requires a peak power rating of approximately one-eighth (9 db) less than that of the AM system. Assuming that an AM transmitter is modulated 100%, the voltage in each of the sidebands is one-half the carrier voltage. If the resistance of the circuit remains constant, the power in each sideband will be one-fourth the carrier power. With a carrier power output of

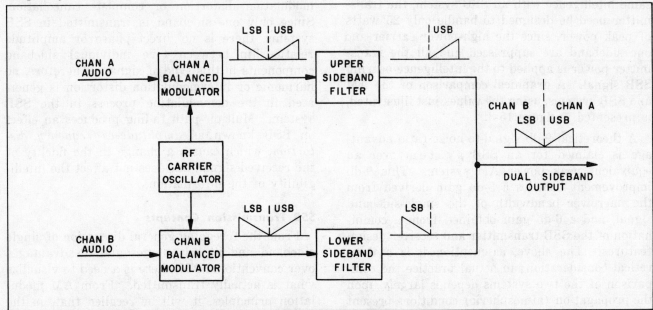

Figure 15-2. Simplified Block Diagram of SSB Dual-Channel System

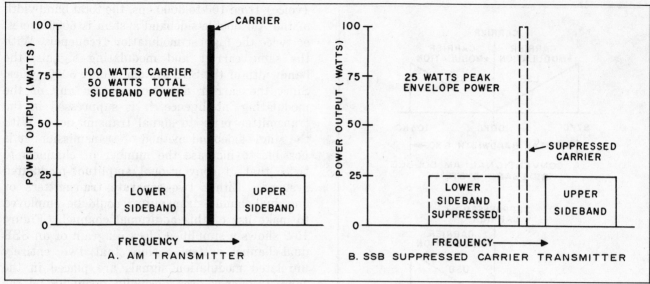

Figure 15-3.   Comparison of AM DSB and SSB Frequency vs. Power Spectrum

100 watts, the power in each sideband will be only 25 watts, giving a total sideband power of 50 watts and an average transmitter power rating of 150 watts. Since the peak voltage (carrier plus sidebands) is twice the carrier voltage, the peak power of the transmitter will be four times the carrier power. Therefore, an AM transmitter rated at 150 watts average power must be capable of handling peak power ratings up to 400 watts. Of the 150 watts average power, only one third (50 watts) is used to transmit the intelligence-bearing sidebands, since the other two thirds (the 100-watt carrier) possesses no useful modulating intelligence. To transmit the same intelligence with an SSB system, the transmitter need be designed to handle only 25 watts of peak power, since the high-power carrier and one sideband are suppressed and all the transmitter power is applied to the intelligence-bearing SSB signal. A graphical comparison of the AM and SSB systems, using the values just illustrated, is presented in figure 15-3.

A theoretical 9-db signal-to-noise ratio advantage is claimed for an SSB s y s t e m over an equivalent peak power AM system. This 9-db improvement includes a 3-db gain derived from the narrower bandwidth of the single-sideband signal, and a 6-db gain obtained from a combination of the SSB transmitter and receiver design features. The above, as mentioned, is a theoretical consideration; in actual practice the comparison of the two systems depends largely upon the propagation (atmospheric) conditions present at the time of comparison. When transmission conditions are i d e a l, neither system has any appreciable advantage over the other; however, when atmospheric conditions are poor and fading of the AM signal occurs, the SSB transmitted signal remains unaffected, thus providing stable communications. The reason for superior results with SSB can be explained as follows: An AM signal can be effectively cancelled at a receiving location because of improper phase relationships between the carrier and sidebands resulting from multiple-path transmission distances. W h e n detected, in the receiver, such signals are effectively a combination of amplitude and phase modulation which can cause harmonic or intermodulation distortion or complete cancellation. Since only one sideband is transmitted in SSB systems, there is no direct phase or amplitude relationship between t h e individual sideband components in this type of signal. Therefore, no harmonic or intermodulation distortion is generated in the demodulating process in the SSB system. Multiple-path fading produces an effect on SSB known as *amplitude-vs-frequency distortion*, which causes a change in the fidelity of the received signal, but does not affect the intelligibility of the information.

SSB Transmission Concepts

From the foregoing general discussion of single sideband and its advantages and disadvantages over conventional AM, there is a need to visualize what is actually transmitted. From AM modulation principles, it will be recalled that, in the process of modulating an r-f carrier with a lower-

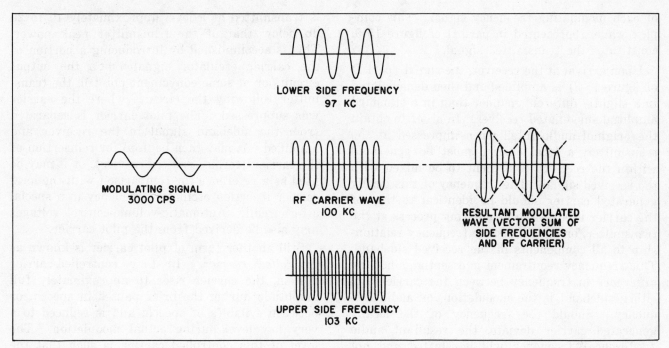

LOWER SIDE FREQUENCY
97 KC

MODULATING SIGNAL
3000 CPS

RF CARRIER WAVE
100 KC

RESULTANT MODULATED
WAVE (VECTOR SUM OF
SIDE FREQUENCIES
AND RF CARRIER)

UPPER SIDE FREQUENCY
103 KC

Figure 15-4. Sideband Frequencies and Resultant Waveform Generated During Amplitude Modulating Process

frequency signal, a heterodyning action takes place in the modulator stage and causes the generation of additional frequencies. If only a single frequency is used as the modulating signal, two such additional frequencies will be generated, as illustrated in figure 15-4. One of these, the upper side frequency, is the sum of the two beating signals; the other, the lower side frequency, is the difference between the two beating signals. Although it is not readily apparent, the resultant modulated wave produced by the modulation process is actually a combination of the carrier wave and the two side frequencies. If a band of frequencies, instead of a single frequency, such as the voice range of 300 to 3000 cycles is used to modulate the carrier, the additional frequencies generated by the heterodyning action produce the so-called upper- and lower-sideband frequencies. These sidebands assume their respective positions in the frequency spectrum, above and below the carrier signal, and the resultant modulated wave is a combination of the carrier and all the frequencies contained in these sidebands. In the process of modulation, all of the intelligence and power of the modulating signal are applied to the generated sidebands. The carrier alone contains none of the intelligence.

In a conventional AM system, the carrier is transmitted and received along with its sidebands, the three components forming a wave envelope,

the carrier of which should normally be in the same frequency and phase relationship to the sidebands as when transmitted. T h i s resultant received signal, when applied to the diode detector o f a superheterodyne receiver, i s essentially heterodyned in the nonlinear device, and the difference (audio signal = i-f carrier – sideband frequency) is the desired intelligence.

In a single-sideband suppressed-carrier system (SSSC), the carrier is suppressed and one sideband attenuated so that the only signal transmitted by the system is the remaining sideband. Figure 15-5 s h o w s a representation of the resultant transmitted signal, assuming that an initial carrier frequency of 200 kc is used. When the carrier is modulated by a 1-kc audio note, the side frequencies generated are 199 kc and 201 kc, as indicated in part A of figure 15-5. Since the carrier and the l o w e r side frequency are suppressed (part B of figure 15-5), the remaining upper side frequency, 201 kc, is the signal radiated by the transmitting system. Part C of figure 15-5 shows the resultant transmitted signal, the amplitude of which is constant for a steady initial modulating tone of 1 kc. When the modulating signal is a voice input covering the range of 300 cycles to 3 kc, the resultant transmitted sideband signal varies in frequency from 200.3 kc to 203 kc at an amplitude determined by the magnitude of each modulating frequency signal. This complex wave, represented in part D of figure 15-5, constitutes the transmitted signal.

Upon arrival at the receiver, the signal (part D of figure 15-5) is amplified and then demodulated in a slightly different manner than in a standard amplitude-modulated receiver. In order to obtain the original audio intelligence impressed at the transmitter, a local carrier must be generated within the receiver equipment to be mixed with the received signal. The frequency of this locally generated carrier should be identical to that of the carrier used in the modulating process at the transmitter, or have the same frequency relationship to all components of the received sideband. This frequency requirement is essential, since the *difference* in frequency between the carrier and either sideband is the modulation, or audio frequency. Should the frequency of the locally generated carrier deviate, the resultant audio (difference) frequency will be shifted and not truly represent the original modulating signal. Deviation in the frequency of the insertion oscillator (carrier-frequency oscillator in the receiver) or any of the heterodyning oscillators greater than approximately 200 cycles (above or below the correct value), may cause sufficient speech inversion to render the received information unintelligible. Thus it can be seen that frequency stability is one of the most critical and important requirements of single-sideband equipment.

To provide some control or means of reference which permits the frequency relationship between the receiver oscillator and the transmitter oscillator to be maintained at a constant value, a pilot carrier is sometimes transmitted. In this system, known as *reduced-carrier SSB*, the pilot carrier is transmitted at a level approximately 10 to 20 db below that of the transmitter peak power. This is accomplished by introducing a portion of the carrier oscillator signal into the output circuits or at some convenient point in the transmitter following the circuits where the carrier was suppressed. The pilot carrier is separated from the sideband signal in the receiver and amplified. It may then be used for reinsertion of the carrier (termed *exalted carrier*), or it may be used as a reference for comparison with the local carrier insertion oscillator frequency in a special a-f-c circuit. Automatic-volume-control voltages may also be derived from the pilot carrier.

Still another form of pilot carrier is known as *controlled carrier*. In the controlled-carrier system, the carrier rises to approximately full amplitude during the brief pauses in speech, or between syllables of speech, and is reduced to a very low level during actual modulation. The level of this controlled carrier is such that the average power output of the transmitter is maintained effectively constant regardless of the presence or absence of modulation. Slow-acting a-f-c and a-g-c circuits are used in the receiver to hold the receiver circuits on the proper frequency during modulation.

In the full-carrier SSB system, the carrier is transmitted at a level of approximately 4 to 6 db below the peak power of the transmitter. The level of the transmitted carrier is sufficient to allow reception of the single-sideband signal with a conventional AM receiver. This mode of transmission is called *compatible single sideband* (CSSB).

In the single-sideband transmission systems discussed above, emphasis has been placed on

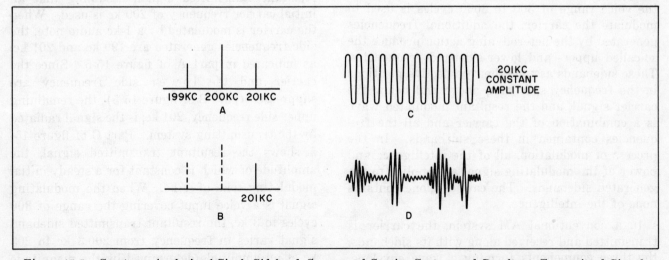

Figure 15-5.   Spectrum Analysis of Single-Sideband Suppressed-Carrier System and Resultant Transmitted Signal

voice communications where the modulating signal is kept within a band of frequencies between 300 cycles and 3000 cycles. When the modulating signal includes extremely low-frequency components (approaching zero frequency), it is difficult to design single-sideband systems which will properly suppress the undesired sideband. To ease this design problem, a small portion of the undesired sideband is sometimes transmitted with the desired sideband. This method of transmission, called *vestigial sideband,* is actually a form of single sideband, and is used extensively in the transmission of television signals. The bandwidth of the vestigial-sideband signal in standard television broadcasting is approximately one-sixth the bandwidth of the full sideband.

15-3 SINGLE-SIDEBAND TRANSMITTERS

There are two basic systems for generating a single-sideband signal — the filter system and the phase-shift system. Although these two systems are basically different in circuit operation, they both produce the same result — the generation and transmission of only one sideband of an amplitude-modulated radio-frequency c a r r i e r. Each system is capable of good over-all system performance, and each provides a gain of approximately 9 db over that of a double-sideband-plus-carrier system. Compared to each other, however, the filter and phase-shift systems have certain advantages and disadvantages.

Filter Method of SSB Signal Generation

Of the two basic methods of generating single-sideband signals, the most widely used is the filter method, illustrated in figure 15-6. Although stability and accuracy of the transmitter are determined mainly by the stability and accuracy

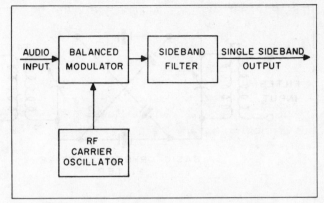

Figure 15-6. Block Diagram of Basic Filter System SSB Exciter

of the r-f carrier oscillator, the balanced modulator and sideband filter circuits are the circuits most important to the generation of the single-sideband signal itself.

There are many variations of balanced modulator circuits, some making use of diode rectifiers and others utilizing vacuum tubes. The basic function of all the various balanced modulators is identical: namely, the generation of a double-sideband amplitude-modulated signal, and suppression of the r-f carrier. The amount of carrier suppression is determined by the degree of balance between the two modulator legs (a balanced modulator can be compared to a bridge circuit). Thus, the output of the balanced modulator illustrated in figure 15-7 consists of only the upper- and lower-sideband frequencies of an amplitude-modulated r-f carrier. The audio input frequency is rejected by normal tuning of the modulator output circuit.

To obtain a single-sideband signal from the balanced modulator double-sideband output, it is

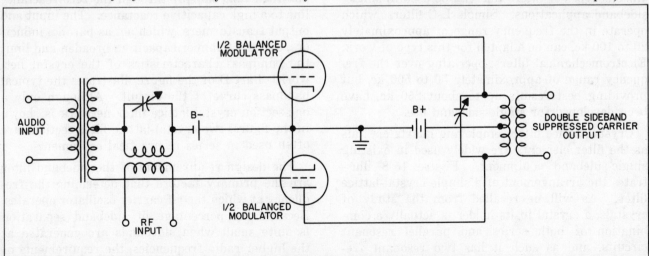

Figure 15-7. Single Balanced Modulator Circuit

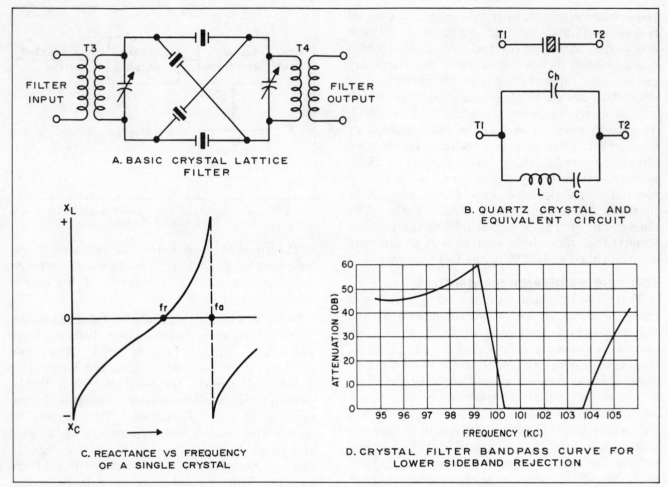

Figure 15-8.   Circuit Characteristics of a Crystal-Lattice Filter

necessary to apply the double-sideband signal to a suitable sideband filter. Either sideband can be rejected or accepted by using an appropriate filter to select one sideband and reject the other. As in the case of balanced modulators, there are various types of filters that can be used in single-sideband applications. Simple L-C filters, which operate in the frequency range of approximately 20 to 100 kc, can be adapted for this type of work. Electromechanical filters, operating over the frequency range of approximately 50 to 500 kc, but providing best results up to about 250 kc, have been developed for single-sideband use.

Crystal-lattice filters employing quartz crystals as the filter elements are widely used in existing single-sideband equipment. Figure 15-8 illustrates the arrangement of a simple crystal-lattice filter. As will be recalled from the study of crystals, a crystal in its holder is actually a combination of both series and parallel resonant circuits, and as such it has two resonant frequencies, as indicated in part C of figure 15-8.

The series resonant frequency f_r, occurs at the point where the reactance curve crosses the zero reactance line; the parallel resonant frequency (antiresonant), f_a, occurs at the point where the reactance curve rises to a high inductive reactance and then falls sharply through the zero-reactance line to a high capacitive reactance. The input and output transformers, which act as parallel inductors, and the trimmer capacitors broaden and limit the bandpass characteristics of the crystal network. Part D of the figure illustrates the typical bandpass curve of the circuit. Although only a one-section crystal-lattice filter network is shown in the figure, two crystal-lattice filter sections are often used in series in practical equipments.

The design requirements of the sideband filter are the primary factors that determine the frequency at which the r-f carrier oscillator operates. Because the percentage of sideband separation is quite small when sidebands are generated at the higher radio frequencies, the requirements of a filter to separate such sidebands are exacting.

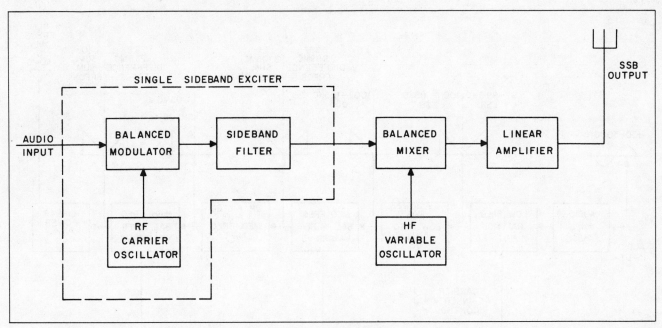

Figure 15-9.   Block Diagram of Filter System SSB Transmitter

To ease these exacting requirements, it is common practice to generate the sidebands at a relatively low radio frequency (usually 100 kc) where optimum operation of the sideband filter can be realized.

A simplified block diagram of a filter-system single-sideband transmitter is shown in figure 15-9.   The single-sideband exciter, as it is termed, contains the low radio-frequency oscillator, the balanced modulator, and the sideband filter. Since these stages operate at relatively low power levels, additional circuits are required to increase both the frequency and power prior to transmission. The circuits following the SSB exciter are in many ways comparable to circuits used in AM systems.   However, since the use of frequency multipliers and class C power amplifiers would impair the frequency relationship between the sideband components, balanced mixer and linear power amplifier circuits are used in the frequency-translating steps in SSB transmitters.

Although only one frequency-translating step is indicated in figure 15-9, two or more such steps are often employed when the transmitter output frequency is very much higher than the frequency of the r-f carrier oscillator.   The primary requirements of the output circuits in transmitting systems are usually low distortion (good linearity) and high power gain.   Since the modulation process is performed at a low level in SSB transmitters, and since any amplification of a signal containing a modulation envelope must be linear,

linear power amplifiers are generally used to satisfy the requirements of the transmitter output circuits.   Basically, a linear amplifier is one in which the output signal is a direct function of, and proportional to, the input signal.   However, high gain is not usually obtained with good linearity.   Therefore, the output amplifiers in SSB transmitters are generally class AB or class B push-pull circuits.

Figure 15-10 shows a block diagram of a typical single-sideband filter-system transmitter. The frequencies indicated for the lower and upper sidebands are typical values used in operational equipment.   The audio amplifier, V1, is a conventional speech amplifier circuit which amplifies audio signals and limits their frequencies to a range of 100 to 3000 cycles.   As explained previously, the low-frequency balanced modulator serves to provide the sidebands of an amplitude-modulated signal and suppress the carrier provided by the r-f carrier oscillator.   The modulator output consists of the lower sideband (97 — 99.9 kc) and the upper sideband (100.1 — 103 kc), as shown. These are amplified and passed through a bandpass filter which eliminates the lower sideband entirely.   The low-level upper-sideband signal is fed into a frequency-translation arrangement consisting of the medium-frequency balanced mixer, the oscillator, and the amplifier-filter.   In these circuits the heterodyning action of the medium-frequency balanced mixer raises the frequency of the sideband signals to obtain

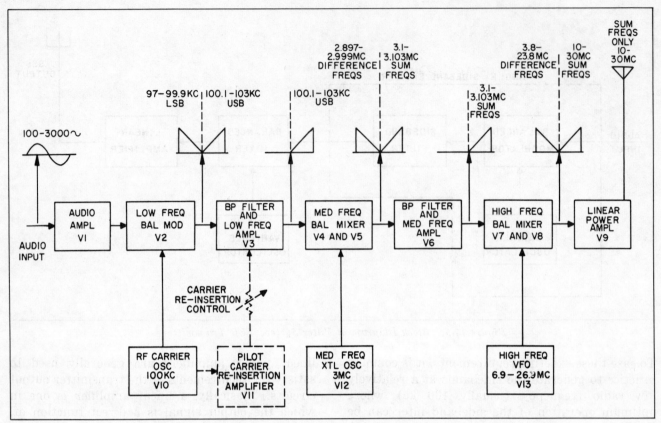

Figure 15-10.   Block Diagram of a Typical Single-Sideband Filter-System Transmitter

the desired upper-sideband translation frequency of 3.1 — 3.103 mc from the medium-frequency amplifier and b a n d p a s s filter. Another frequency translation takes place, using the high-frequency variable-frequency oscillator, the high-frequency balanced mixer, and the linear power amplifier. Heterodyning again occurs in these stages to increase the resultant output sidebands to the desired transmitter frequency. Note that the high-frequency oscillator is a variable-frequency oscillator, capable of being varied from 6.9 to 26.9 mc. This allows the resultant transmitter output frequency to be varied over a specified range of frequencies. The absence of a bandpass filter following the high-frequency balanced mixer is accounted for by the fact that the linear power amplifier and the antenna circuits are tuned to the sum frequencies and therefore will not pass the u n d e s i r e d lower-sideband difference frequencies.

The above discussion of the block diagram covered the circuits that are associated with a single-sideband transmitter using a completely suppressed carrier (SSSC). For transmission to receivers which employ the controlled-carrier or reduced-carrier principle, the transmitter would include the dotted circuits in figure 15-10 to provide the desired percentage of radiated carrier for system operation.

Phase-Shift Method of SSB Signal Generation

In the phase-shift single-sideband transmitter the audio input amplifier, the r-f oscillator, the balanced modulator, and the linear power amplifier circuits serve the same basic functions as their equivalent circuits in the filter-system method. The principal difference between the two systems is in the method used to produce the desired sideband and reject the undesired sideband. Instead of using crystal-lattice or electromechanical filters to accomplish this sideband rejection, the phase-shift system operates on the principle of removing the undesired sideband by a balancing or cancelling process based upon the phase relationships between the sideband signals generated in two separate balanced modulators. Figure 15-11 shows a block diagram of a practical phase-shift single-sideband transmitter. In this circuit arrangement the input (audio) modulating signal is applied to a 90-degree phase-shift network to produce quadrature audio signals.

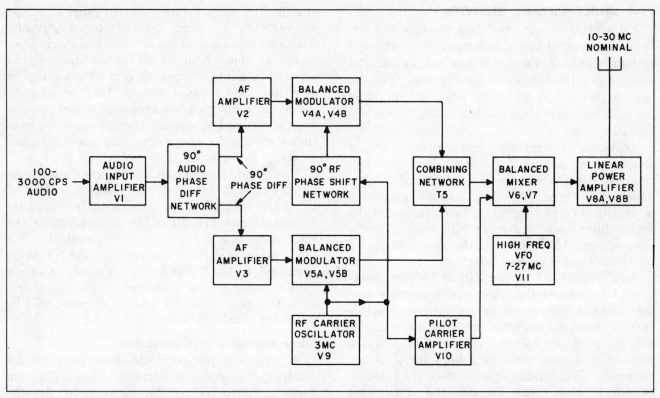

Figure 15-11. Block Diagram of Practical Phase-Shift-System Single-Sideband Transmitter

These quadrature audio signals are amplified in the audio amplifiers, which also isolate the phase-shift network from any loading due to the balanced modulators.   The r-f carrier oscillator is applied directly to one balanced modulator, and through a 90-degree phase-shift network to the other balanced modulator.   The individual carriers cancel in the balanced modulators, while the generated upper and lower sidebands constitute the output from the balanced modulators. The effective phase relationships of the outputs of of the individual balanced modulators are such that there are 90-degree differences between the upper and lower sidebands, in a d d i t i o n to 90-degree differences between both balanced modulators.   These sideband s i g n a l s are then combined in the adding n e t w o r k in such a manner that the upper sidebands from both modulators aid each other and add, while the lower sidebands of both modulators oppose each other and cancel.   The net result is that only the upper-sideband frequencies are applied to the third balanced mixer which, in conjunction with the high-frequency VFO, provide the desired frequency translation for the required transmitter frequency output.   The linear amplifier serves the same purpose and meets the same requirements as the amplifier used in the filter method.

Comparison of Filter and Phase-Shift SSB Generation

The choice of the basic method of single-sideband generation primarily hinges upon two factors — relative cost, and transmitter stability and maintenance requirements. The filter system is by far the most costly of the two systems because of the initial high cost of the filter networks and the number of frequency-translation steps required to obtain the desired frequency of operation. However, once the system is adjusted, it will provide stable and relatively trouble-free operation.

The phase-shift system is less costly than the filter system in that it requires fewer circuits to achieve the necessary frequency translation and the need for expensive sideband filters is eliminated.   However, adjustment of the phase-shift networks is quite critical for optimum system performance, thus increasing the maintenance time required to assure equipment stability.

Discussions of dual-channel DSB systems and other methods of sideband generation can be found in engineering texts covering single-sideband transmission. These systems will not be covered in this volume.

15-4 SINGLE-SIDEBAND RECEIVERS

AM reception requires interception of the desired transmitted signal by means of an antenna system, amplification of the selected signal, and detection of the impressed intelligence. The detection process, as has been explained, requires the presence of the sidebands and the r-f carrier signal.

Reception of single-sideband signals is not as simple as ordinary AM reception, because detection requires the mixing of the sideband (either upper or lower or both) with a locally generated or amplified carrier signal. Therefore, one of the major differences between an SSB receiver and a conventional AM receiver is the provision in the SSB receiver for carrier insertion.

Two methods of accomplishing carrier insertion at the proper frequency are in common use. One method makes use of an extremely stable carrier insertion oscillator, and the other amplifies the pilot, or reduced, carrier (when transmitted) to a level sufficiently high for detection purposes. The relationship between the inserted carrier frequency and the sideband frequencies must be identical to that between the carrier frequency of the transmitter and the sideband frequencies.

Superheterodyne receivers are widely used for AM reception because of the selectivity, high gain,

and quality performance inherent with this type of receiver. The same type of receiver, usually with multiple conversion, is used for single-sideband reception. Multiple conversion improves the selectivity, gain, and overall performance, and is generally used because filtering may be accomplished more easily at low frequencies and because several steps of frequency translation make possible the reduction of spurious responses by proper choice of heterodying frequencies.

Similar to the single-sideband transmitter, the single-sideband receiver may employ either of two basic methods of processing the received information and providing for demodulation: the filter method and the phase-shift method. The various circuits which can perform the functions indicated in the following block analysis of an SSB receiver are too numerous to discuss; therefore, the principles, not specific circuits, will be the main consideration.

Filter Method of SSB Reception

A typical simplified double-conversion single-sideband receiver is illustrated in block diagram form in figure 15-12. The figure illustrates the general circuit requirements for both a suppressed-carrier system and a pilot-carrier system.

The r-f high-frequency amplifier is a conventional circuit similar to the r-f amplifier employed in a standard AM receiver. Circuit requirements

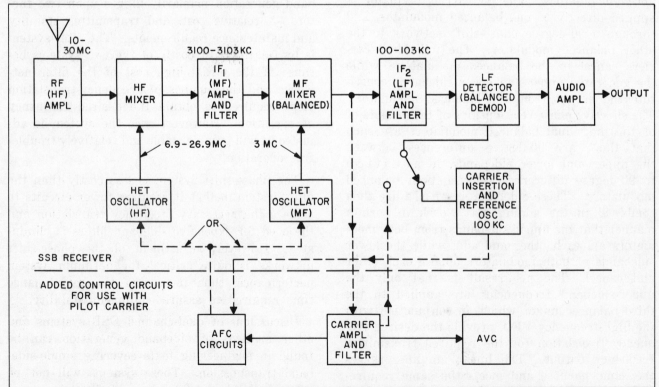

Figure 15-12. Block Diagram of a Double Conversion Superheterodyne SSB Receiver

as to selectivity and bandpass characteristics are identical to those in conventional AM in that the bandpass must be sufficient to pass either the upper or lower sideband, or both. As would be expected, the high-frequency (r-f) amplifier is tuned to the desired incoming-signal frequency received from the antenna circuit, and performs the functions of preselection and amplification.

The amplified sideband signal is then applied to the high-frequency mixer. This circuit mixes the signal from the high-frequency amplifier with the output of the high-frequency oscillator. In the mixing process, heterodyning action between the two signals produces a third, or difference, frequency. This process is the same as that used for normal AM reception by the frequency-conversion (heterodyning) method.

The high-frequency oscillator may be variable-tuned within the frequency range of the receiver. The oscillator frequency is normally below that of the received input signal. The oscillator tuning is extremely critical, and frequency stability is essential, since the full wave envelope is not present. Any deviation of oscillator frequency with respect to sideband frequency will result in frequency distortion in the output of the receiver.

The medium-frequency (high i-f) signal resulting from heterodyning the incoming signal and the local-oscillator output is still only the upper sideband, converted to a lower frequency. The carrier may be present, if it is being transmitted; however, it has not yet been added.

The output of the high-frequency mixer is filtered to eliminate all but the desired upper-sideband information converted to a medium frequency which may or may not include the carrier. The filtered signal is then amplified in the medium-frequency stage. Since only one sideband is received, the filter and amplifier require only one-half of the bandwith that would be required for normal AM reception. This reduction in bandwidth usually results in an improved signal-to-noise ratio. However, the i-f transformer tuning is usually broadened slightly to insure reasonably flat response to all frequencies in the pass band of the filter.

For a better understanding of the principles discussed above assume that the carrier is transmitted at 10 mc. This carrier heterodyning with a local-oscillator signal of 6.9 mc would then produce an i-f signal of 3100 kc. Now assume that the same carrier is voice-modulated with frequencies limited to a range from 100 to 3000

cycles per second. If this were an AM transmission with both sidebands, a bandwith of 6 kc would be required in the r-f and i-f sections, and the i-f stage would be center-tuned to 3100 kc. If the modulation of the received signal included music, or frequencies up to 10,000 cycles, the receiver bandwidth for full reproduction would have to be at least 20 kc wide for AM, or 10 kc for SSB. Since the receiver under consideration is designed for single-sideband voice frequencies limited to a range from 100 to 3000 cycles, the bandwith need only be one-half that required for double sideband, or 3 kc instead of 6 kc. Also, since the filters are fixed-tuned (crystals or mechanical filters), it is desirable to depend on the filters alone to limit the bandpass, and to tune the i-f transformers (and the beating oscillators) to correspond to the filter frequencies.

The output of the medium-frequency amplifier is applied to the medium-frequency balanced mixer. Here the medium frequency is heterodyned with the output of the medium-frequency oscillator to produce the low-frequency i-f signal. A balanced mixer (same type of circuit as a balanced modulator) is used at this point too, since its operational characteristics offer certain advantages which are favorable to single-sideband systems. The frequency of the medium-frequency oscillator is selected close to the frequency of the input to the medium-frequency mixer. For example, if the input to the medium-frequency balanced mixer is 3100 kc (3.1 mc) as assumed previously, the selected frequency of the medium-frequency oscillator will be 3000 kc (3 mc). The balanced mixer will provide cancellation of the 3-mc oscillator frequency and allow only the difference frequency to appear as the low-frequency i-f signal.

To avoid any confusion in the use of the balanced modulator, or mixer, remember that sidebands are sum and difference frequencies. The output of the medium-frequency balanced mixer is tuned to a 100- to 103-kc difference frequency, or the lower sideband of the signal produced by heterodyning of the 3-mc oscillator signal with the 3.1- to 3.103-mc signal. This should not be confused with the fact, however, that the frequencies between 100.1 and 103 kc are still the upper sideband of the original received pilot carrier, the frequency of which is now 100 kc. All have simply been converted to a lower frequency.

The 3-mc, or medium-frequency, oscillator must also be extremely stable, to prevent any shift in the sideband frequencies which may cause unintelligibility of the resultant audio output.

As can be seen from the diagram, the 100- to 103-kc output of the medium-frequency mixer is applied to the low-frequency amplifier with its bandpass filter circuit, and to the carrier amplifier, which contains a sharply tuned filter circuit. Here the pilot carrier is separated from the sideband signal, if carrier comparison circuits are included in the receiver. Conventional i-f circuitry is used in both amplifiers (i-f$_2$ low-frequency amplifier and carrier amplifier), except for the filters. The filter in the sideband channel is tuned to provide a bandpass of from 100.1 to 103 kc, corresponding to the upper sideband frequencies, and has a very sharp cutoff at the lower side of its frequency range, so as to reject the carrier frequency. The carrier channel and its associated filter are sharply tuned to the 100-kc carrier frequency.

The output of the low-frequency amplifier (sideband channel) is applied to the low-frequency balanced demodulator, together with the output of the carrier insertion and reference oscillator. Note that the reference-oscillator frequency of 100 kc corresponds to the frequency of the carrier (if present) which was rejected by the filter network of the low-frequency amplifier. Since the sideband-channel signal contains only sideband frequencies, it cannot be detected properly with the conventional diode, or envelope detector, because the complete wave envelope is not present. To permit proper detection, the 100-kc oscillator re-inserts the necessary carrier.

If a pilot carrier is received, it may be used instead of the output of the 100-kc oscillator for carrier re-insertion. However, since the pilot carrier is greatly reduced in amplitude, it must first be reconditioned and amplified to the same relative strength as the original modulating carrier (at the transmitter) to avoid causing the effects of transmitter overmodulation and serious distortion. To provide the correct relationship for demodulation, the carrier amplifier section must be capable of a constant output voltage of approximately 10 times the sideband voltage. This output is applied to the carrier input of the balanced modulator.

Under conditions of selective fading, when the carrier is subject to serious fading while the sidebands are not affected, it is preferable to use the 100-kc oscillator for carrier re-insertion. Use of this oscillator is of course a necessity for the reception of suppressed-carrier signals. In the receiver block diagram a switch is shown for selection of either the reconditioned received carrier or the locally generated carrier insertion output.

A highly stable crystal oscillator is customarily used in this circuit to provide the necessary stability. The output of this oscillator must be high, similar to the reconditioned carrier, with respect to the sideband level at the demodulator, so that proper envelope shape into the demodulator will result. After carrier re-insertion, the signal may be detected with a conventional diode or other type AM detector. However, the use of frequency conversion results in a higher signal-to-noise ratio and less cross modulation and intermodulation from unwanted carrier and/or sideband beats than detection by rectification. This method also corrects, to some extent, the effect of the inherent phase distortion common to single-sideband systems. A convenient method of detection by frequency conversion is the use of a balanced detector.

The low-frequency demodulator is essentially a balanced detector. The theory and design considerations of balanced detectors (demodulators) are the same as those of the balanced modulators used in the generation (frequency translation) of the transmitted SSB signal.

The output of the low-frequency demodulator is applied to an audio-amplifier circuit. Since this circuit and the power supply circuits are conventional, an analysis of these circuits is not necessary. In the audio-amplifier circuit audio filters may be used, if necessary, to further separate audio components. The power supply should include a well regulated plate voltage for the oscillator circuits, to aid in assuring the required frequency stability.

Referring to figure 15-12 note that an a-f-c circuit is incorporated in the receiver to control the high-frequency oscillator. The frequency stability of this oscillator is an important factor, because any frequency shift of the oscillator with respect to the frequency of the transmitter carrier oscillator, unless c o m p e n s a t e d for elsewhere, will cause a shift in the audio output of the receiver, which will be apparent as frequency distortion.

If a pilot carrier or a controlled carrier is received, the amplified carrier is taken from a convenient p o i n t, usually the output of the medium-frequency mixer; it is sharply filtered and amplified in the carrier filter and amplifier circuit, and the amplified signal is applied to the comparator type a-f-c circuit, along with the output of the carrier insertion oscillator. A shift in carrier frequency (if not too great) or a shift in the local low-frequency oscillator, or any difference between the two, will then result in a corresponding change in the frequencies and phases of the control voltages in the a-f-c circuit, and a subsequent change in frequency of the high-frequency oscillator, thereby maintaining s t a b l e communications. Many types of a-f-c circuits are available; however, the most popular are the discriminator-reactance t u b e system and the balanced modulator-motor drive system. The balanced modulator-motor drive system can provide positive control capable of correcting the oscillator frequency to within 1 cycle. This type of electromechanical circuit, which drives a variable capacitor in the h-f oscillator, has been in common use in transoceanic telephone service, and its reliability is established and recognized in this field.

The a-v-c circuits are included when a carrier of some type is received to control various sections of the receiver. In a suppressed-carrier receiver, or when no pilot carrier is received, the a-f-c and a-v-c circuits are inoperative or may be omitted entirely from the receiver design. When a receiver is designed specifically for suppressed-carrier operation, a crystal oscillator is usually used in place of the h-f variable-frequency oscillator. The use of a crystal oscillator, to provide stability, presents no problem for single-frequency operation, and crystals may be switched for multi-frequency operation.

Phase-Shift Method of Detection

A phase-shift method of detection may be used in SSB and DSB receivers to eliminate the need for sideband filters. This method is similar to the phase-shift method of SSB modulation at the transmitter, and is well suited for the reception of signals transmitted by this method. The principles involved are the same in both cases. Such a demodulator is shown in block diagram form in figure 15-13. Since no filters are necessary in the i-f stages, these stages may employ conventional AM circuitry, and the chief requirement in the circuits preceding the detector stages is oscillator stability. Thus the output of a conventional AM receiver i-f section may be applied to an adapter using the circuitry illustrated.

In the phase-shift method of detection, two balanced demodulators are used in parallel, and

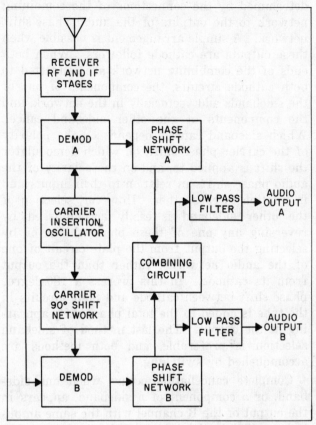

Figure 15-13. Block Diagram of Phase-Shift Method of Single-Sideband Detection

the inserted carrier is shifted 90 degrees before being applied to one of them. The output of the two balanced demodulators will therefore have a quadrature relationship to each other. Each output is applied to its own wideband-audio phase-shift network. The degree of phase shift in each network (input to output) will vary up to several hundred degrees; however, a 90-degree shift is maintained between the outputs of the two networks over the entire desired audio-frequency bandpass of the receiver. Frequencies slightly above and below the design limits of the filter will be passed, but may be somewhat distorted because of a shift in phase greater or less than 90 degrees.

The 90-degree phase-shift network in the carrier oscillator signal i n p u t circuit to the demodulators and the two audio phase-shift networks in the output circuits of the balanced demodulators are similar to circuits used for the phase-shift type of modulator. The outputs of the two audio phase-shift networks contain in-phase and out-of-phase components of the audio derived from either or both sidebands. These are applied to a resistive combining network. Sideband selection from the combining network is determined by the connections of the combining network to the outputs of the audio phase-shift network. A simple arrangement is possible when these outputs are cathode followers. When both ends of the combining network are connected to both cathode circuits, the components of one of the sidebands add vectorially in the network, and the components of the other sideband cancel. Which sideband cancels depends on the polarity of the carrier phase shift, on which demodulator the shift is applied to, and on the polarity of the audio phase shifts in relation to their inputs and in relation to each other. However, selection of the other sideband is easily accomplished by reversing any one of these phase shifts, or by selecting the output from the plate circuit of one of the audio networks, rather than the output from its cathode. In this process a 180-degree phase shift between cathode and plate circuits in the tube is added to the total phase shift appearing at the output. The last method of sideband selection is preferable, and both methods are accomplished by switching.

Complete cancellation occurs when one sideband, or a component of a sideband, appears in the output of the B channel with the same amplitude as that in the output of the A channel, but exactly 180 degrees out of phase with it.

15-5 OTHER SINGLE-SIDEBAND SYSTEM ARRANGEMENTS

In this relatively short discussion on the basic principles of single-sideband transmission and reception techniques, only the more important circuit arrangements that can be used to provide this mode of communication have been considered. In both the filter and phase-shift method of single-sideband reception, circuit additions and changes can be made to allow these systems to become dual single-sideband receivers, which can receive two separate pieces of information simultaneously, one on the upper sideband and the other on the lower sideband.

In addition, there are other types of SSB transmitting systems, such as the envelope elimination and restoration SSB transmitter, and other types of receiving systems, such as the synchronous receiver and the diversity receiving system. These systems employ variations of electronic circuits to provide the desired operational characteristics.

15-6 SUMMARY

The usefulness of single-sideband communication has become more apparent in the last few years because of the overcrowded conditions which exist in the communications radio-frequency spectrum. Single-sideband principles have been known and used in telephone applications for a number of years. With the advent of improved circuit techniques, the use of single sideband and double sideband is becoming more popular as a means of communications in the high-frequency range.

An important consideration in any of the methods of producing and receiving a single-sideband signal is stability of the frequency-generation portions of the system. The use of balanced modulators and demodulators or phase-shift circuits are the most common methods of removing and inserting the carrier in both civilian and military equipments.

REVIEW QUESTIONS

1. Define the term *single-sideband communications*.
2. State the relationship between the peak powers required, to achieve transmission over a given distance, for a standard AM transmitter and a suppressed-carrier single-sideband transmitter.
3. What is the theoretical signal-to-noise advantage claimed for a single-sideband receiver over a conventional AM system?
4. Does the carrier wave in a standard AM broadcast radiated signal contain any of the modulation information?
5. If the last frequency-translation oscillator in a suppressed-carrier single-sideband system is adjusted to 6.9 mc, and the input sideband signal to the last balanced modulator is 3.1 to 3.103 mc, what is the frequency of the resultant upper sideband that is transmitted?
6. Name the three types of SSB systems which employ some means of including a portion of the basic carrier in the radiated signal.
7. What is vestigial-sideband transmission and where is it most commonly employed?
8. Describe two basic systems used in generating a single-sideband signal.
9. Which of the two systems, filter or phase-shift, will produce the most reliable operation?
10. Can the receiver of a single-sideband system be synchronized in any way with the transmitter? If the answer is "yes," state how.

Appendix A

FORMULAS

Ohm's Law for D-C Circuits

When two d-c circuit values are given, the unknown value may be determined by the application of the Ohm's Law formulas for d-c circuits:

$$I = \frac{E}{R} \qquad I = \frac{P}{E} \qquad I = \sqrt{\frac{P}{R}}$$

$$E = IR \qquad E = \frac{P}{I} \cdot \qquad E = \sqrt{PR}$$

$$R = \frac{E}{I} \qquad R = \frac{E^2}{P} \qquad R = \frac{P}{I^2}$$

$$P = EI \qquad P = I^2R \qquad P = \frac{E^2}{R}$$

where:
- I = current in amperes
- E = potential in volts
- R = resistance in ohms
- P = power in watts

Ohm's Law for A-C Circuits

When two a-c circuit values are given, the unknown value may be determined by the application of the Ohm's Law formulas for a-c circuits:

$$I = \frac{E}{Z} \qquad I = \frac{P}{E \cos \theta} \qquad I = \sqrt{\frac{P}{Z \cos \theta}}$$

$$E = IZ \qquad E = \frac{P}{I \cos \theta} \qquad E = \sqrt{\frac{PZ}{\cos \theta}}$$

$$Z = \frac{E}{I} \qquad Z = \frac{E^2 \cos \theta}{P} \qquad Z = \frac{P}{I^2 \cos \theta}$$

$$P = EI \cos \theta \qquad P = I^2 Z \cos \theta \qquad P = \frac{E^2 \cos \theta}{Z}$$

$$P = I^2R$$

where:
- I = current in amperes
- E = potential in volts
- Z = impedance in ohms
- R = resistance in ohms
- P = power in watts
- θ = phase angle in degrees (see PHASE ANGLE and POWER FACTOR)

Resistance

Resistors in series:

$$R_t = R_1 + R_2 + R_3 + R_4 \ldots$$

Resistors in parallel:

$$R_t = \frac{1}{\dfrac{1}{R_1} + \dfrac{1}{R_2} + \dfrac{1}{R_3} + \dfrac{1}{R_4} \ldots}$$

Two resistors in parallel:

$$R_t = \frac{R_1 R_2}{R_1 + R_2}$$

Capacitance

Capacitors in parallel:

$$C_t = C_1 + C_2 + C_3 + C_4 \ldots$$

Capacitors in series:

$$C_t = \frac{1}{\dfrac{1}{C_1} + \dfrac{1}{C_2} + \dfrac{1}{C_3} + \dfrac{1}{C_4} \ldots}$$

Two capacitors in series:

$$C_t = \frac{C_1 C_2}{C_1 + C_2}$$

Quantity of electricity stored in a capacitor:

$$Q = CE$$

where:
- Q = quantity stored in coulombs
- E = potential across the capacitor in volts
- C = capacitance in farads

Capacitance of a parallel plate capacitor:

$$C = 0.08842 \, \frac{KS (N-1)}{d}$$

where:
- C = capacitance in $\mu\mu f$
- K = dielectric constant
- S = area of one plate in square centimeters*
- N = number of plates
- d = thickness of the dielectric in centimeters*

*If the S and d values are given in change constant 0.08842 to 0.2244.

Capacitance of a single wire parallel to ground:

$$C = \frac{7.354l}{\log_{10} \dfrac{4h}{d} - S}$$

where:
- C = capacitance in $\mu\mu f$
- l = length in feet
- h = height above earth in feet
- d = diameter of wire in feet
- S = a constant (see table 1)

Capacitance to ground of parallel wires of the same height joined together:

$$C = \frac{7.36l}{F}$$

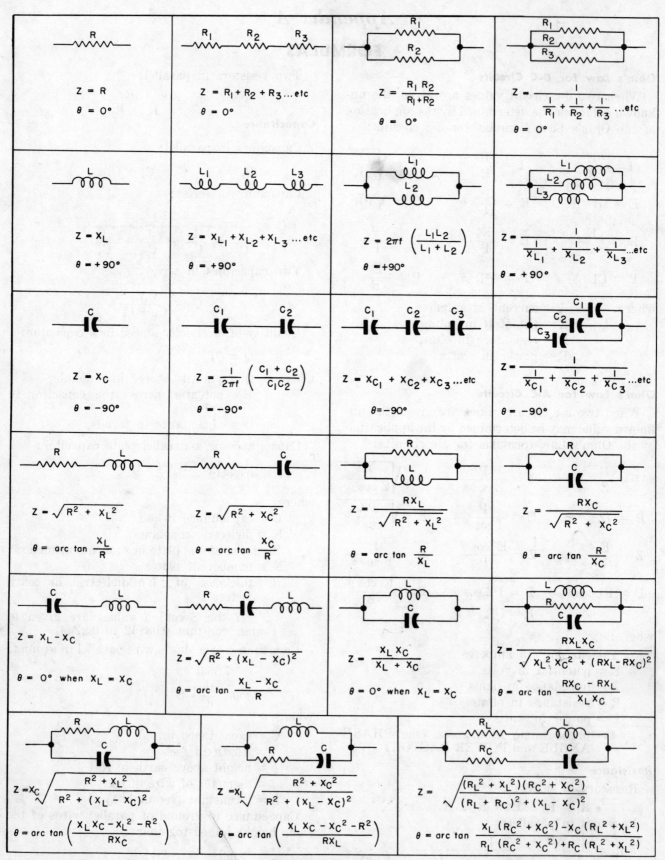

$$Z = R$$
$$\theta = 0°$$

$$Z = R_1 + R_2 + R_3 \ldots \text{etc}$$
$$\theta = 0°$$

$$Z = \frac{R_1 R_2}{R_1 + R_2}$$
$$\theta = 0°$$

$$Z = \frac{1}{\frac{1}{R_1} + \frac{1}{R_2} + \frac{1}{R_3} \ldots \text{etc}}$$
$$\theta = 0°$$

$$Z = X_L$$
$$\theta = +90°$$

$$Z = X_{L_1} + X_{L_2} + X_{L_3} \ldots \text{etc}$$
$$\theta = +90°$$

$$Z = 2\pi f \left(\frac{L_1 L_2}{L_1 + L_2} \right)$$
$$\theta = +90°$$

$$Z = \frac{1}{\frac{1}{X_{L_1}} + \frac{1}{X_{L_2}} + \frac{1}{X_{L_3}} \ldots \text{etc}}$$
$$\theta = +90°$$

$$Z = X_C$$
$$\theta = -90°$$

$$Z = \frac{1}{2\pi f} \left(\frac{C_1 + C_2}{C_1 C_2} \right)$$
$$\theta = -90°$$

$$Z = X_{C_1} + X_{C_2} + X_{C_3} \ldots \text{etc}$$
$$\theta = -90°$$

$$Z = \frac{1}{\frac{1}{X_{C_1}} + \frac{1}{X_{C_2}} + \frac{1}{X_{C_3}} \ldots \text{etc}}$$
$$\theta = -90°$$

$$Z = \sqrt{R^2 + X_L^2}$$
$$\theta = \arctan \frac{X_L}{R}$$

$$Z = \sqrt{R^2 + X_C^2}$$
$$\theta = \arctan \frac{X_C}{R}$$

$$Z = \frac{R X_L}{\sqrt{R^2 + X_L^2}}$$
$$\theta = \arctan \frac{R}{X_L}$$

$$Z = \frac{R X_C}{\sqrt{R^2 + X_C^2}}$$
$$\theta = \arctan \frac{R}{X_C}$$

$$Z = X_L - X_C$$
$$\theta = 0° \text{ when } X_L = X_C$$

$$Z = \sqrt{R^2 + (X_L - X_C)^2}$$
$$\theta = \arctan \frac{X_L - X_C}{R}$$

$$Z = \frac{X_L X_C}{X_L + X_C}$$
$$\theta = 0° \text{ when } X_L = X_C$$

$$Z = \frac{R X_L X_C}{\sqrt{X_L^2 X_C^2 + (R X_L - R X_C)^2}}$$
$$\theta = \arctan \frac{R X_C - R X_L}{X_L X_C}$$

$$Z = X_C \sqrt{\frac{R^2 + X_L^2}{R^2 + (X_L - X_C)^2}}$$
$$\theta = \arctan \left(\frac{X_L X_C - X_L^2 - R^2}{R X_C} \right)$$

$$Z = X_L \sqrt{\frac{R^2 + X_C^2}{R^2 + (X_L - X_C)^2}}$$
$$\theta = \arctan \left(\frac{X_L X_C - X_C^2 - R^2}{R X_L} \right)$$

$$Z = \sqrt{\frac{(R_L^2 + X_L^2)(R_C^2 + X_C^2)}{(R_L + R_C)^2 + (X_L - X_C)^2}}$$
$$\theta = \arctan \frac{X_L (R_C^2 + X_C^2) - X_C (R_L^2 + X_L^2)}{R_L (R_C^2 + X_C^2) + R_C (R_L^2 + X_L^2)}$$

IMPEDANCE CHART

where:

$$C = \text{capacitance in } \mu\mu\text{f}$$

$$F = \frac{P + (n-1)Q}{n} - S_n$$

$$P = \log_{10} \frac{4h}{d} - S$$

$$Q = \log_{10} \frac{2h}{D} - S$$

l = length of wire (assumed same for all wires)

h = height above earth in feet

d = diameter of wire in feet

n = number of wires

D = spacing between adjacent wires (assumed to be the same for all adjacent pairs)

S = a constant (see table 1)

S_n = a constant (see table 2)

Note: This formula assumes that the ratio D/d is large.

Capacitance to ground of a single vertical wire:

$$C = \frac{7.36m}{\log_{10} \frac{2h'}{d} - k}$$

where:

C = capacitance in $\mu\mu\text{f}$

m = length of vertical wire in feet

h' = height of lower end of wire above earth in feet

d = diameter of wire in feet

k = a constant (see table 3)

TABLE 1.
VALUES FOR CONSTANT S*

$2h/l$	S	$l/2h$	S	$l/2h$	S
0	0	1.00	0.336	0.50	0.541
0.1	0.042	0.95	0.350	0.45	0.576
0.2	0.082	0.90	0.364	0.40	0.617
0.3	0.121	0.85	0.379	0.35	0.664
0.4	0.157	0.80	0.396	0.30	0.721
0.5	0.191	0.75	0.414	0.25	0.790
0.6	0.223	0.70	0.435	0.20	0.874
0.7	0.254	0.65	0.457	0.15	0.990
0.8	0.283	0.60	0.482	0.10	1.155
0.9	0.310	0.55	0.510	0.05	1.445
1.0	0.336	0.50	0.541		

*Use either $2h/l$ or $l/2h$ whichever is less than unity.

TABLE 2.
VALUES FOR CONSTANT S_n

n	S_n	n	S_n	n	S_n	n	S_n
2	0	8	0.347	14	0.550	20	0.688
3	0.067	9	0.388	15	0.576	30	0.847
4	0.135	10	0.425	16	0.601	40	0.970
5	0.197	11	0.460	17	0.625	50	1.063
6	0.252	12	0.492	18	0.647	100	1.357
7	0.302	13	0.522	19	0.668		

TABLE 3.
VALUES OF THE CONSTANT k*

h'/m	k	h'/m	k	m/h'	k
		0.3	0.280	1.0	0.207
0.02	0.403	0.4	0.261	0.9	0.202
0.04	0.384	0.5	0.247	0.8	0.196
0.06	0.369	0.6	0.236	0.7	0.190
0.08	0.356	0.7	0.227	0.6	0.184
0.10	0.345	0.8	0.219	0.5	0.177
0.15	0.323	0.9	0.2125	0.4	0.170
0.20	0.305	1.0	0.207	0.3	0.162
0.25	0.291	—	—	0.2	0.153
0.30	0.280	—	—	0.1	0.144
—	—	—	—	0	0.133

*Use either h'/m or m/h' whichever is less than unity.

Self-Inductance *

Inductors in series:

$$L_t = L_1 + L_2 + L_3 + L_4 \ldots$$

Inductors in parallel:

$$L_t = \frac{1}{\frac{1}{L_1} + \frac{1}{L_2} + \frac{1}{L_3} + \frac{1}{L_4} \cdots}$$

Two inductors in parallel:

$$L_t = \frac{L_1 L_2}{L_1 + L_2}$$

*Inductors not coupled

Coupled Inductance

Inductors in series with fields aiding:

$$L_a = L_1 + L_2 + 2M$$

Inductors in series with fields opposing:

$$L_o = L_1 + L_2 - 2M$$

Inductors in parallel with fields aiding:

$$L_a = \frac{1}{\frac{1}{L_1 + M} + \frac{1}{L_2 + M}}$$

Inductors in parallel with fields opposing:

$$L_o = \frac{1}{\frac{1}{L_1 - M} + \frac{1}{L_2 - M}}$$

where:

L_a = total inductance with aiding fields

L_o = total inductance with opposing fields

L_1, L_2 = self-inductance of coil

Mutual Inductance

The mutual inductance between two coupled r-f coils is given by

$$M = \frac{L_a - L_o}{4}$$

where:

M = mutual inductance
L_a = total inductance of L_1 and L_2 with aiding fields
L_o = total inductance of L_1 and L_2 with opposing fields

Inductance of Small Air-Core Coils

For single-layer wound coils:

$$L = \frac{(rN)^2}{9r + 10l}$$

and;

$$N = \frac{\sqrt{L(9r + 10l)}}{r}$$

For multi-layer wound coils:

$$L = \frac{0.8(rN)^2}{6r + 9l + 10b}$$

For single-layer pancake coils:

$$L = \frac{(rN)^2}{8r + 11b}$$

where:

L = self-inductance in microhenries
N = total number of turns
r = mean radius in inches
l = length of coil in inches
b = depth of coil in inches

Coupling Coefficient

When two r-f coils are inductively coupled, the coefficient of coupling is given by

$$K = \frac{M}{\sqrt{L_1 L_2}}$$

where:

K = coupling coefficient ($K \times 100$ = coupling coefficient in %)
M = mutual inductance
L_1, L_2 = self-inductance of coil

Reactance

Inductive reactance:

$X_L = 2\pi f L$

Capacitive reactance:

$$X_c = \frac{1}{2\pi f C}, \text{ or } X_c = \frac{.159}{fC}$$

where:

X_L = inductive reactance in ohms
X_c = capacitive reactance in ohms
f = frequency in cycles
L = inductance in henries
C = capacitance in farads
2π = 6.28

Resonance

When X_L is equal to X_c, the circuit is resonant at a particular frequency. Combining the two reactance formulas, the formula for resonant frequency is found to be

$$f_r = \frac{1}{2\pi \sqrt{LC}}, \text{ or } f_r = \frac{.159}{\sqrt{LC}}$$

also;

$$L = \frac{1}{4\pi^2 f_r^2 C}$$

and;

$$C = \frac{1}{4\pi^2 f_r^2 L}$$

where:

f_r = resonant frequency in cycles
L = inductance in henries
C = capacitance in farads
2π = 6.28
$4\pi^2$ = 39.5

Wavelength and Frequency

To convert from frequency to wavelength:

$$\lambda = \frac{3 \times 10^8}{f} \text{ (meters)}$$

where: f = frequency in cycles

also;

$$\lambda = \frac{3 \times 10^5}{f} \text{ (meters)}$$

where: f = frequency in kilocycles

and;

$$\lambda = \frac{300}{f} \text{ (meters)}$$

where: f = frequency in megacycles

To convert from wavelength to frequency:

$$f = \frac{3 \times 10^8}{\lambda} \text{ (cycles)}$$

also;

$$f = \frac{3 \times 10^5}{\lambda} \text{ (kilocycles)}$$

and;

$$f = \frac{300}{\lambda} \text{ (megacycles)}$$

where: λ = wavelength in meters

Conductance

Conductance in a d-c circuit is the reciprocal of resistance and is expressed by

$$G = \frac{1}{R}$$

conversely;

$$R = \frac{1}{G}$$

where:

G = conductance in mhos
R = resistance in ohms

When resistors are connected in a parallel d-c circuit, the total conductance is given by

$$G_t = G_1 + G_2 + G_3 + G_4 \ldots$$

and the total current by

$$I_t = EG_t$$

In terms of conductance, Ohm's Law may be stated as follows:

$$I = EG$$

and;

$$E = \frac{I}{G}$$

Susceptance

The susceptance of an a-c series circuit is expressed by

$$B = \frac{X}{R^2 + X^2}$$

where: B = susceptance in mhos
R = resistance in ohms
X = reactance in ohms

Admittance

The admittance of an a-c circuit is expressed by

$$Y = \frac{1}{\sqrt{R^2 + X^2}}$$

Since admittance is the reciprocal of impedance:

$$Y = \frac{1}{Z}$$

also;

$$Y = \frac{I}{E}$$

where: Y = admittance in mhos
R = resistance in ohms
E = potential in volts
I = current in amperes
X = reactance in ohms
Z = impedance in ohms

Impedance

When values for R, X_L, and X_c are given, the impedance in ohms and the phase angle may be computed by the following formulas:

For a series a-c circuit:

$$Z_t = \sqrt{R_t^2 + X_t^2}$$

and;

$$\theta = \text{arc tan} \frac{X_L - X_c}{R}$$

For a parallel a-c circuit:

$$Z_t = \frac{1}{\sqrt{G_t^2 + B_t^2}}$$

and;

$$\theta = \text{arc tan} \frac{RX_c - RX_L}{X_L X_c}$$

where:
Z = impedance in ohms
R_t = total resistance of circuit in ohms
$X_t = (X_L - X_c)$ = total reactance of circuit in ohms
G_t = total conductance of circuit in mhos
B_t = total susceptance of circuit in mhos
θ = phase angle in degrees

Q Factor

Q is a figure of merit which is widely used in the design of electronic equipment. The term may be applied to a single component such as a coil or a capacitor, or it may be applied to an entire circuit composed of a number of resistive, inductive, or capacitive components. The Q factor is the ratio of reactance to resistance, and for an inductor or a circuit having inductance and resistance it is expressed as

$$Q = \frac{X_L}{R_L}$$

For a capacitor or a circuit having capacitance and resistance:

$$Q = \frac{X_c}{R_c}$$

When a circuit contains a combination of inductive and capacitive reactance as well as resistance, the Q of such a circuit is usually expressed only at the resonant value of the reactances. Therefore:

$$Q = \frac{1}{R} \sqrt{\frac{L}{C}}$$

where:
Q = figure of merit
X_L = inductive reactance in ohms
X_c = capacitive reactance in ohms
R_L = resistance in ohms in series with inductor or the R-L circuit
R_c = resistance in ohms in series with capacitor or the R-C circuit
L = inductance in henries
C = capacitance in farads

In a single tuned circuit, Q may be determined by the relationship between the resonant frequency and the bandwidth between the 3-db (half-power) points. When

$$\frac{E}{E_o} = 0.707 \text{ (3 db down)}$$

then;

$$Q = \frac{f_r}{2\Delta f}$$

where:

Q = figure of merit

f_r = resonant frequency

Δf = deviation from resonant frequency

$2\Delta f$ = bandwidth (width between the two half-power points)

Phase Angle

The phase angle is the angle, expressed in degrees, by which the current lags the voltage in an inductive circuit, or leads the voltage in a capacitive circuit. For purely reactive circuits with no resistance (a theoretical concept) the current lags by 90° in an inductive circuit and leads by 90° in a capacitive circuit.

In a resonant circuit where $X_L = X_c$, the total reactance is resistive and the phase angle is 0°. Similarly, in a circuit consisting of resistance alone, the current and voltage are *in phase* and the phase angle is 0°.

In series circuits containing reactance and resistance, the phase angle is equal to the angle whose tangent is indicated by the ratio

$$\frac{X}{R}$$

and is expressed by

$$\theta = \text{arc tan} \frac{X}{R}$$

where:

X = inductive or capacitive reactance in ohms

R = non-reactive resistance in ohms

arc tan = "the angle whose tangent is . . ."

In parallel circuits containing reactance and resistance, the phase angle is equal to the angle whose tangent is indicated by the ratio

$$\frac{R}{X}$$

and is expressed by

$$\theta = \text{arc tan} \frac{R}{X}$$

Phase angle formulas for various combinations of R, X_L, and X_c in series, parallel, and series-parallel circuits may be found in the chart under IMPEDANCE.

Power Factor

The power factor of an a-c circuit is equal to the ratio of the true power in watts to the apparent power in volt-amperes. Since

$$P = EI \cos \theta$$

and

$$P_a = EI$$

therefore; $PF = \dfrac{EI \cos \theta}{EI}$

or

$$PF = \cos \theta$$

where: PF = power factor

P = true power

P_a = apparent power

θ = phase angle

Example, using phase angle and power factor:

A series circuit has an inductive reactance of 100 ohms and a non-reactive resistance of 100 ohms. Find the phase angle.

$$\theta = \text{arc tan} \frac{X}{R} = \text{arc tan} \frac{100}{100} = \text{arc tan } 1$$

from a table of natural trigonometric functions
      arc tan 1 = 45°

therefore θ = 45° (lagging)

however; $PF = \cos \theta$

and $\cos 45° = 0.707$

therefore;   PF = 0.707 or, in percentage, 70.7%

Consequently, for true power in watts in the circuit described:

$$P = EI \cos \theta = EI \times 0.707 \text{ watts}$$

Vacuum Tube

The dynamic plate resistance, r_p, of an electron tube is the resistance of the electron path between cathode and plate. It may be calculated by effecting a small change in plate voltage, and dividing this by the corresponding change in plate current, with the grid voltage held at a constant value. The dynamic plate resistance (r_p) in ohms is given by

$$r_p = \frac{\Delta E_p}{\Delta I_p}$$

with E_g held constant.

The amplification factor, μ, of a vacuum tube is the ratio of the change in plate voltage to the opposite change in grid voltage required to maintain the plate current at a constant value. The numerical value of μ is given by

$$\mu = \frac{\Delta E_p}{\Delta E_g}$$

with I_p held constant.

The transconductance, or mutual conductance, g_m, of a vacuum tube is equal to the amplification factor divided by the plate resistance. Therefore, the transconductance is equal to the change in plate current divided by the change in grid voltage, with the plate voltage held at a constant value. The transconductance (g_m) in mhos is given by

$$g_m = \frac{\mu}{r_p} = \frac{\Delta E_p / \Delta E_g}{\Delta E_p / \Delta I_p}$$

or

$$g_m = \frac{\Delta I_p}{\Delta E_g}$$

with E_p held constant.

The voltage amplification, or voltage gain, of a vacuum tube in a grounded-cathode circuit is expressed by

$$A = \frac{\mu R_L}{R_L + r_p}$$

also

$$A = \frac{g_m R_L r_p \text{*}}{10^6 (R_L + r_p)}$$

In cases where $r_p \gg R_L$, the formula may be simplified to

$$A = g_m R_L$$

* In this formula, g_m is expressed in micromhos.

The voltage gain of a v a c u u m tube in a grounded-grid circuit is expressed by

$$A = (1 + \mu) \frac{R_L}{R_L + r_p}$$

The voltage gain of a v a c u u m tube in a grounded-plate (cathode follower) circuit is given by

$$A = \frac{R_L}{r_p + (1 + \mu) R_L}$$

where

r_p = dynamic plate resistance in ohms
E_p = plate voltage
E_g = grid voltage
I_p = plate current
μ = amplification factor
g_m = transconductance in mhos (multiply by 10^6 for transconductance in micromhos)
R_L = load resistance in ohms
A = gain of tube
Δ = change in value, either increment or decrement

The voltage gain of an amplifier with feedback is given by

$$\text{Gain with feedback} = \frac{A}{1 - A\beta}$$

where

A = gain of amplifier without feedback
β = fraction of the output voltage which is fed back

If the expression $1 - A\beta$ is less than unity, the feedback is said to be regenerative. This type of feedback, common in oscillator circuits, is not used in conventional amplifiers because of the distortion introduced by it. In amplifiers, therefore, the feedback is usually negative and the fractional part of the output voltage which is fed back is $-\beta$. For negative feedback, then, the formula becomes

$$\text{Gain with negative feedback} = \frac{A}{1 + A\beta}$$

Hence, the expression $1 + A\beta$ is greater than unity and the feedback is degenerative. When the gain of the stage, A, is large compared with 1, the formula may be expressed by

$$\text{Gain with negative feedback} = \frac{1}{\beta}$$

BIBLIOGRAPHY OF PUBLICATIONS
USED AS REFERENCES IN
THE PREPARATION OF THE TEXT

TEXTS

1. *Principles of Radio*, Henney and Richardson, John Wiley and Sons, Sixth Edition, 1955.
2. *Elements of Radio*, Marcus and Horton, Prentice-Hall, Second Edition, 1949.
3. *Practical Radio Communicaton*, Nilson and Hornung, McGraw-Hill, Second Edition, 1943.
4. *Fundamentals of Radio*, Terman, McGraw-Hill, 1938.
5. *F-M Simplified*, Kiver, D. Van Nostrand, 1947.
6. *FM Transmission and Reception*, Rider and Uslan, John F. Rider, 1948.
7. *Transistors Handbook*, Bevitt, Prentice-Hall, 1956.
8. *Transistors in Radio and Television*, Kiver, McGraw-Hill, 1956.

TRAINING MANUALS

1. *Homestudy Course Device, 26-K-2*, U. S. Naval Training Devices Center, 1957.
2. *Electronic Power Supplies*, Department of the Army, 1951, TM 11-663.
3. *C-W and A-M Radio Transmitters and Receivers*, Department of the Army, 1952, TM 11-665.
4. *F-M Transmitters and Receivers*, Department of the Army, 1952, TM 11-668.
5. *Troubleshooting and Repair of Radio Equipment*, Department of the Army, 1958, TM 11-4000.
6. *Basic Theory and Application of Transistors*, Department of the Army, 1959, TM 11-690.
7. *Radio Communication System Measurements*, Philco Corporation, 1952, AN-252.
8. *Electronic Circuit Directory*, Philco Corporation, 1953, AN-296.
9. *Antennas*, Volume 1, Philco Corporation, 1956, AN-374.
10. *Single Sideband Communications*, Philco Corporation, 1957, AN-401.
11. *Field Engineers' Data Handbook*, Philco Corporation, 1957, AN-407.
12. *Basic Electronic Circuits and Systems Training Course*, Philco Corporation, 1957, AN-217/218.

Index

T   tera - 10^{12}

G   giga - 10^{9}

M   mega - 10^{6}

μ micro - 10^{-6}

n   nano - 10^{-9}

P   pico - 10^{-12}

Gain on   AC-DC Panel Radio

RF Voltage Amplifier 23 - input .0118 v output .8

RF Converter 24 - input .36   output .8

IF Amplifier 25 - input .8   output 5.

Diode Detector and A-VC 26 - input 5. output 14.

Audio Voltage Amplifier 27 - input .8 output 24

Phase Splitter 28 - input .08   output .38

Audio Power Amplifier 29 - input 2. output 44.